The Joys of
Beekeeping

The Joys of Beekeeping

by Richard Taylor

Illustrated by Meri Shardin

ST. MARTIN'S PRESS • NEW YORK

What god, ye Muses, what god disclosed to us this art?

—VIRGIL

Contents

The Joys of Beekeeping

Preface

Books on apiculture describe how to produce honey but they neglect to note how beautiful it is. They explain how to tend bees but they do not say how joyous this can be. They describe swarms but say nothing of how inspiring it is to behold one. It is omissions like these that I have tried to rectify. I have tried to give an intimation of the sources of happiness that beekeepers have discovered and to convey my own philosophy that is so closely interwoven with my beekeeping. I have also described how I do certain things connected with bees.

In doing so, I have had in mind readers who have never seen a beehive and who have no intention of ever owning one but who might want to know how things are done by devotées of this strange craft. I have also had in mind my fellow victims of this obsession, hoping that I have expressed something of their own joys and supplied them with a new idea or two.

Some of the things I have written have appeared in the pages of *Gleanings in Bee Culture* as part of my column "Bee Talk."

I am grateful to the editors for letting me use the material again here.

ONE

The Taste of Joy

My book is a rejoicing, and I have no other objective in writing it. It is not primarily meant to be instructive, except indirectly with respect to that most elusive of goals, the achievement of happiness. I can write of this because I have tasted it or indeed, because I have been expressing it in countless ways most of my life. This is not a boast but a thanksgiving, for there is nothing here for which I can credit myself. I love nature, and honeybees are among the most exquisite and inspiring expressions of nature. The life that the husbandry of them has styled for me is the source of my rejoicing.

My bees have not made me rich. Had it been otherwise, had this way of life been a source of wealth, as business and speculation sometimes are, then I would have had my reward, but that reward would not have been happiness. Yet the knowledge that I could have depended upon my bees for at least a meager livelihood has given me a sense of independence, which is itself a joy.

Such joy is no passive delight. Keeping bees in a serious way, with concentration and art, is toilsome, sometimes exhausting, frustrating and discouraging. But it is also made the more joyous for the overcoming of all this. The image of happiness is not that of the patron of an amusement park, nor is it that of someone burdened with galling work, nor that of greed measuring up its gold. Part of the image, at least, is that of a challenge met, a purpose achieved—and achieved with great effort.

The basic reason for any pursuit is to find happiness. Many persons seek it through wealth, power or prestige, and while some of them do find these things, it is doubtful whether they ever find more than the most specious happiness. The ancients, who thought more deeply about happiness than we do, were unanimous in rejecting these goals as sources of it. They thought that happiness consisted of having a good demon, so they called it eudaemonia. There is no doubt that the honeybee has been my demon, and an immeasurably good one as long as I can remember. Happiness cannot depend upon the gifts of our fellows, nor upon their approval, for what they bestow today they can as easily withdraw tomorrow.

We are all the creation of the same nature, or as some perceive it, of God, and we share this lovely earth with a multitude of things great and small. We were not given the world to dominate it, to subdue it or exploit it as though it were a kind of warehouse placed at our disposal and for our exclusive benefit. Rather, we were given it to make our home in it, to share it, to glorify it and to glory in it.

One's happiness is, of course, something personal, something more his own than any possession. We do not all find it in the same way. Some never find it at all. Possibly most never do, even when the means are at hand. But I have found my bees and all the countless things I associate with them a constant and unfailing source of it. I know that not all persons are of this temperament. Some look upon this obsession of mine with incomprehension, some with amusement or curiosity, while I in turn pity them, for they lack the capacity for these particular joys so fulfilling to me.

I can only thank God that, in creating this bounteous earth, He included these tiny creatures whose organization still defies the sublimest intellects and whose labors yield the golden honey that has been prized by human beings since before recorded history. Without bees my own existence would be a shadowy thing, like a world without flowers or without stars or without the songs of birds. The world of men is always uncertain, seldom inspiring, often a source of discouragement and dismay. But the keeper of bees, like anyone who has welded his life to the cycles and patterns of nature, can always turn to his tiny creatures and his craft. The bees have a perpetual store of surprises in readiness for their owner, but they also have a constancy beneath it all. No doubt, there are many foun-tainheads of happiness, but none equals those nature has provided from the beginning of time. Certainly human artifices, even those we have been taught to consider great, are nothing in comparison. They are not needed, in fact, are dismissed as encumbrances, by those who have tasted the changeless serenity that nature so freely offers.

Even as a boy, driven by the passions and impulses that make youth so tumultuous and blind and filled with folly, I noted this serenity in beekeepers. From time to time I would see one sitting out in his battered chair, basking in the peace and sweetness of the setting, surrounded by his hives of bees, his orchard, his small parcel of land, his quiet and ordered world. Overhead soared the purple martins belonging to the large apartment birdhouse he had erected for them on his barn roof, while around him, in spring, the cherries bloomed and the bees hummed, just as they had for a million springs gone by, and as they will for more millions to come.

There was another beekeeper who was old and had lost some of his strength. I occasionally helped him in his bee yards. One of these yards was set in a beautiful grove of locust trees on the side of a hill, outside of town, and we sometimes went there together in his ancient car, an open Model T Ford, which in those days could be purchased in running condition for ten dollars. I was surprised then how happy I was, riding along in the open air with this old man, an object of curiosity to my friends, giving him a hand, and in turn learning about bees. I had not expected this reward of inner happiness, but having found it I never forgot it.

In the meantime, I had my own hive of bees, purchased for four and a half dollars. Soon I had two. The second was the crude product of one of my early attempts at carpentry. I sold the comb honey to my neighbors for fifteen cents each, a good price in those days, and I have never forgotten the beauty and goodness of that honey made from the sweet clover that then bloomed everywhere. When my studies, followed by military service, forced me to abandon for a time the small beginning I had made in apiculture, I nevertheless preserved my memories of it. In whatever part of the world I found myself, my thoughts went back to my bees, to the fruit trees in full bloom and the beehives beneath them, to the old man who taught me and to his apiary set out in the grove of black locusts, to the soft maple in the spring ringing to the hum of the bees, and all the numberless associations of those golden hours.

I have often thought since then that anyone who does not taste happiness in his youth is in danger of never finding it. Those who do find it, on the other hand, are likely to return to those sources of it, sooner or later, as I certainly did. How blessed I am to have grown up in a village where bees were kept, to have known beekeepers who taught me about them and to have had a loving family to encourage my interest in them. I believe this has been the constant source of the most lasting joys of my lifetime, and my existence would have been indescribably poorer without it.

TWO

The Language of Beekeeping

My book is written for all who love nature—for those who have tended bees most of their lives as well as those who have never seen a beehive and who know nothing of beekeeping except what they have gathered from enjoying honey occasionally, sometimes seeing a bee on a flower and perhaps at some time or other receiving a sting. For these I am going to briefly explain the words we beekeepers use, thereby saving the need to explain them as they come up. This language is not esoteric. It only seems so to those whose ears are unfamiliar with it.

To begin with then, a *hive* is a man-made boxlike container in which bees live and establish their colony, sometimes inappropriately called their "nest." The *colony* is a social unit dwelling within the hive (or, in nature, within a hollow tree) and consisting normally of one *queen*, or female, several hundred *drones*, or males, and thousands upon thousands of *workers*, appropriately so-called, who perform every task of the colony except reproduction.

My *apiaries* are groups of beehives, sometimes twenty or more, at a given place. I also call them my *bee yards*, or simply

9

yards. I do not, with the exception of my home yard, actually own these places, although of course I own the hives that are kept there. Instead, I have persuaded farmers to let me use out-of-the-way nooks and corners of their land, which they are happy to do in return for pollination and some free honey from time to time.

Now for the hive itself. A *frame* is a wooden rectangular device within which the bees are induced to build *comb*. Normally a single-story hive contains ten such frames arranged side by side, and hence ten combs. The more typical two-story hive contains twice as many frames. The comb is a complex waxen structure, built by the worker bees and composed of thousands of hexagonal cells on both sides. Since a frame is removable, I can at will remove combs, shift them from hive to hive, spin the honey from them, do whatever I wish with them. This fact constitutes the basis of modern apiculture.

A *brood frame* is one containing a comb that is used by the bees for raising their young. The queen lays eggs therein, one egg to each cell of the comb, and these hatch into tiny grubs that soon metamorphose into adult bees. An *extracting frame* is a frame containing a comb used by the bees for honey storage, and hence one from which I spin (or "extract") delectable honey that then appears on my customers' tables. Brood frames and extracting frames are identical, except that the latter are often smaller. By means of an unbelievably clever ruse, I can induce the bees to build their combs in the frames where I want them built, rather than where nature would guide them: I insert in each frame a sheet of pure beeswax called *foundation*, which has the pattern of the honeycomb embossed on each side. The bees, coming upon this sheet of foundation, take it to be the beginning of a honeycomb. They simply complete it, or as beekeepers say, "draw it out." I do not actually make this foundation, and hence can claim no credit for its ingenuity. Instead, I deliver beeswax to the bee supply factory and for a small "work up" fee, they convert it to foundation for me.

A hive consists of several stories, normally two at the beginning of the season, then more as greater quantities of honey come to be stored there. The bottom story is called the *brood chamber*, for here is where the queen normally lays thousands upon thousands of eggs, in the brood frames. The second story is called the *food chamber*. It is identical to the brood chamber, and is used for much the same purpose, except that in the fall it is mostly filled with honey upon which the bees subsist through the winter; hence its name. These two stories make up the beehive proper.

All stories above these two are called *supers*, since they are the stories superimposed upon the hive. These contain only extracting frames. Here is where the bees store all the *surplus* honey, which, at the end of the season, I harvest. In a normal year I take about one hundred pounds of honey from each hive, sometimes less, but sometimes much more.

Beeswax is exuded by the workers from special glands as tiny white flakes and then sculpted and molded by them into the exquisite and complex geometric pattern of the honeycomb. It is, like honey, ultimately derived from the nectar of flowers, although it bears no other resemblance to honey. It is unique among waxes for its hardness and beauty and is an extremely valuable byproduct of beekeeping.

Propolis is a fragrant, gumlike substance gathered by the bees from various trees and plants and used by them to caulk holes and cracks. The word is Greek and means literally "before the city." The ancients apparently believed that this substance is used by the bees as the foundation of their city, or *polis*.

A *queen* is a female honeybee and the mother of the entire colony. For most of recorded history she was called the king bee, after human analogy, until it was finally noticed that she laid eggs. Normally there is only one queen in a hive. She is created by the workers from the tiny grub that would normally become only another worker bee. Nothing is understood of the organic chemistry of this remarkable transformation, except that it is achieved by a hormonal secretion from the pharyngeal glands of the workers, called "royal jelly," with which the developing larva is lavishly fed. The queen is capable of laying more than a thousand eggs in a day, and in the springtime she does so. She has no other function.

A *drone* is a male bee that has no other function than to mate with a queen. A queen mates early in her adult life, soon after she has acquired wings and learned to use them, for mating takes place high in the air. She never mates again the several years of her normal life. Therefore very few drones ever actually mate with any queen. After mating the drone immediately dies. When the autumn frosts come and the drones are no longer needed, they are mercilessly thrown from their hive by the workers, to perish in the cold.

All the other bees in the hive are workers. There may be fifty thousand workers in a hive at the peak of the summer. The role of a worker within the unbelievably complex social structure of the colony is determined by its age. Only the older ones fly forth to forage for nectar and pollen. The younger ones remain behind performing janitorial functions, tending the young, building combs and performing the numerous other exact and specialized tasks of the colony. During the active season a worker lives only about six weeks, spending the last two or three of these going to and from the hive and fields, sometimes over distances of miles.

A *swarm* is a large, often enormous, assemblage of bees that has left the hive in order to establish a new colony someplace, sometimes miles away. After issuing from the hive in a roaring cloud, normally during the swarming season of late spring, the bees form a large cluster on any nearby object and remain there, occasionally for several days, while scout bees search the countryside for a suitable place to establish their new colony. This is usually a hollow tree, which will henceforth be a *bee tree*. The swarm consists of the queen mother, a few hundred drones and thousands of workers. Left behind in the hive from which it issued are still thousands of bees and a young *virgin queen*, or sometimes many special *queen cells* from which virgin queens will shortly "hatch," or emerge. The first to emerge immediately destroys all the others in their cradle cells before they can come out. If, however, two such queens emerge and encounter each other they engage in combat and only one survives, this being the only time in her long life that the queen draws her stinger.

I take the honey from my hives by removing the supers and taking them home, having first trapped the bees out of them by a remarkably handy little device called a *bee escape*. The frames of honeycomb, filled with honey and neatly capped over, are then spun in my *extractor* or *spinner*, which whirls the honey out by centrifugal force after the surface cappings of the combs have been sliced off with a warm knife. Other than the straining-out of bits of beeswax, honey requires no processing, although most commercial honey has also beem warmed and filtered in order, as its processors imagine, to make it more "attractive" to purchasers and to retard the tendency of virtually all honeys to granulate or turn crystalline.

Comb honey, once common but no longer so, is simply pure honey comb constructed by the bees within the very containers in which it is eventually sold to consumers. It is one of the most beautiful products of nature, the only strictly natural honey there is and, indeed, the only truly natural sweet known to mankind. It is expensive, because it requires special skill to get comb honey. The relatively few apiarists who have mastered and still cultivate this art are justly proud, for they have forsaken the greater profits of extracted honey for the deeper satisfaction of meeting a more demanding challenge.

As in all crafts, there is a more specialized vocabulary covering the more recondite aspects of apiculture, but these are the basic words and, indeed, the basic facts of this ancient art.

THREE

The Bee Yard

One needs a sanctum, a quiet retreat, a place safe from intrusions, a place to work out one's thoughts, dwell in feeling on the moment, on the sweetness of the hour, the arising and passing of things. This may have been easier when people lived in cabins and got around by foot or by horse, so that a greater part of life was lived at a quiet pace. Perhaps then the solitary hours, at least for country people, were not so hard to find. Now, with engines ubiquitous and the general race against time that seems to characterize the life of most, the hours of seclusion must be sought and are not always easily found.

The bee yard, for its master or mistress, is a natural sanctuary whose visitors are welcome ones. People almost never intrude in my yards, for hardly anyone knows where they are, and the fear of stings forms an invisible fence to any who do. Occasionally, a beekeeper friend may call, or the bee inspector, who is always welcome. But I rarely encounter the bee inspector in any of my yards. He comes only about once a year, and I can always sense his recent presence—the brick of one of my hives is out of place or a burnt match lies where I did not drop it or a tire track tells the tale. I then find his note, saying he was there, what irregularities he may have noticed that I should know about and

15

otherwise declaring all to be well. When I occasionally come upon him, I do not regard him as an intruder. He can talk about bees while being paid to do his work and I can ask all sorts of questions about what he has found on his trips around the countryside, how the honey flow seems to be shaping up and things of this sort. There is a feeling of sodality between us, a sense of common understanding. We possess a shared initiation into the mysteries, and numberless things are instantly understood without needing to be said.

But the bee yard, when not the scene of herculean labors, as at harvest time, is largely a place of quiet where one feels not alone but rather an integral part of the scheme of things. Solitude is not really the word for it. Communion is. One is not separated from company but only from distraction. One's thoughts and feelings are not imposed from without but elicited from within, rising in absorption with the vast surrounding nature.

The hum of the bees overhead, which in spring and during a honey flow approaches a roar, is to me what the sound of the surf is to the beachcomber. It is not a menace or warning, but a reassurance, almost a voice speaking. It would instantly carry the thoughts of others, the uninitiated, to the association with stings. The sight of the bee master, placidly standing in the midst of this roar, would give an outsider no reassurance at all. The rare intruder who comes upon me in one of my yards therefore retreats, and the yard and its master are again as secure as if surrounded by a high wall.

Smaller visitors, feathered and furred, come and go at will, of course, as oblivious to the bees as the bees are to them. The chatter of the birds is unabated, and my appearance produces a squeak from an occasional chipmunk. Off in the meadow a pheasant gives warning to her chicks. But in general all these

living things share the peace with me, and I shall always keep it
with them. The bees themselves have very few enemies, and I
am glad to move about my yard with the understanding that,
from the standpoint of nature, this domain is primarily theirs.

If it is about midday and I have come to work with my bees, I
can first rest in the shade with a bit of fruit, my jug of water and

a sandwich, my good dog joining me there for the hundredth time. There I get in mind the best way to proceed with whatever needs to be done. I do not know how one could be richer than I am at such moments. Certainly, one's world is not really enlarged with possessions, except by first reducing the world in one's own conception. The setting I am immersed in—the infinite sky overhead, the warm earth, the living woodland, the fields and the many creatures nature never endowed with a sense of property—all this is enough, and the price of it is simply acceptance.

Nothing is despoiled, nothing destroyed or reduced to ugliness or ruin by the presence of a bee yard. The bees themselves forage over literally thousands of the surrounding acres, inconspicuously flying for miles and then returning unerringly to their own hives and no others, but the treasure they bring back is no fruit of plunder. On the contrary, nature has been enriched by their work, for the millions of flowers that have yielded this treasure have in turn received a great gift from the bees, the very gift of life for their seeds. Without the visitations of bees most of these flowers would exist to no purpose, dry up and die without leaving seedlings behind to carry their species into another season.

Honeybees in particular are their saving angels, for unlike other bees and insects that transport the precious, life-giving pollen, the honeybees concentrate upon single species in their foraging. They do not wander aimlessly from one kind of flower to another, which would accomplish little from the plants' point of view. Having started with a particular kind of plant—with an apple blossom, for example—they stay with it. Thus nature and, incidentally, the harvests of men are made more bountiful, and at no price, for the bees also have their reward. One of my yards is tucked off inconspicuously in the corner of the holdings of a large orchardist, who has not only hundreds of acres of fruit trees, but melons and other fruit as well. He knows, as I do, that the honey my bees gather there is a small compensation for the enormously increased yields of his acres.

The beehives themselves involve no assault upon nature or upon the senses. They blend with everything as nicely as a bee tree would. They are, in fact, not substantially different from bee trees. Things have been arranged for the greater convenience of the beekeeper, but the bees take no notice of this. There is nothing unsightly about an apiary, nothing to suggest disharmony. Nothing conveys the impression that, for example, a hydroelectric plant set next to a beautiful stream does or a factory rising in what was recently farmland. On the contrary, an apiary is a lovely thing to see, and beehives are even considered ornamental in gardens and lawns.

The hives need no painting, although there is no harm in doing it if their owner wants to please his own eye. The bees find their way to their own hives more easily if the hives do not all look alike. I rarely paint mine, and as a result no two are quite alike. Most have the appearance of many years of use and many seasons of exposure to the elements. Some were once white, some green, brown, a few even red, having once been painted with leftover barn paint. Most are now weathered, faded and peeling. It does not matter. If I get a hive or super that has never had a coat of paint, which is seldom, then I give it a coat of creosote. This violates the most dogmatic recommendations of the beekeeping manuals: they all contend that creosote never dries and that the bees detest it, both of which statements are false. Before long my creosoted hives have a weathered, inconspicuous and practical look that is pleasing to me and obviously unobjectionable to the bees.

About the only thing that is uniform about my yards, other than the size of the hives, which are all standard ten-frame ones, is that the hives are raised from the ground and arranged in pairs. I find them easy to keep track of that way and I can learn their individual peculiarities. I form a positive fondness for some of them, as though they were friends. A hive stand to support two hives is cut from a ten-foot length of two-by-four, made to form a rectangle and held off the ground by a rock or brick at each corner. Beyond the few cents for the big nails, these stands cost me nothing, because discarded two-by-fours can be found all over for no more than the price of picking them up. It makes no difference if they are filled with nails. They keep the bees up off the damp ground. Dampness is the bees' worst enemy, and the one most easily foiled.

By raising the hives, mice are also discouraged from slipping into them in cold weather when the bees are dormant, and the hives themselves are protected from rot. Of course, many animals find shelter beneath my hives, within the cozy space provided by these simple stands—not only mice, but sometimes snakes, once even a hen and her chicks and once the bees themselves. This last resulted from my hiving a swarm which, incomprehensibly, chose to set up housekeeping *under* the hive rather than *in* it.

Beekeepers are always tempted to build their hive stands with a little ramp sloping down from the hive entrance to the ground. They think that the bees, falling short of their door, can walk up this ramp, but there is nothing to this whatsoever. None of my stands has such an alighting ramp. A bee rarely misses its door. When it does it does not crawl to it. Rather it takes wing and makes a fresh approach, flying right in the second time. The sloping ramps beekeepers feel obliged to supply express some felt need of their own, not of the bees.

Every hive has a brick on top. This custom, quite universal among apiarists, probably originated with the desire to keep the cover on in a strong wind. Doubtless it serves this purpose, at least in winter, and a hive would seem incomplete without the brick. But besides this the brick serves as an excellent device for keeping records, and I can tell at a single glance at a yard any special conditions of any of the hives. The brick in its usual position, fore and aft, means that all is apparently normal with that colony. If standing on end it tells me that the colony was filling its combs with honey last time around and is now either in need of another super or of harvesting the ones that are there. If laid crosswise, the brick indicates that the colony is seriously abnormal—that is has no queen, for example, or that it has laying workers, which is a fatal aberration and will require prompt attention before the colony perishes and the hive is taken over by wax moths. If the brick is lying crosswise on the edge, this means that there is some question as to whether all is well and that I should now have another look.

Usually, of course, all or nearly all of the bricks are in their normal position except during a honey flow or just before harvest. Then nearly all are cheerfully pointing upright, conveying instantly the anticipation of a bountiful honey harvest. It is a rather good system and gives me the additional assurance that no one has tampered with the hives since my last visit, even though little assurance of that kind is needed. If the bricks appear undisturbed I feel that no one else has been near them, for they speak a language invented by me.

Few things are so satisfying to a beekeeper as the sight of a well-tended apiary, especially when it is ringing with the hum of the bees and the hives are towering with supers, presumably loaded with honey. A beekeeper, finding himself in unfamiliar territory, has his eye peeled for the sight of an apiary. I do not know why. Nothing is learned just from seeing an apiary from the car as one drives along, but it is always rewarding somehow. Perhaps it is a reminder that there is still another person who shares some of one's own feelings and joys.

Among beekeepers there is a tradition that they not own, or even in any formal sense rent, the land on which their apiaries are set up. I know of no other branch of husbandry of which this is true. Certainly I would never approach a total stranger and ask if I could put sheep on his land. It is perfectly acceptable to ask that question about beehives. The hives take up little room and, with a bit of inquiring around, one can always find out-of-the-way places for them. It is surprising how many farmers and other country people are pleased, sometimes even eager, to have bees around. Thus I acquire a spot for my bees, for which I do not even have to pay taxes, and the bees themselves acquire thousands of acres of forage land over which they can come and go as they please, gathering the bounty it offers. They do not care who owns those acres, nor do the flowers that bloom in them, nor do I.

Of course I always reciprocate, giving the owner of the patch whatever honey he needs. My rule of thumb is a gift of two pounds of honey for each hive I have set on his land, which may be as many as twenty or so. It is a rough rule, never mentioned to the owner himself, and casually acted upon. Sometimes it is more, sometimes less, but in any case, it is cheap enough. The hive from which he gets two pounds yields perhaps a hundred for me. One owner prefers an occasional bottle of whiskey, left near one of my hives where he, but not his wife, will find it, and this works out all right. I have in the back of my mind a rough idea of when another bottle is due, but we never discuss it. I rarely see the landowners, except when I pull up to their doors with honey for them, and then of course I am welcomed.

How do I find these apiary locations? By asking around. Sometimes I simply go to the door and put the question to whoever answers: How would they feel about having some bees there? Usually the answer is negative, but it is also usually polite. Even those who are appalled at the thought of bees on the place can often point out some crazy neighbor who they think would probably be delighted at the idea. So in one way or another apiary sites are turned up. Of course, as the manuals say, the apiary should be on the brow of a hill that slopes off to the south or the east, but not one of my yards meets those ideal standards. I am content if the spot is sufficiently elevated to avoid dampness, reasonably safe from vandals and convenient to an accessible drive or lane. This last is the one essential requirement. One can walk a distance to and from his bee yard with pleasure until harvest time. When that time comes one must be able to drive a vehicle close to the hives, for the alternative would be to break one's back with the labor of harvest.

My yards present a great variety. There is none I do not enjoy, but some are more rewarding than others. Some I have arranged with better sense than others, so that my chores there are easier—the hive stands are well spaced, for example, or the wild raspberries and cockleburrs are not a problem. Some reward me with honey flows that come faster and heavier than in others. Approaching one of these yards, I can always hope to find a large crop of honey gathered since the last visit. The hope is often rewarded and thus kept alive from one year to another. Another yard is the occasional source of some unusual honey, perhaps of a kind that is much sought after, such as buckwheat. Here, although my hopes are rewarded less often—sometimes three years or more go by with only disappointment—when the reward comes, it is a foretaste of heaven.

I have one yard in the corner of a woodlot that differs from all the others in that way. Overall, my honey harvest there is less than from the others. The area is agriculturally poor, and one finds there more of the works of nature than the works of men. Farms are for the most part in a state of collapse and neglect. Yet, because the soil is poor, the few remaining farmers do sometimes grow buckwheat. These buckwheat fields are discovered by the bees, but almost never found by me, however long I might search. And sometimes, from the eighteen hives I keep there, I harvest a huge crop of this incredible honey. Some years there is little, if any, although I generally get a decent crop from other plants at this place.

I shall never abandon that spot if I can help it. Apart from the occasional buckwheat, there is no more pleasant place to be, just because it is so isolated, so abandoned by people and repossessed by nature. The corner of the woodlot, which I of course do not own, and whose owner I have seen only once in the past decade, is a tiny Garden of Eden. Because the hives are shaded, my bees rarely swarm there. For the same reason they are never encumbered or obstructed by weeds. The animal population is large and varied, providing a constant source of delight. And sometimes there is that sweet reward that is the ostensible point of it all—honey supers crammed to the last cell with dark, rich buckwheat honey. I need then only post a sign at my cottage door, BUCKWHEAT, and those who know what it means beat a path to the door to get it.

Each yard has its own rewards. The home apiary, which is the only one standing on land that I own, is for comb honey, which makes it unique and exciting. Another is a reliable source of alfalfa honey, while still another is located near wild raspberries. By speading them out over the countryside, I of course increase the distances I must travel to tend them all, but it is worth it, not only for the variety, but also in terms of spreading my risk. In any given year one yard or another may not do particularly well, but it would be rare indeed for all to do badly; in fact, this has never happened. Discouragement in one place is compensated by bounty in another, and I feel more in tune with things when I dwell more on the latter than the former.

FOUR

Spring

Like the bees themselves I come to life in the spring, and my rebirth is as sudden as the season's. Last week the bees were clustered in their hives, miraculously maintaining the hive temperature at 65°F., while winter, yielding reluctantly, piled the bee yard with snow drifts and hurled its winds against the hives. The bees knew it was the season's dying effort, for weeks ago they began preparing for warmth. The queens began laying eggs again before there was the slightest hint of spring to my limited perception of things. They began tentatively, with just a few eggs in the deepest center of the hive, as far from the hostile elements as possible and protected by living blankets of workers, layer upon layer.

Then, as the days gradually lengthened, the brood nest was carried outward.

Thus the bees gained an advantage. Already new members of the colony were at hand, filling the places left by their exhausted predecessors. It is no wonder that the hives, so lethargic when I "put them to bed" in October, burst into life with such explosive suddenness the moment the warm spring air sends the snow into streams in thousands of rivulets and stirs the life underneath the earth.

The colony has been preparing for this day, as I have, they in the darkness of their hive and I in my warm shop, getting ready, waiting, keeping an eye on the portents of spring and the first stirrings of the hives, watching the course of the sun and the changing colors of the willows. What was a desert of snow quickly becomes spangled with the glow of dandelions whose pollen will feed the larval bees emerging in such countless numbers in the hives. Spring peepers suddenly fill the night with their low whistling, reviving in me the sweetest memories of youth. Soon afterward the skeletal black locusts will be heavy with their creamy blossoms, saturating the air with their scent and, if the weather is kind, filling the honeycombs with one of the earliest and loveliest of honeys.

Spring does not creep up on us slowly in these parts, which everyone refers to as "upstate." It and the seemingly invincible New York winter engage in a death struggle, winter reasserting itself time after time, refusing to let go until that moment when resistance becomes futile and spring triumphs in a blaze of glory. Then, virtually overnight, the white of the wild cherry replaces the winter cape, and the life of the beekeeper assumes a new tempo.

Woe to the beekeeper who has not followed the example of his bees by keeping in tune with imperceptibly changing nature, having his equipment at hand the day before it is going to be needed rather than the day after. Bees do not put things off until the season is upon them. They would not survive that season if they did, so they anticipate. The beekeeper who is out of step will sacrifice serenity for anxious last-minute preparation, and that crop of honey will not materialize. Nature does not wait.

My bee yards are scattered about over a wide area, and this

apparent inconvenience allows me to savor spring in its different aspects. My two most distant yards are about seventy-five miles apart, with others strung between. It adds to the driving, but my bees are mostly near routes I must travel from time to time anyway, so my bee trips are often combined with other missions.

Some of these yards are at the edges of meadows, in the full sun. They say that locating them this way gets the bees up earlier in the morning, especially if their hive entrances face east, but I do not entirely believe this. The bees in my woodlot yards seem to do just as well, and they swarm less. Still, some variety is pleasant.

Besides this, I have friends in all these different spots. Out in my meadow yards first thing in the spring I have the company of an occasional pheasant. She lets go with an alarmed squawk to her chicks suddenly warning the whole meadow of my intrusion, even though I have been there for more than an hour. Here and there a snake has sought protection under a hive, with not the slightest objection from the bees. The field mice come too, and one of these can be terribly destructive if allowed inside a hive. The bees cannot deal with him after the frost has driven them into cluster and dormancy in the fall, so the mouse, warm blooded, can ravage to his heart's content. Still, I will not destroy him. It is my own fault for not inserting the entrance guards in time. I am entitled to a few epithets and curses, but the field mouse is still entitled to his life. The beekeeper's craft is made better if he sees it, not as an assault upon nature, but as a pursuit that fits in with the total scheme. The mouse is part of that scheme, as are the snakes, the pheasants, the bees, and indeed, as I am.

In my woodlot yards the scene is rather different from the

meadows. Here the chipmunk is my constant companion, though he cautiously keep his distance. He has no use for bees and never ventures toward them, but near my cottage he makes his winter's bed in the old beehives piled in back of my shed and usually steals a fair amount of my smoker fuel for his bedding. I cannot think of a better use for it, and it cost me nothing anyway—old burlap bags, wads of baler twine and some chunks of rope. The chipmunk sleeps more profoundly through the winter than the bear, I am told, and probably has a regular apartment down there in those hives, with pantry, lavatory and everything. Sometimes he slips into my kitchen when I am away, stealing every last kernel of my popcorn without leaving a trace—which is how I know it was not a mouse. The chipmunk is welcome to that too. Fifty cents worth of popcorn will carry him through a good part of the winter, and I feel I have more than my money's worth.

One of the joys of a woodlot yard is to look skyward in the spring, through a break in the foliage, to see the thousands of bees cascading in like a waterfall and rising in equal numbers to scatter over the countryside for miles around. How they do this without constant collision I cannot imagine. They stream upward and downward without any interference whatever, threading their individual irregular paths with such speed that it would be difficult to follow them if there were not such numbers. They are oblivious to me, even though I may be standing directly beneath the break in the foliage that is their entrance to the yard. They swoop past me on every side, then each to its own hive, which is indelibly fixed in its memory from among the twenty or more hives that are there.

The spectacle is greatest in spring, when each bee seems to feel that the destiny of the race depends upon its wings. I may stand directly in front of a hive, into which the bees were pouring a moment ago until I obstructed the approach, but they do not dream of attacking. They are driven by the need to forage, gather and bring home. But when I step aside, restoring the familiar sight of the hive, they descend upon it in a cloud. They display every color of the rainbow, for they are carrying large and colorful pellets of pollen on their hind legs, gathered from dandelions, willows, rockets and other spring flowers. This pollen is the "bee bread," as beekeepers call it, intended, not for themselves, but for their rapidly developing larval brood. It is an inspiring spectacle. I have kept bees in the heart of a large city, on the flat roof of my garage, where they were sheltered by shade trees and used such an overhead opening in the foliage as their gateway to the world. Although thousands of bees constantly rose and descended through this opening, neighbors only thirty or forty feet away were aware only of the low droning hum of their wings, and sometimes would not hear even this without listening for it.

The first jobs in spring are to make sure that the hives are still clean and that the entrances are not obstructed by dead bees, then to check for the invasion of any mice, to see whether any colonies have perished and which ones may have squeaked through on a prayer and now urgently need to be fed to survive the season's final trial. Those few hives that have suffered severely must be dismantled and their entrances cleared.

In the fall I tilt each hive foreward just slightly, slipping a stick or pebble underneath it to hold it in that position. As a result the melting snow does not run into them and most of the dead bees that drop at the entrance do not accumulate there. My hives are never wrapped or insulated against the winter cold, for I learned long ago that it is moisture, not cold, that works hardship. Each hive is provided with ventilation to eliminate excess moisture. Over the years many have developed cracks and holes, which, if not too large, serve perfectly to insure the desired ventilation. In addition, the bees use these openings for coming and going, for back or side entrances. This introduces a bit of irregularity into the apiary but it somehow suits my sense of how things should be. On newer hives, which so far lack such imperfections, I leave the crown board open to provide ventilation. This permits moisture to escape but keeps wind and melting snow out.

It is a simple matter to see whether the hives are clean inside, for any refuse there is accumulates at the bottom. I insert a long, slender stick into each entrance and remove it with a sweep. If all is well then nothing of significance is swept out. It is pleasant indeed to go down an entire row of hives with this result, for I then know that I have wintered my bees well. Instead of spending the next hour or so dismantling and cleaning bottom boards I can sit down nearby with a banana and my thermos of hot tea, watch the bees and listen to their dense hum, congratulate myself on how well I have done here and in my imagination raise up the crop of honey that is sure to follow.

Some beekeepers, trusting the ways of bees less than I do, at this point routinely "switch hive bodies," that is, switch the positions of the two stories of each hive, thinking that this will induce the queen to increase her egg laying and distribute it more widely through the hive. I doubt, however, that any such result is accomplished, and in any case I have long since found that such planning is best left to the bees.

There is no more doleful sight in a bee yard than a winter-killed colony. I have never lost a colony to dampness since I learned of the importance of hive ventilation, but sometimes a colony is lost to starvation. This is a hard thing to admit, for in principle there is no reason for any colony to perish from this cause. It is simply a matter of my hefting each colony from behind in the fall to make sure it is tolerably heavy and hence amply provided with honey for the impending winter. But what is a simple matter to describe is not always so easy to practice. October is likely to find me rushing against time to get the last of the crop harvested before snow is on the ground and before the late fall honey from the goldenrods and asters has begun to granulate in the combs. Just as spring can come suddenly, so can winter, and one must do first things first. More than one hive is likely to begin the long trial of winter with its meager stores of honey supplemented only by a prayer on the lips of its owner. If everything were as it should be, if I never let myself fall behind and the weather steered a predictable course, if people made no pressing demands upon me at critical times when my bees demand my time just as urgently, then colonies would perhaps never be lost to the winter.

But things are never perfect. I see my bees for the last time in October. By then the first frost may have come, the drones have been hurled from the hives and the bees are languorous even on the occasional warm days. The flowers are all gone and the gray skies promise a sudden snowfall at any moment. It is a rush just to get the entrance wedges all in place to keep the mice out. The bees are now resigned to the long and difficult months ahead. Some of the hives are nice and heavy. I have no idea what they weigh, but experience has taught me that when they feel that way all is well. Others I wish were a bit heavier but it is past doing anything about it now. The honey they need has gone to the honey house instead, and some of the fall flowers I counted on failed. I shall worry about these hives, but when spring returns, it is always surprising to see how well they made it. A few may have succumbed, if the winter was long and hard, and many more may have made it only by a hairsbreadth. With the very first appearance of any bloom these will be entirely rejuvenated.

One year, when the goldenrod in the area failed that fall, a whole yard was light. I thought I would be lucky if three of the sixteen colonies survived. Thirteen made it, and of the three that did not, two had been toppled by vandals. It was a gratifying reassurance to check that yard in the early spring, with snow still on the ground, to peer ever so briefly into the crown board opening of each hive and to see that the bees were alive. By the time the dandelions had come and gone, each of those hives was again as heavy as stone, loaded with the treasures of honey and pollen.

It is perfectly easy to tell whether a colony has perished from starvation rather than some other cause: there is no honey in the combs. What one finds instead are dead bees, masses and masses of them, tightly clustered, the combs filled with them, so that each cell has become a tomb rather than the larder it was meant to be. The dismal spectacle appears hopeless—moisture has invaded the hive and turned its contents to a "mouldering mass of sodden corruption," in the perfectly chosen words of some writer of long ago. Vermin have moved in, parts of the combs themselves disintegrate at touch and the temptation is to cast the whole forsaken mess upon a good fire.

Textbooks in beekeeping rarely mention this problem. Evidently their authors are reluctant to admit that it arises. The beginner is thus left in the dark, depressed and dismayed. There is no need for this, however, for here one learns again of the bees' capacity to work together in the performance of unbelievable feats.

I dismantle the dead hive and scrape its bottom board, which takes only a second or two. Next the two stories of the hive are separated and the combs from each removed, one at a time. Most of the dead, soggy mass of bees falls to the ground as combs are separated. The rest I scrape loose with my hive tool, but there is nothing I can do about the thousands of bees filling the cells of the comb or about the bluish mold that has settled. No matter. I do what I can and replace the combs. Now at least air can get inside, the mold is checked and the hive will begin to dry out.

In a week or two, when the opportunity presents itself, I hive a swarm in this salvaged hive. Since it is spring and the season of swarming there is usually no dearth of swarms for this purpose. From then on it is as though nothing had happened. The bees clean the hive and combs within a few days, repair broken comb and restore everything to its original condition. The truly monumental work of apiculture is always done by the bees themselves.

Sometimes a swarm takes over a dead hive at its own initiative, greatly simplifying my work. It is a great satisfaction when I find this has happened. I go to my yard, set for the depressing task of cleaning up a dead hive and discover that the hive is quite alive, that it has been resurrected by an industrious swarm, and that thousands upon thousands of bees are doing the very work I had planned for myself. One winter, because of an early frost that destroyed the fall flowers, my losses were very heavy. My best yard, normally stocked with twenty-two colonies, lost five, which is unusually severe. I was late getting these five cleaned, and by the time I finally did, three had been taken over by swarms. I gave them a hand, cleaning out the bulk of the dead bees and decay and clearing the bottom boards, but it was astonishing how much these bees themselves had already done. The swarms had not been there long, for the queens had only recently begun laying eggs.

On my early trips to the yards in the spring I take jugs of sugar syrup to carry over any colonies that may be in need of emergency relief. No hives are opened yet, for there may still be patches of snow on the ground. I simply heft them from behind, an inch or so, to get the feel of their weight. Any light colony is given a gallon jug of life-saving syrup. It tips the balance. I pick up these wide-mouthed gallon jugs at lunchrooms, usually at no cost, where they were used for mayonnaise, relish and such. I punch four small nail holes in the center of the lid, dump in a five-pound bag of sugar, fill the jug with hot water and stir. The jug is them inverted over the crown board opening of a light colony and the bees empty it in a week or less. Of course there is no danger of any of this sugar syrup finding its way into honey, for the bees consume it at once, and in any case no extracting supers will go on the hives for some time.

Spring is the time of gladness for a beekeeper, not because of what he has accomplished, of course, but for what is promised. This is when I am nourished by hope. The season lies ahead. I always feel sure it will be the record one, and past disappointments do nothing to dampen that hope. Life quickens on every side. The signs of winter's decay subside and are replaced by renewal, not only in the hives, but in the warm earth, in the meadows and woods, and in the air, where every motion and sound declares life. Now is when I not merely know what I have known all along, but deeply feel what I know, that I am alive and intensely aware, in every cell and every thought and feeling, and I rejoice.

FIVE

Swarms

A beekeeper has few memories that rival those of the swarms he has seen. It is a thrill unique to this craft. It seems to me I remember all I have ever dealt with, hundreds by now. My thoughts still go back to a distant boyhood, and I see myself bicycling home, barefooted, a large swarm of bees enclosed in a burlap bag and held at arm's length so that none would be injured as I peddled along. The thrill and fascination that filled me then as I watched large swarms stream into hives has never weakened. I still sit in silent wonder, when now, alone, in one of my yards, I hive a new swarm. It follows exactly the pattern established millions of years ago. It is at this point in the colony's cycle that the psychology of the bees becomes most wondrous. It is now that the habits and orientations that have governed their every movement from the moment they first took wing are abruptly halted, to be replaced by a totally new orientation, as though the former had never existed. It is as though they were determined by a destiny laid down in advance. The phenomenon draws a philosopher's attention to the mystery that inhabits every pocket of creation. We see only a small part of the surface of things. The rest will be forever hidden from us, to be appreciated for its felt but unfathomed presence.

Swarms almost invariably issue before noon and, in my latitude, in the months of May and June, reaching a peak of frequency early in June. By the Fourth of July I have ceased giving them much thought. If several days of rain in the spring are followed by clear, warm mornings, then swarms are likely to issue from the hives in great numbers. Of course wet weather does not by itself cause swarming. The underlying causes are much deeper and are not really understood by anyone.

The preparation for swarming takes about ten days, eight at least, for bees will not swarm until they have reared a number of new queens so that one of them can remain behind to perpetuate the parent colony. It is seldom that uninterrupted rain lasts that long. Therefore, the colonies that swarm in such numbers following wet weather have been preparing to do so before the rain began; the weather only forced a postponement. Although it is considered one of the few near certainties of apiculture that bees will swarm on a warm day that follows days of rain during the swarming season, I have nevertheless made the rounds of my yards on such a day without finding a single swarm. On other days, when for one reason or another I expected to find few or no swarms, I have found a dozen.

Hives headed by queens three or more years old are almost certain to swarm. A colony with a queen less than a year old will seldom swarm unless goaded to it by an inept apiarist. This suggests that swarming might be controlled by requeening one's colonies every year, and in fact this is good advice to one who has only a dozen or so hives. One who has a hundred or more must be content with a less perfect scheme, for otherwise one's beekeeping would consist of little more than requeening.

It is not clear why old queens should be the ones to head swarms, and yet there is a certain abstract intelligibility to it. Although old, she is perfectly capable of founding a new colony with her worker daughters. When she is gone, perhaps soon, one of these daughters will have been miraculously transformed into a new queen, assuring the ongoing life of the colony. In the meantime a new young queen has remained behind to perpetuate the "parent" colony.

Given the spectacular character of swarms of bees it is surprising that they are so seldom seen. Even beekeepers, who are constantly on the alert during the swarming period, seldom see them except in their own bee yards or when summoned by someone else who has discovered one, probably for the first time in his life. The swarm, after it issues from the hive, is in the air rather briefly. For those few minutes it is awesome. The sight fills the beekeeper with excitement and, if the swarm is from one of his own hives, with consternation, for he sees in it the destruction of his hopes for a large harvest of honey from that hive.

People unfamiliar with bees and unattuned to nature are filled with terror by the sight and flee with their hands on their heads. In fact, there is nothing personally threatening about a swarm of bees. Without being hurt one can stand in the very midst of it, the thousands upon thousands of bees swirling about on every side, a few alighting on one's head or on an ear or a shoulder, then taking wing again to rejoin the foray. Provided one gets one's spirit in tune with the excitement and is careful not to crush a bee inadvertently or to let one become entangled in clothing or hair, the chance of being stung is exceedingly remote.

After such a commotion silence soon falls upon the scene, and the swarm now hangs quietly and inconspicuously on some nearby branch, bush or post. The colony that produced it has resumed its accustomed activity, as though nothing whatever had happened, and even the most expert beekeeper finds it hard to say which colony this is unless he was there to see the swarm come out. Now one understands why swarms are seen so seldom. It would be easy to stand within a few feet of this clustered mass, composed of perhaps twenty thousand bees, and not know it is there. Even an experienced beekeeper seldom finds stray swarms. In his own bee yard it often happens that a swarm, which he had not suspected was there, suddenly breaks cluster almost at his elbow, and he stands in helpless dismay as it moves off across the meadow in a vast cloud, never to return, to store in some hollow tree all the honey that he thought would be his. Now is the time for the beekeeper to remind himself that nature recognizes no principle of human ownership. Certainly the bees do not.

During the swarming season people discover clustered swarms in their yards in what seem to be extraordinary places. This is when I receive telephone calls from persons I have never heard of, whose anxious inquiries have turned up my name, as well as from the police and fire departments. The bees' choice of a clustering point is generally arbitrary. It can as well be some lamp post or traffic light as an isolated tree in the country. I have been summoned to the heart of the city to deal with a swarm clustered on a fire hydrant and arrived to find the street barricaded and the police directing traffic clear of the danger point, keeping the curious at a safe distance and being careful to maintain that distance themselves. This is evidently one of the hazards of police work not dealt with in police manuals. To appear in such a setting clad in sandals and tennis shorts and

deal casually and expertly with the cause of all this alarm, accompanied by many "ohs" and "ahs" from the bystanders, is a pleasure that can be matched in few crafts.

The occasion also offers a good opportunity to convey to people that the danger exists only in their confused perception. Bees possess stings only for the protection of the hive. Swarming bees have no hive to protect, and therefore no inclination to sting. I gently dislodge them into my big swarm funnel and swarm box, occasionally brushing a stray bee from my ear or nose or clothing, then drive off, as tranquility settles once again on the human scene.

People are sometimes terrified to discover a swarm in their yard and will eagerly pay an exterminator any fee to dispose of it. If boys discover it they treat it as a target for stones. Often the impulse to mutilate and destroy seems to arise spontaneously in people when they are confronted with something unfamiliar in nature. More than once I have been told of a swarm of bees and, arriving upon the scene, have found ashes, char, and the odor of kerosene, and many thousands of lovely honeybees scattered on the ground, dying or dead. One would think it enough to tell people that bees are essential to the natural ecology and agriculture. Those who cannot understand this will hardly understand that nature labored millions of years to perfect these beautifully complex creatures, and that they have as much right to be in the world as their frightened tormentors.

The swarming season is always filled with surprises. One of the happier ones was the most recent. I saw a huge swarm in the very top of a large apple tree near my home apiary, far beyond reach of any combination of ladders and poles that I could assemble. So I ruefully abandoned it to nature. Within an hour, standing again near that spot, I was astonished to find this enormous limb on the ground, as though by a divine intervention, and there, before my unbelieving eyes, was my great swarm, confused but still together, within a foot of the ground and a few feet from the empty hive into which I forthwith dislodged it. That limb had withstood storms and gales for the better part of a century, and then chosen this moment, when there was no wind, to collapse. The weight of the swarm seemed hardly sufficient to make the difference.

Driving to and from my yards one spring, a spring when swarms had been unaccountably scarce and I was wishing I might come upon a few more, I suddenly had the fleeting feeling that I had espied one from the corner of my eye, a great distance away across two widely separated lanes of highway and in the middle of a woodlot. Just for that instant it seemed to me that I had caught a glimpse of its catenated silhouette against a patch of blue sky. Such discoveries almost always turn out to be illusions arising from hope, as the "swarm" materializes into a collage of leaves or the refuse of tent caterpillars.

This one, however, turned out to be real, as I found when I had maneuvered my car back to the spot. There were no apiaries around there that I had ever seen or heard of, but that fact was not by itself remarkable. Swarms often travel great distances and recluster along the way. I took the spare hive that I keep in the car for just this purpose, set it under the swarm, which was only a few feet from the ground, dislodged the swarm in front of it as I had done countless times before, then continued on toward home and supper. A week or so later I returned to find the hive where I had set it, now taken over by the bees, as I had fully expected. Since the day was wet and few bees were flying, I slipped a screen into the entrance and carted the hive off to my buckwheat yard in the woodlot. That was many years ago, but I can still point to the colony established that day. Now I can never drive past the spot where the swarm was first seen without looking over to it again, as though expecting to see another. In fact, I like to recall how I discovered it, over that considerable distance and while driving along, for it was truly a feat of sorts, the kind of thing that happens very rarely in a lifetime. I take pride in it, even though it is of no significance to anyone else in the world. That colony has never failed to store up a good crop.

So just as nature sometimes reclaims my bees and distributes them to the safety of tree hollows, so also does she sometimes freely give.

Few things are so remarkable as the abrupt change in the bees' psychology that is wrought by their swarming. Normally, they mark the location of their hive with precision, unerringly returning to it after a foraging flight of many miles. If the hive is moved as little as a foot to one side the bees go first to the spot where it had been before making a fresh approach. This orientation is totally disrupted by swarming, so that the bees appear to suffer a complete loss of memory. If, for example, the swarm is hived, and the new hive set alongside the very hive from which the swarm issued, the bees will nonetheless disregard the original hive—the one into which they were born and to which they had unfailingly returned hundreds of times. Nothing will induce them to enter it again so long as their new hive is there.

Indeed one would suppose that any stray bees from the swarm that were in the air or off scouting when the swarm was hived would easily find their way back to one of the other of these two hives. They would be welcomed at either, although instantly assaulted by the guard bees if they attempted to enter any other hive in the apiary. But they cannot find their way to the hive from which they issued, nor to the one next to it, in and out of which their sisters now freely pour, even though these hives may be only a dozen feet away. Days later one can return and find these stray bees still aimlessly circling, their orientation changelessly fixed to the cluster spot the rest of the swarm has abandoned. They retain their futile attachment to that spot until, days later, they perish within sight of what was so recently their home.

On the other hand, if the queen is removed from a clustered swarm, within only a few minutes all the bees return to their hive—not in a random and haphazard way, but en masse, as if at a signal. So they have not forgotten at all! One sometimes reads that if a handful of bees from a clustered swarm is shaken about in a bag of flour and then released, one can then tell from which hive they came by seeing to which one they return. This has never worked for me, and I believe it is something writers have fabricated. The dusty bees in my experiments were irrevocably oriented to their swarm cluster, and no signal that I was capable of producing was able to budge them from it.

How are such things explained? No one knows. Perhaps someday someone will be able to explain them, perhaps not. But I believe there are bees, indistinguishable from the others, who somehow direct the rest, and that the swarm is entirely dependent upon signals from them, instantly understood by the bees but still hidden to us. One naturally imagines that the queen would play this role, so appropriate to a monarch, but this is certainly false. The queen is the most helpless, least resourceful bee in the entire swarm, displaying nothing but fear, stupidity and an eagerness to do whatever her daughters tell her to do.

Why do bees swarm? One might as well ask why the heart beats, why birds nest and spiders spin, why the earth turns.

Abstractly, the phenomenon is quite understandable. The perpetuation of the species cannot be assured simply by colonies of bees becoming ever more populous. Beyond a certain point the size of a colony serves no purpose whatever. Although a colony of bees in a tree hollow might become ever so populous, this does not in the least insure that the tree will not be lost to a fire or to the ax of a woodsman. From the standpoint of the life of the species, then, nothing is accomplished by sheer numbers. If, on the other hand, that colony has given rise to others like itself in other trees and hollows, then nothing of significance is lost when it perishes itself, as sooner or later it must. Other colonies are now in the world to carry on the life that it is the mission of every living thing to perpetuate.

SIX

Controlling Swarms

While there is no such thing as *the* cause of swarming, there are certain factors that precipitate it. The main one, already mentioned, is the diminishing fecundity of the queen as she ages. Another, also mentioned, is a period of rainfall followed by a burst of sunshine and warmth. Overcrowding within the hive does not, as beginners often suppose, cause swarming, but it does aggravate the tendency. I therefore make the round of my yards early in May to get the first supers on the hives, giving the bees room to store honey and something to distract them from swarming. Any obstructed entrances are also now opened, even though there may still be a frost or even another light snowfall. One shallow super is given to each colony the first time around, then another in a couple of weeks as honey begins to appear in the first ones, then a third a bit later and, in the case of very strong colonies, eventually a fourth.

The colony is thus able to grow and expand, and my eyes are treated to the sight that, from the beekeeper's point of view, is the purpose of it all—new, crystal-clear honey in the combs and snow-white flecks of wax capping it over. The sweet odor of the apiary tells me, before I look, that the bees have found great sources of nectar and that the weather has favored the gathering of it. Colonies that a couple of weeks ago would be lifted almost effortlessly would now strain the back of any strong man; the difference is the honey that is rapidly filling the supers.

Of course I hate to see my colonies swarm, as this means the depletion of the force of foragers at the very moment they are needed for gathering nectar. It is a blow to the spirits to open a hive that a few days ago was boiling over with bees and find its population depleted. Foraging is brought nearly to a standstill just when the fields and meadows and trees are filled with the blossoms of clover or yellow rocket or locust. There is not much change in the apparent population of the hive below, but the supers, where the honey goes, are depleted. The swarmed colony will eventually regather its strength, and with decent luck provide a fair crop of honey from the autumn flowers, but it will be less that I had hoped for.

Swarming is of course essential not only to the survival of the species but also to nature itself, for without bees the many plants—both wild and cultivated—that depend upon them for the viability of their seed would also be threatened with extinction. They even have their place and value to apiculture. A newly hived swarm is usually the hardest working colony in the yard. If hived on foundation in a single-story hive (but not if hived on drawn comb), it can usually be depended upon to make beautiful comb honey because of its excessive industry. Swarms also draw foundation beautifully and can be utilized to get perfect brood combs that will last for decades. These are the very foundation of practical beekeeping. Swarms are also useful for making up for winter losses and getting the hives back to use before mice or wax worms take them over. And finally there is the sheer delight in gathering them, adding needed colonies when one is expanding a beekeeping operation.

I have heard it claimed that by picking up stray swarms, one risks bringing disease to the yards, to which I can only say that none of the countless swarms I have added to my yards over many years has resulted in a diseased colony. A colony weakened from foulbrood, a bacterial disease that attacks honeybee larvae, would not be likely to throw swarms, and in any case the risk of disease is greatly reduced by hiving swarms on foundation. Any diseased honey is thus converted to beeswax and its potential danger is eliminated.

There seems to be no practical way of preventing swarming, and sooner or later beekeepers need to conquer their anxiety over it. One must here, as in so many things, be content with something less than perfection, doing what one can to reduce swarming and, beyond that, hoping for the best. Someone with only a few hives, who does not depend on his bees for any significant part of his livelihood, can undertake herculean preventive measures that sometimes work, but this is no pattern for the beekeeper whose bee yards are spread over the countryside and who must make every hour he spends with them count.

If the queen's wing is clipped she cannot, of course, fly off with a swarm, and there is no harm to her in clipping it provided she has mated. The only time she will need wings is when the swarm issues. Without them she falls helplessly in the grass in front of the hive while the swarm swirls overhead, but they will not leave without her and in moments they return. They won't stay, however, for virgin queens with very good wings are about to emerge within the hive, and in a day or two the swarm is ready to take wing again, this time with one of the virgins. Hence nothing has been gained, unless the beekeeper happened to be on hand to see the original swarm come out. In that case he can put a new hive on the original stand and let the swarm with its old clipped queen run into that, moving the parent colony off to a new spot.

Some beekeepers go back one step further in their effort to combat the swarming impulse, destroying all the queen cells in the hive. This sometimes works. The bees will not swarm without leaving behind cells to provide a young princess to fill

the place abandoned by the queen mother. The bees, however, driven by the swarming impulse, replace the queen cells as fast as the beekeeper mutilates them. Normally this replacement takes at least ten days, but in this war with their supposed master they sooner or later decide to swarm on a seventh day, before the queen cells are even sealed, and the work of trying to keep them eliminated has all been wasted. And what work it is:

examining the frames closely one after another every week, greatly disrupting the colony each time, and then in the end losing the battle as the bees fly merrily off.

Beekeepers have invented all sorts of clever manipulations to combat swarming, all of which involve separating the queen either from the young brood or from the foraging force. Bees will not swarm unless queen, brood and foragers are all present. Thus, for example, the brood is all moved to the top of the hive and the queen confined below on mostly empty combs. There are many variations on this idea, but all involve considerable extra work and equipment, which makes them of doubtful value—and still the bees may swarm.

Probably the only reasonably sure way of preventing a swarm is by what is quaintly called "shook" swarming the colony. To speak of this as prevention is misleading, however, for it really involves the beekeeper's creating a swarm. All he gains is the choice of time. The method consists of setting the entire colony off to one side, putting a new hive in its place, and then shaking perhaps half or more of the bees off the combs in front of the new hive, together with the old queen. The original hive, now on a new stand with all the brood, eventually raises a new queen, or can be given a new one, and both colonies then gather strength and eventually store a fair crop of honey.

The effect of that operation is the same as if the bees had swarmed and the swarm had been hived at its original location but in a new hive. The foraging bees return to their old stand, greatly augmenting the force of bees there, and the moved colony, deprived of its foragers, does not swarm. It is all rather fun, if the beekeeper has time for this sort of thing, but then he does end up with two colonies where before he had only one, and he may not have wanted this. A variation upon this system involves hiving the shook swarm, not in a regular hive, but in a shallow super of foundation and then using it to raise comb honey. This can sometimes be done with spectacular results.

If a colony is moved to a new location in the same yard on a warm day when the bees are foraging, it seldom swarms unless it was on the very brink of throwing a swarm when moved—all the foraging bees return to the original location. But then, of course, the beekeeper has the problem of providing a new hive at that original location. Otherwise, the foragers, returning by the thousands, have no place to go.

Sometimes one can simply interchange a strong colony, which is likely to swarm, with a weak one, which is not. In this case the weak one is strengthened by the foragers of the other, which in turn is not likely to swarm. These same foragers, however, are quite likely to murder the foreign queen that they suddenly find occupying the hive at their location; so what was a promising colony is now likely to dwindle to nothing.

Still another method I have used with some success, but which is really only a variation upon these, is to remove the strong colony to a new location in the yard, and on its old stand put a new hive with three or four combs and the queen from the original hive. This usually works but again one ends up with two colonies where before there was one.

After trying them all I decided some time ago that swarm-prevention measures are a will-o-the-wisp; each has its price and none its guarantee, for bees have ways of confounding the most resourceful of schemes. Bees are not like the domesticated mammals and fowl over which human beings have so totally triumphed. They are still untamed and uncorrupted. I hope they will always remain so. If men were to conquer the bees, bending them entirely to human ends, then there would doubtless be rewards of some sort in terms of increased honey production. But something very precious would be lost. The bees we know care no more for our hives than for a hollow tree; they are as much at home in one as the other, and during the period of swarming they are ready to abandon either for the other. The step to nature is for them a very short one. Indeed, it does not even exist. By inducing the bees to make their homes in the hives we provide, we gain control over their location and enable ourselves to reach into those homes and take what we will, but we gain little control over the bees themselves.

I profoundly hope it will always be so. The claims of human beings are not the only ones that are made in the natural realm, and there is something to be said for the spirit of adaptation and acceptance instead of conquest. We have conquered so much, and in the process laid waste to so much. If now this tiny insect adamantly refuses to yield its own nature to us then a certain balance of things will remain as it should. The beekeeper will always be there, with the hum of the oblivious bees overhead. When he sees a prime swarm fill the air and move off to the woods, following the pattern set millions of years ago, he can draw from the sight an inner satisfaction that transcends consideration of material gain.

SEVEN

Swarm Gathering

A beekeeper can hardly sit still or put his mind to any other work at the peak of the swarming season. Over the years I have managed to bring this anxiety under control to some extent, at least to the point of more or less putting out of my mind what might be happening in my more distant yards when it is not possible to find out. Nothing is gained by imagining large prime swarms there. Experience has taught me that if I rush to my yards, summoned by such specters, I will probably find no swarms anyway. Still, it is not easy to relax on one of those warm spring days when I am tied to other responsibilities. The rest of the world goes on in a state of relaxed enjoyment, as though nothing were different, while a beekeeper feels as though he were sitting on pins.

Sometimes, though, that warm spring breaks on just the day I have set aside for a tour of my yards, and this, if all goes tolerably well, is like heaven. There is a thrill in gathering swarms, especially if I have suffered winter losses and have some hives standing empty. At this time of the year every apiary can be a source of surprises. I might find an enormous swarm, several, none at all, or perhaps three or four tiny ones clustered here and there. These little "after swarms," as they are called,

57

have issued with virgin queens after the prime swarm and mother queen have left. It is not clear why they emerge, or why they sometimes do and sometimes do not. They seem to be symptomatic of the colony's "swarm fever," as beekeepers call it, which is sometimes slow to abate. In any case, they are a delight to find if one is needing swarms, for even one of these, smaller than a football, can grow to a powerful colony and fill a super with honey the first year. Just the virgin queen by herself is worth a considerable sum as soon as she is mated.

The unique reward of any swarm, particularly a large one, is seeing it. Of course, a swarm gathered early in the season represents a potential honey crop of significant value, but a beekeeper who lets his thoughts stop there views his craft with an astigmatism. The manner in which a swarm takes over a new hive is always the same, and the thrill of seeing it is always the same, even though it may be the hundredth time.

I dump a prodigious mass of bees in front of a hive, as casually as if it were a bushel of beans, usually onto a cloth that I have spread to prevent entanglement with grass and weeds. There is a momentary confusion as bees move aimlessly and a few of them take wing. Then a few approach the hive, recognize its potentiality and signal to others by raising their tails high and fanning their wings. The signal is quickly picked up by the other bees, which duplicate it, and within seconds most of them are facing the hive, heads low and tails high in the air as though bowing to Mecca. The mass of bees starts approaching the hive, slowly at first but gathering speed as they come closer and start pouring in.

At this point it is always worth searching for the queen. She can usually be found somewhere among those thousands upon thousands, clumsy and frightened and beautiful to the eye of a beekeeper, and having the least idea of any bee in the throng what is going on and what is expected of her. Certainly she in no sense leads the other bees. If she is removed, however, it produces a visible consternation throughout the entire swarm. The new hive, which roused in the bees such excitement a minute ago, now ceases to have the slightest interest to them until they have her back. When I find her I usually pick her up gently, especially if she seems headed off in the wrong direction, and drop her near the hive entrance. She dashes in at once, away from the unfamiliar daylight and back to the security of darkness. The bees know approximately when this critical event has occurred, when their queen is safe in the hive, and a sense of contentment settles over the entire colony.

This is their home, from that moment and very likely for decades to come. What was before a lifeless thing, without significance, becomes now the foundation of their city and their destiny. From miles around they will henceforth return to this spot, and this one alone. In the course of a few minutes it has become the center of their universe, any other object on earth having meaning for them only in relation to it. They will build it up and protect it with their lives. Nothing will be permitted to befoul this hive, nothing other than a bee will be permitted to enter it, and indeed no worker bee except one belonging to this hive. As these bees themselves perish and are replaced by new generations, they will fall outside the hive or be quickly carried out.

The ease with which a swarm is hived is astonishing, but of course not every swarm gets hived. Sometimes the swarm is high, inviting the beekeeper to risk a broken neck. More likely, he simply does not see it until too late. Sometimes I first learn of the presence of a swarm nearby by hearing it take wing, and sometimes a swarm takes wing right before my eyes just as I am making preparations to gather it and then, as all the literature of beekeeping expresses it, "absconds" over the horizon while I watch in dismay.

It is an inspiring spectacle, if one can overcome frustration sufficiently to appreciate it. The cluster of bees that has hung there sometimes for days, until this moment placid, quiescent, hardly resembling a living object, suddenly begins to disintegrate, as though it had received a signal. Within a minute the air is filled with a vast cloud of bees hovering at the spot and keeping themselves together as one. The purpose of this is to insure that the queen is present, to make sure she has had time to take wing and join them. The destiny of the colony for generations and, in fact, for eternity rests in the tiny cells of her body, and there alone. Without her, the swarm would be meaningless. Soon the cloud rises and expands, the individual bees threading their way within it in a pattern of zigzags. It begins to drift away, and for a few minutes one can accompany it over the meadow. Then as they become assured that all is as it should be, the bees gather speed and vanish over the hillside, leaving behind the vacuum of silence, as though nothing had happened. In the presence of such a sight a beekeeper can rise above his limited animality and, for a moment, sense, if not understand, the eternal assurances at which nature forever hints.

I have worked up a few simple swarm-gathering tools and techniques, and the tools are always at hand during the swarming season. One of these is a strong ten-foot pole with a heavy hook screwed into its end. This brings most swarms within my reach, though sometimes I must also stand on top of my truck. Another device, and without doubt the best single discovery of my beekeeping career, is an enormous funnel, about two feet wide at the top and narrowing to about four inches at the neck. Rather than hiving swarms where and when they are found —which is strangely a common practice among beekeepers—I merely dislodge them into screened swarm boxes, using the funnel, then hive them at times and places of my own convenience. In addition to these two special swarm-gathering implements, I have the usual ones—pruners, both large and small, a small buck saw, a length of cord and clothesline and a few small queen cages.

Ideally a swarm should select as its clustering point the end of a fairly small branch of worthless sapling about four feet from the ground. And actually they do that, more or less, fairly often. I then merely prune the branch near the cluster, trim away twigs and leaves, and either dislodge the swarm into one of my swarm boxes or carry it to a nearby hive in need of occupants and dislodge it there. If I use a swarm box, I can cart it home and, if necessary, store it in my cool basement for a few days, then deal with it at my leisure. The bees do not mind this in the slightest, just so long as their queen is with them.

Usually, however, swarms are found clustered in less convenient places—in a thornbush, for example, or a tangle of vines. I prune it away as best I can, taking care that the cluster does not get broken up or scattered if this can be helped. If at all possible in such cases it is best to get the funnel and swarm box under the bees, then shake them all in as well as one can. Bees that are left outside will cluster on the outside of the cage in a few minutes, provided, again, that the queen is inside it.

Of course, the swarm is likely to be overhead. The pole will usually bring it down to within reach. If it would require a ladder to get the swarm I usually force myself to ignore it, to pretend I never saw it, and proceed with other things. No swarm is worth the risk of getting hurt.

If, however, I feel I must recover the swarm, then the following strategy usually works. I tie a small stone to a cord and get it over the branch near the swarm, either with a fishing pole (if one is at hand) or an accurate throw. The stone is joggled down to within reach and a clothesline tied to the other end of the cord and pulled on over the branch. Next I tie a small basket to the end of the line and put a comb containing unsealed brood in this. The brood comb can come from any hive. Basket and brood are now raised to the bees so that they touch it. In a half hour or so they become clustered around that comb and in and around the basket, and can be lowered and hived very simply. The last time I used this somewhat troublesome technique I was glad I had, for it was a large, early-season swarm. It made more than a hundred sections of comb honey for me that first season. The time spent on that one was very well spent indeed.

I have oftened wondered how I ever got through season after season of beekeeping without my swarm funnel and swarm boxes and I wonder still why these are not basic tools of other apiarists. They shorten the time spent in apiaries during the swarming season and put me in control of the bees instead of the other way around. Traditionally, beekeepers cart empty hives around to their yards and hive swarms in them as they are discovered. It is not unusual for me to find a half-dozen swarms in a single tour of my yards, and twice that number is not unheard of. Sometimes I will find several hanging about in bushes and trees in a single yard. Without a funnel and swarm boxes one needs to have perhaps a half-dozen hives on hand at all times while checking the yards for swarms.

Nor is this the only problem. Bees once hived do not always stay hived, especially if the operation is performed in the heat of the day. Their cluster point still draws them like a magnet and the beekeeper, after a half hour's struggle to get a swarm down, often faces the frustration of repeating the task or even seeing the swarm he thought he had properly hived take wing and fly off. Again, it is not always practicable to bring a swarm to a hive; sometimes the hive must be taken to the swarm for it is

sometimes impossible to move whatever it happens to be clinging to—a tree trunk, thorn bush, heavy post or something of
that sort. The bees must then be hived at that spot, which is
usually not where the beekeeper wants an additional hive. Once
the bees are hived there that is where they will forever want to
remain, so one must either leave things that way or come back
later and move the hive to a new spot miles away.

All such difficulties are abolished with funnel and swarm
boxes. It usually takes only a few minutes to knock a swarm into
a swarm box, which can then be handled at the beekeeper's
convenience and at whatever yard he chooses. There is no
returning to pick up hives, and the swarm boxes themselves
take up little room in a truck or car.

I also mentioned small queen cages as being among my
swarm-gathering tools. What are these for? Actually, they are
seldom of use, but they take so little room and are sometimes of
such great value that it is worth having them along. I often spot
the queen, and occasionally, if I am quick and alert, I can catch
her in my hand. Once she has been popped into a queen cage
there is no problem. The swarm is then entirely in my control,
for the bees will not abandon her, no matter where she is. If I
slip the queen, cage and all, into a hive with a handful of bees,
then the rest of the bees will soon follow. Or I can suspend her in
her cage with a bit of wire from a convenient small branch and
soon all the bees will be on that branch. Or I could, though I
never have, clip cage and queen under my chin to produce a
large beard of live bees. This is a standard stunt of beekeepers
and it never fails to stun audiences.

Capturing the queen is always fun as well as useful. The sheer
exercise of skill and dexterity in plucking that one bee from the
midst of her thousands upon thousands of daughters is a deep

satisfaction. Once I even plucked her from the air. I heard the swarm emerging from a hive I kept on my porch, and as I stood there watching them I suddenly had the sense of spotting the queen in the cloud of insects that filled the air in front of me. With a quick grab I suddenly, miraculously and unbelievably had her in my hand. The rest of the bees then clustered near the door of a fairly disagreeable neighbor who had always been far from enchanted by my keeping bees there. I slipped the queen into a queen cage and fastened this on a bush in my own yard, next to a black sock that the bees immediately noticed, and within minutes the rest of the bees all came there too, before my neighbor was aware that anything had happened. On other occasions I have spotted the queen at the hive entrance just as she was emerging with a swarm. She is always worth watching for there, if one knows that a swarm is issuing, for she seems never to be among the first to come out. If you are very quick you can pick her from the alighting board before she spreads her wings. I have never been able to pluck the queen from the swarm after it has clustered, but often she can be found as soon as the cluster is dislodged. Occasionally, the bees themselves betray her location by forming a tiny cluster around her.

When a swarm is awkwardly located and it is impossible to get the whole thing in one stroke there is always the question of whether one has the queen. Is she in the swarm cage or still with those bees at the cluster point? Or is she in any of several possible spots to which the bees have been scattered? This question is always easy to answer by noting the behavior of the bees themselves. If the bees in cluster settle down contentedly the queen is with them. If they are agitated she is not with them. If large numbers of bees are bowing in more or less the same direction and fanning their wings, perhaps over an area of several square feet, then the queen is near where they are all pointing. With help of this kind it is much easier to find the queen than one might imagine.

Beekeepers cannot help loving their queen bees, and the queen must be an object of awe to anyone who understands what she is. She is at once beautiful and singularly stupid, a prisoner of her own fantastically specialized function. A swarm of bees is only imperfectly appreciated if the queen is not spotted within it, for she is its heart and soul. Twenty thousand swarming bees divested of their queen are without significance from the standpoint of nature, while a swarm with its queen seems to manifest nature's deepest workings and mysteries. This perception was expressed to me once by the landowner to whom I pay my rental fees with an occasional bottle of whiskey. He emerged from his house as I was hiving a swarm in his yard, having first gotten a few nips under his belt. We both watched spellbound as the throng of bees began pouring into the hive and I wordlessly pointed to the queen among them. He exclaimed: "And to think some folks say there ain't no Almighty." I do not suppose a swarm of bees rationally proves anything of theological significance, yet it did seem to me that my friend had found precisely the words to express the wonderment of the quiet spectacle before us.

EIGHT

Friends

A beekeeper has a chance to make lots of friends. I am not speaking now only of the human kind, who are not always the most constant, but of the countless others that relieve what could otherwise be an awful loneliness in the bee yards, woods and fields. We tend to take the song of birds, the squeak of the chipmunk and the scurrying of the red squirrel for granted. We may go hours without noticing them. But how desolate our world would be without them, and how desolate our lives! The hum of the bees lifts the spirits, but it is not enough. We need the whole of nature, and we need to be reminded that we are a part of it. The same life that pulsates in us, the same yearning and striving, the same love of existence fills everything around us. These things are not foreign, they belong to us and we to them. It is not our role as human beings to conquer, exploit and destroy, but to build up, protect and love in the spirit of acceptance the natural order into which we have been placed.

These thoughts are never far from me, and I was forcibly reminded of them one day when I began making preparations to move one of my yards to a more promising location. Beneath the old boards and odds and ends that I throw in front of the hives to keep the weeds down, and under many of the hives themselves, I found numerous snakes, curled up in what they thought was the inviolable safety of those retreats. They were not attracted there by the bees, for I have never heard of any snakes having the slightest interest in a beehive. They were simply secure and, I suppose, warm places. It gave me a good feeling to discover them there, to learn that some of my hives and stands were serving this unintended purpose, and to know that, whatever may have been the snakes' terror at being so suddenly exposed to the light and impending destruction, they were perfectly safe from me. After a moment of that fixed stare and flagellating tongue, inimitable by any other animal, they slid casually into the surrounding weeds. I was sorry to cart off their roofs, but I needed them too.

Once, years ago, I was astonished to find a hen nesting beneath one of my hives. She had found a place safe from the entire world, protected as it was by legions of bees who would have no interest in harming her chicks. I managed to do my bee work there without disturbing her, and I have no doubt her chicks were hatched and brought into the world in good shape, although I was not at hand to witness this.

The kingbirds come around to my home yard, and these are officially described in beekeeping literature as enemies of bees. I suppose they are, in the strictest sense, for they eat them—they drop down and pluck them right from the air, near the hives. But are they not entitled to? As we rob the hives of their honey, the kingbirds rob them of a bee now and then, and the right to do either seems hardly less violable than the other. I do not know how many bees one of the birds may eat. Perhaps quite a few if one were to number them singly. But certainly the number is insignificant in terms of the teeming population that a hive of bees supports. In any case, it is quite certain that the kingbird takes no more than he needs. Can we always say the same for ourselves? I have no objection to the kingbirds, and if my hives, in addition to the bounty they yield to their keeper, give up also a bit of nourishment to these graceful birds, then I have one more reason to be glad that I have them. Certainly, the kingbirds have never reduced my honey crop so much as a pound. They perch along the utility wire that runs across my front yard, spending much more time there than in the pursuit of bees, and in the few minutes they are perched there, far more bees are emerging from the brood combs in the hives than all these birds could catch in an entire afternoon. They follow their ancient patterns, as nature prompts them.

Of course the thought crosses my mind: would a kingbird hesitate to snatch a queen bee departing or returning on her nuptial flight, thus imperiling an entire colony? But then I realize that the likelihood of such an event is so infinitesimal as to be hardly worth the moment it takes to consider it. One could probably keep bees for a thousand years before it would happen.

Skunks visit the hives at night, scratch at the entrances, then snatch the bees that appear in the darkness in response to the disturbance. I find the image of this droll. I have never seen it happen, and probably never will, but more than once my dogs have gone boldly forth in the night to investigate and then returned to throw the household into shocked dismay, the skunk having known exactly how to deal with that threat. Still, I do not know what it would be like to live in the country without that singular odor of the skunk in the air from time to time, so I count its source among my friends. I can get on with him, and he with me; we simply keep our distances. Anyway, I have always thought that the Almighty was waxing whimsical when He created this remarkable animal and its extraordinary defense. The skunk can have a few bees and I shall not mind. I induced the bees to make their home in my hives, but I did not create them. As things are reckoned by men I own them, but in the order of nature I own them no more than the skunk does. The man whose thought would here turn to traps is still infinitely far from that sense of nature and spirit of acceptance I have spoken of.

Mice are a different story, and it would not be hard to learn to hate them if it were not such a perfectly simple matter to avoid their depredations. Various species of mice, a few of them quite beautiful, find an empty beehive a perfect haven. An occupied hive suits them in late fall, after the bees have clustered and become too torpid to put up a defense. The mouse chews out a hollow, ruining many valuable combs in the process, and stuffs it with the sort of trash it considers appropriate for a nest. A beekeeper should blame himself for this, however, and not the mouse, for it takes nothing more than a wedge of wire screening in the entrance to protect the hive completely. The mesh is large enough for the bees to pass through easily but too small for the mouse. Unless they become trapped inside and have no other way to escape, mice never, as far as I have been able to discover, chew holes in the hive. Nor do they ever climb up the side of the hive to take advantage of openings higher up. Of course, if, as in my yards, unused covers and bottom boards are kept in the apiary, to be at hand when needed, then mouse nests will frequently be found in them, often with baby mice. There is no harm in this. The worst that can happen is delay in the use of the equipment until the tenants have abandoned it. There is no need to dump the tiny creatures out to perish. Whatever task required the use of that equipment can usually wait until the next trip around.

Toads appear once in a while. It is impossible to think of them as enemies, although I have seen them included in that extensive list of "enemies of bees" in one of the leading treatises on apiculture. They may menace hives in tropical climates wherever hives are not raised from the ground, but certainly they pose no threat in more temperate areas. If they ever catch bees, which I doubt, they must get only a few of them. The toad squats Buddhalike, with boundless patience, certain that some sort of insect will come within reach of his tongue before starvation approaches. He impresses my own less trusting mind. I usually move him to my garden and hope he will stay there, but if he prefers to lumber back to the apiary I do not mind.

My friends are beyond numbering. At one yard, but only at one, the indigo buntings come around year after year. I have singled out these finches as special friends because of the indelible impression one of them made upon me when I was a boy. It was the first I had ever seen. Its beauty was exquisite, and I treated it as messenger of hope.

A woodchuck, too, comes around. He once squared off against my dog, who fortunately had the good sense not to draw too close. The 'chuck gets fatter and fatter until, by late summer, his sleek and portly bulk seems more to roll over the ground than to walk. I believe he is the champion hibernator, far exceeding the bear in his capacity for sleep. By the time he has sunk into his deepest torpor and begun the slow consumption of that great layer of fat his pulse will have slowed, I am told, to only four beats per minute. Then, according to quaint legend, as spring enters, he will rouse himself for the sole purpose of examining his shadow.

Even the crickets fit into the cycle, filling the meadow with their stridence at harvest time. It is hard to disassociate them in my imagination from heavy combs of bright new honey. They are drawn inside to the warmth of my potbelly stove when October's chill puts a frost on the grass, and there they add their singing to the otherwise somber autumn days. The stove seems to affect them in much the same way it does me. It holds the winter's sleep at bay just a bit longer and rekindles fading life. As winter begins to replace the fall I sometimes move a few of the crickets from my honey house stove to my cottage, there to make their home in a tiny bamboo box, sing by my bedside, and gain a further reprieve from winter.

I shall never understand nature, this earth, the bees, the buntings—all the myriad forms. No one ever will. I have no need to. I gaze in unuttered reverence, and I am fulfilled.

NINE

The Honey Flow

The time of honey flow is the one of quiet excitement for a beekeeper. It fills him with a sense of culmination, of a goal near fulfillment. Swarming is past, the supering is done, and the labor of the harvest will soon begin. In this interlude I can sit out among my bees in the home yard and hear the hum of their industry, smell the sweet redolence of incoming nectar and speculate upon its source, estimate my impending crop and gauge my riches.

Paradoxically, the period of the honey flow is the most relaxed time of the season. The activity is feverish, unremitting, but it is the bees that are working. Their owner is waiting, watching the weather, noting the blossoms, timing the opening of the bloom, keeping an eye on the scale hive and nourishing hope. All this is in vain, for there are no reliable signs. I can only wait and see how the flow develops. Still, no beekeeper can help watching for signs, however illusory. I note whether the basswoods have bloomed yet, and if they have, whether there are bees in the flowers. I check the patches of alfalfa, look to see whether bees are on the sumac bobs, note the flight of the bees at the hive entrances.

But the only real test is to peer into a few hives to see how the top supers are filling. By this time almost every hive has three supers, some four, and since the top one went on last it will be the last to be worked in. If there is honey in that one there usually is more in those underneath it.

I am always astonished by the volume of honey the bees store up in a short time during a good flow. A bee can carry only a drop of nectar and must usually fetch that from a considerable distance, sometimes from a source miles away. Furthermore, the nectar is more than half water and must be distilled before any honey results. Knowing these things, I repeatedly underestimate the speed with which supers can sometimes fill up. I arrive at one of my yards to find the supers full and the bees needing more in a hurry. No matter how much nectar is in the fields, it will not end up in the hives or add a drop to my crop or a cent to my purse if the bees have no place to store it.

Having supers fill up with honey faster than empty ones can be prepared is sometimes a real problem, but it is also the nicest problem a beekeeper can have. When I push my hive tool under the crown board and find that it is well stuck down, I can sometimes sense that I am going to see lots of newly stored honey underneath it. The crown board comes off, and before my satisfied eyes are thousands of gentle bees, oblivious to this intrusion, and white combs bulging with honey. Bits of burr comb have been broken by my entry and the bees gather to lick up the pure honey, keeping everything dry and neat. Where all this honey comes from, how the bees could have gathered it so fast, each carrying so tiny a load, is a mystery. We sometimes imagine we know all the answers, but we never do, and even a beekeeper with a lifetime of experience is still often surprised. If the honey that drips from that broken burr comb has a deep mahogany color, however, and if it is late August, then I know

where it came from, for this tells me that the buckwheat flow I
so fervently hoped for has materialized and I am suddenly rich. I
do not think I could find a surer happiness.

In the intense hum of the yards during a flow the bees are
quite literally working themselves to death. Those that emerge
just prior to the flow will perish after about six weeks, having
done what their instinct has driven them to do to insure the
colony's survival. Of course you do not get this impression of
desperate, driving work when you visit the bees. All you see are

bees coming and going in great numbers, perhaps alighting a bit heavily at the hive entrance. Their morale is high and they do not sting me even though I may be sitting only a foot or two away. They are fulfilling their purpose without inhibition. There is no need to sting, no inclination to relax. If a bad turn in the weather at this point forces them to stop collecting nectar, allowing them to relax and extend their individual lives by an enforced rest, then they become irritable, which in their case means they become prone to sting.

I can tell when a honey flow begins by finding a dramatic rise in the readings of my scale hive. This is the special hive that rests permanently on a set of platform scales in my home yard. But this does not tell me where the honey is coming from, which is often a mystery. I am, as often as not, unable to find any conspicuous sources. But of course the sources can be inconspicuous. Unless examined closely, sumac blossoms do not even look like blossoms to us, but the bees assess them differently. One may observe dozens of bees moving from bob to bob of a sumac, touching for only the briefest instant each of the tiny flowers clustered together. The nectar gathered from such a blossom is microscopic, but to form the true picture of things one must multiply that molecular bit by the millions of such blossoms that are displayed and the thousands upon thousands of bees foraging over them for miles around. Other blossoms, such as basswoods, are similarly inconspicuous, except, perhaps, to beekeepers, who are always looking out for such things. It is not, after all, for our pleasure that flowers bloom; they bloom to attract insects.

Still other sources may be distant, their existence unknown to the beekeeper but perfectly known to the bees. It is universally claimed in the literature of apiculture that bees rarely fly more than two miles from their hive, and ordinarily much less, but I have reason to think that greatly extended flights are not uncommon. I have often found buckwheat honey in my hives, sometimes in great quantity, when I was quite certain there were no fields of buckwheat within two miles. Snow white fields of buckwheat, unlike basswoods or sumacs, are not nectar sources I could easily overlook, for I am constantly searching them out. Normally, there is not much else in bloom in the late summer when the buckwheat blossoms open, and the bees must either fly to those fields, at whatever distance, or not forage at all.

Although this is the period of the most intense and driving activity of the bees, it is, strangely and admirably, not competitive. The cooperation within the colony, which has been the foundation of the bees' survival over millions of years, appears to be carried over to the fields as well. Thirty hives sitting side by side exhibit not the slightest sign of rivalry for the bounty—or the scarcity—of the fields, each carrying on its work as though the others did not exist. Of course this mutual acceptance can suddenly terminate when special adverse conditions arise. If a colony becomes seriously weakened, for example, and the weather or advance of the season brings the honey flow to an end, a strong colony might "rob out" the weak one, taking every drop of its stored honey and leaving it to starve. This is rare, however, and is in fact almost always brought about by the bumbling of the beekeeper himself. If a worker bee enters the wrong hive, which is a fairly common occurrence when there are similar hives placed side by side, inhabitants of that hive are likely to attack it. Drones, on the other hand, can fly from hive to hive at will, and a worker that happens to arrive at the threshold of the wrong hive laden with honey or pollen will usually be admitted.

This spirit of cooperation, the avoidance of debilitating

rivalry, carried over even to the foraging areas, is one of the foundations of apiculture. Bees are never found fighting over discovered sources of nectar. Bees from a dozen hives can fill a single basswood tree without the slightest hint of conflict or rivalry. Two worker bees from different hives, which would fall into immediate combat if they were to encounter each other at the entrance to one of their hives, meet on a sumac blossom with only the barest sign of recognition. Under no circumstances do they race against each other to gather the nectar. Instead, one of them simply moves off to a different blossom, leaving the immediate field to the other. More than this, a given source of nectar never seems to be visited by more bees than can effectively and efficiently gather from it, even during periods when nectar is scarce. Thus the number of bees gathering from a patch of alfalfa or the blossoms of a fruit tree is proportionate to the abundance of nectar available there. As this diminishes so does the number of bees; they do not fall to fighting over the dwindling supply. If the source is a field of buckwheat it is visited by great numbers of bees in the morning, when the nectar is flowing, but by midday, the number diminishes to none.

When we marvel at the prodigious feats wrought by the bees, when we are staggered to incomprehension by the vast quantities of honey that can be stored by a single hive, we are likely to overlook what is surely part of the explanation: that the energy of the bees is directed entirely to this result rather than being spent in competition. Cooperation and mutual restraint are of course not unknown among other animals, nor among men, but I believe that nowhere else in creation does it approach this level, extending beyond the hive to the distant fields. To this the bees owe their survival; to this the beekeeper owes his harvest.

TEN

Getting Honey

To speak of *the* honey flow is misleading, suggesting that there is some identifiable time of the year when the bees gather honey, comparable to the flow of sap from maples. A honey flow results whenever any honey plant blooms in sufficient abundance and the weather conditions bring about nectar secretion. Both conditions are essential. Sometimes an entire field will bloom in beckoning profusion, yet be entirely empty of bees because the weather conditions are, in some undetectable way, imperfect. Thus there can be a succession of flows, waxing and waning, some heavy and others light, some long and some brief and some overlapping. They are seldom the same from one season to another, although in a given area there are likely to be one or more identifiable *primary* flows each year.

The earliest flows, from dandelions, fruit blooms and other spring sources, are used by the bees to build up their populations. These "spring buildup" flows in my area are sometimes followed by flows from the locusts, basswood, sumac, clover, alfalfa and other flowers. If things go very well, later on there may be a flow from buckwheat. Then finally in September come the goldenrods and asters, which under favorable conditions of moisture and warm weather produce heavy "fall flows," putting the hives in condition for winter. The season comes to a close with the first frost early in October.

Sometimes a few days can be critical, and whether or not I get honey from a given source can be determined very quickly. The locusts do not bloom very long, for example, and many years they hardly bloom at all. If during the few days they are in bloom it rains on just the wrong one, confining the bees to their hives and washing the nectar from the blossoms, then there may be no locust honey at all. In the fall a shower a week early or a week late, in relation to the goldenrod, or a few days that are too cold or too hot, can make the difference between supers that are full and supers nearly empty. And so it is through the seasons. It is all in the hands of the gods from week to week. It is very rare for every major source to fail, but it is also rare for conditions to be favorable even for most of them. It is doubtful, for example, whether I shall ever in the same season garner good crops from locusts, basswoods and buckwheat, but I would be distressed if in any season I did not get one of these.

During a heavy flow, particularly at the beginning of the season when the work of the bees is most feverish, their drive is so great that nothing can divert them. I can leave my honey house door wide open, which would at other times be an invitation to disaster, and the bees ignore the odor of sticky cappings and combs. They are intent upon the more abundant offerings of the fields. Usually during these heavy flows the days are hot and humid and the nights warm, and every sunset finds the hives settled into a soft murmur, audible at some distance. This arises from the thousands upon thousands of wings fanning and miraculously evaporating and distilling the nectar into the golden richness of honey.

My sets of platform scales, each large and rugged enough to support a hive of bees the year round, year after year, are a source of joy, timing and measuring the flows, telling me at a glance what the bees are doing from day to day. I have two sets of these scales, one for a yard in the north, the other for my cottage yard to the south. Most of my other yards are scattered between these. The scales stay outside all winter each covered with only a bag, which is likely to be torn to pieces by squirrels looking for something for their winter beds. Still the scales continue to tell me what I want to know, season after season. Sometimes the gain is thirty or forty pounds in a few days, sometimes a dozen pounds from one sunrise to sunset.

When I multiply figures like that by my total number of hives and realize that I am the owner of approximately *that* much more honey, I think of the investor watching the rise and fall of the value of his holdings, his wealth varying from hour to hour; except I would rather watch the rising and falling of my platform scales, set out in the shade of a tree, than watch a tape or board in some windowless room. The scale hives provide one of those little extras. Each morning during the warm months, as I watch the various blooms unfold in succession and speculate over breakfast upon what the day will hold, I look forward to joggling that little brass weight down the scale to see where the balance will be struck that day.

Although two or more honey plants are commonly in bloom at the same time, the bees tend to gather from only one of them—whichever yields nectar more copiously. The pear trees may be in bloom and contain nectar in their blossoms, for example, but the bees of a given colony, and in fact all the colonies in the apiary, are likely to ignore them in favor of the dandelions that usually bloom at the same time. This creates a difficulty in the pollination of pears. The minor sources of nectar, such as certain garden flowers that do not bloom in profusion, are likely to be passed over by the bees completely if major sources are available to them. This disappoints beekeepers who have planned their flower gardens partly with the bees in mind.

On the other hand, this selectivity of bees is of great value, not only to farmers in terms of pollination, but also to beekeepers in enabling them to keep various honeys more or less separate. Ordinarily, if a honey flow has been strong, supers are likely to be filled exclusively, or nearly so, with honey from that source. If the honey is harvested at regular intervals as the season progresses there is a succession of honeys that are predominantly of a given type. There is likely to be a considerable mixture of the early honeys, but these are usually all light, mild ones that blend well anyway, so there is little point in trying to separate them. Every effort should be made, however, to get the honey harvested and empty supers on the hives before the buckwheat blooms, as this dark and distinctive honey is exceedingly valuable if kept separate from the others. The fall honey, mostly goldenrod, should also be kept separate, although it blends very nicely with the early light honeys. In these considerations we find the answer to a question that is frequently put to me by my customers: how I control what flowers the bees visit, thereby keeping the various honeys unmingled. Of course I have no such control, but the bees do, and I simply collaborate with their responses to the flows.

Honey supers can be either regular hive bodies, in which case they are called "full-depth supers," or they can be less deep, in which case they are called "shallows." A beekeeper with an unbreakable back who is assured he will suffer no loss of strength as his years increase can use the full-depth supers to advantage. He can interchange them with hives—with brood and food chambers—and he needs to handle only one super, whereas the beekeeper using shallows must handle two.

These advantages are, however, more than offset by the considerations that no man's back is unbreakable and even beekeepers grow older. When full, a mere shallow super is heavy, weighing forty pounds or more. Deep supers, when filled, are ponderous beyond practical limit. Of course, if one has a helper or hive-loading machinery, it is different, but this only calls attention to the disadvantage all over again—one is committed to hiring a helper or investing in such machinery.

Beyond this single, overwhelming consideration in favor of shallow supers, there are others that are not insignificant. It is, for example, much easier to keep honeys from different sources separate by using shallows. A deep super, taking twice as long to fill, is far more likely to contain a mixture from successive flows. The shallow frames, too, are easier to uncap and extract, and they are much less likely to contain honey that has not been capped over and is therefore "unripe." I decided upon shallows long ago and the wisdom of my choice has been confirmed many times. Beekeeping is hard, back-straining work, especially in the yards at harvest time. There is little to be gained in making it more laborious.

To facilitate uncapping them, only eight frames are used in the shallow supers instead of the normal ten. The importance of this can hardly be exaggerated. The combs are thick and can be uncapped in a single deliberate stroke. If foundation has been used, then nine frames are needed, for with fewer frames the bees build the combs irregularly and sometimes between frames. Once the foundation has been drawn and the honey harvested from them, however, eight is the proper number.

The principle behind these observations is that of the so-called bee space, a principle of utter simplicity discovered by the great American beekeeper Lorenzo Langstroth. It revolutionized beekeeping to the point of making genuinely commercial beekeeping possible. The principle is that bees can be absolutely depended upon to leave a space of one-fourth to three-eighths of an inch everywhere in the hive, and hence between combs. Given a larger space, they will build comb in it, while smaller spaces will be chinked with propolis. If eight drawn combs are more or less regularly spaced in a super, then the bees draw them out to the point where they are separated by the bee space and then cap them. This gives the beekeeper precisely the right comb to permit easy uncapping, as well as a good harvest of beeswax from the cappings.

Any beekeeper loves to have supers of beautiful white or near-white combs for the bees to fill; but things in nature are seldom that perfect, and with the passage of years the combs never stay white. The extracting combs become darkened, especially after brood has been reared in them, as it almost always is. Sometimes honey granulates in the combs before they can be spun out, in which case it is likely to be there the next year when it is time for the supers to go back to the hives. Eventually wax moths find some of the combs in storage, so that supers sometimes get wax worm webs between the combs. How does one deal with problems of this sort?

Dark combs are no problem. The color of the comb has nothing to do with the color, taste or quality of the honey that is stored in it. I have been using some of my extracting combs for twenty years. Over that time they have become dark, but they are still perfectly good combs, strong, well formed, and easy to uncap. The honey that comes from them is indistinguishable from the rest. When returned to the hives each season, they acquire the snow-white patina of wax at the commencement of the flow, and the cappings are, of course, renewed each year. There is no need to cull them merely because they are dark. The time do do that is when they have become broken, irregular or warped so they do not uncap easily.

Granulated honey in the combs, although a common problem, is also not a serious one. The bees eventually clean it out, but it may take more than one season. So here again, as in so many aspects of beekeeping, the bees solve the problems and do the work, restoring to use what would otherwise be of little value to the beekeeper, and correcting what are often the results of his own blunders.

Wax worms in the combs are similarly dealt with by the bees, so long as the combs themselves have not been broken down. The bees quickly remove every trace of the web before using the combs for honey storage. Of course there is a limit here to what one can expect of the bees. If the combs themselves are damaged and some of the moth larvae have spun cocoons here and there, then the frames must be cleaned out and fitted with fresh foundation.

Some apiarists have worked out ingenious ways to get extracted combs free from all stickiness before storing them for the winter. One can, for example, stack empty shallow supers, a half dozen at a time, over the crown board of a hive with only a tiny hole about the size of a pencil for the bees to pass through. The bees soon scour the combs of every trace of honey without storing fresh honey there or clustering in the supers, provided the hole for their passage is kept very small. There is no need for any more complex arrangement to achieve this result. I nevertheless always store my supers away sticky and return them that way to the hives the next year. I do this because it is easier, because I have seen other highly successful beekeepers do it and because winters where I live are sufficiently long and cold to prevent the residual honey from fermenting. There is another advantage. When the supers are returned to the hives in the spring the bees move right up into them without pausing a moment. They love those sticky combs, take them right over, clean them up at once and go right to work in them.

But I must confess there is also a disadvantage to this. The sticky combs in my open truck are frightfully attractive to the bees in my home yard, especially after the first spring flows. So I have to get everything in readiness first, back the truck up to my honey house, load up the supers quickly and be off and on my way before the bees realize what is going on. Otherwise, the whole place becomes bedlam in a matter of minutes, and my dear wife again presents me with the now-familiar ultimatum: either her and my happy home or this mad obsession with bees. It would be terrible to be forced into actually having to make a choice, for it would be impossible to abandon either.

ELEVEN

Puttering

Beekeeping charms the naturalist, the philosopher and the putterer. If one happens to be all three the blessings are uncountable. The bees and their astonishing order open the eyes of the naturalist to what others behold without seeing. The philosopher is able to view mankind in the context of a far greater creation. He sees nature not merely as a stage for the unfolding of human history but as a cosmos, a great thing of beauty (which is what the word meant to the Greeks) in which every facet of creation has its place and purpose.

We are not, however, just beings who observe and think. Our joys are sometimes found, not in the contemplation of wonders, but in our fingertips, in doing things, inventing, fabricating or, to use the best word of all, in puttering. Here the child in us, which the poet declared is the father of us all, finds his playful outlets. Here is what is sometimes needed to make us come alive—to be concocting schemes, seeking out little things, preparing surprises for ourselves, testing our own cleverness, sometimes experiencing success and then stepping back to look at some trivial thing we have worked up and thinking: Lo, what I have wrought!

I do not think I have ever known a serious beekeeper who was not a putterer. It is one of the great joys of the craft, and when beekeepers get together for their annual regional conference there is almost certain to be, alongside the honey and beeswax displays, a special gadget show, with premiums awarded to the cleverest and best. The creators of these are usually near at hand to explain them to any who show the slightest sign of interest. This attention to gadgetry is a little surprising when one considers that the basic equipment and paraphernalia of apiculture have not changed much in a century. I sometimes find in old catalogs of bee supplies, put out at about the turn of the century, many of the same things that are shown in catalogs today. It would appear that the tools of the craft have become perfected and fixed, but not so. Every beekeeper introduces his own variations and improvements and, inevitably, his own inventions, things hitherto unknown that he—and perhaps he alone—finds indispensable.

Under the head of puttering I shall include all the activity ancillary to beekeeping that has to do with tools and equipment, whether they are things invented by the beekeeper or familiar things picked up and sometimes put to novel use. This latter is extremely common. Indeed, the really passionate beekeeper can never pass a junk shop without going in to see what he might find to use in his tool box or honey house —something to use in melting beeswax, an old burner for making steam, a useful scraper, whatever. Thus did I acquire my lovely old potbelly stove for a few dollars, attracted as much by its beauty as by its anticipated utility. By now it has become the soul of my honey house, transforming it into a place of comfort and warmth. My honey house is filled with such things, ranging from a fine brass fire extinguisher I found in the road and recharged, good as new, to all sorts of pans, and dippers, strainers, mixers and spoons. It would be almost impossible to inventory them all. Many were made up out of my head, some picked up here and there. I make it a rule, however, not to collect junk, and as soon as I discover that I am not using some bit of equipment, out it goes.

Still, there is plenty left, and the overhead beams of my honey house are covered with nails from which hang these dozens of bewildering objects. Things that cannot be suspended from nails have their places on the many shelves erected here and there. These are themselves old bookshelves and cabinets that someone had thrown out. It is seldom that some tool I need is not in sight and close at hand. My eye is constantly open for things I can bring home. Even when the reward is nothing more than a pile of baler twine or some old burlap bags that a farmer has cast aside, still, they will fuel my smoker for many weeks to come.

For several summers farm auctions were a rich source of gadgets. When commercial farming began replacing family farms not long ago there were left behind many farmhouses and buildings, still inhabited, but not by families engaged in farming. Over the years many of these were abandoned and their contents auctioned off in the yard. Attending these auctions, I always hoped that some past tenant had been a beekeeper, and that his things, as well as old books on beekeeping, would now be unearthed. And sometimes the hope was rewarded. It was in this manner that I acquired some of my best smokers, sometimes offered by auctioneers under such strange names as "bee lamps," and as unfamiliar to the bidders as to him. One auctioneer was glad to let me have a considerable stack of hive bodies for five cents each, there being no other beekeepers in the

audience to offer ten. It was through farm auctions that I got two splendid sets of platform scales, one for a dollar, the other for seven. Both have been of inestimable value in helping me plan my work and schedule my harvests.

These auctions have other rewards, too. At one I found a fine old bee book, of no particular monetary value, and one I already had. Having nothing else to wait around for, I moved it to where the auctioneer would pick it up, thinking I might offer fifty cents. This gesture of mine was noted by an antique dealer, however, who interpreted it as a sly one and inferred that I had discovered something of rare value. Soon she and another dealer in collectors' items were bidding against each other furiously until one of them triumphed with an outrageous bid. I believe I enjoyed this display of uninformed greed more than I would have enjoyed owning the book, which I would only have given to a friend.

My most memorable auction came as a total surprise. I drove off to it with no special expectation and saw nothing about it to stir any interest, until suddenly my eye fell on a bundle of top bars to frames, neatly tied, dusty, but unused. That was all —nothing else to suggest bee things. It was like finding a diamond in a coal yard. How did these get there? Could there be more of this stuff somewhere about? There had to be, it would seem. But aside from this one tantalizing item I could find no evidence of any bee equipment anywhere on the place. I went poking all over, but in vain. Deeply puzzled, I returned to where I had discovered the top bars and probed deeper. Suddenly my heart stopped as there was revealed, beneath a miscellaneous pile, a mountain of bee supplies—box after box of valuable foundation, frames, a copper steam generator of just the kind I needed, and evidently lots more, all old, dusty, but mostly unused, judging from what I could see.

Now I began to eye the crowd to see whether any of the others looked like beekeepers. One gentleman who seemed interested in my discovery pointed out the little steam generator and informed me that it was an "extractor." I decided there would be little competition there. The auctioneer drew closer, and I assumed the appropriate uninterested expression, concealing the excitement and anticipation within. Just as it was the business of the auctioneer to get bids up as high as he could, it was mine to hold them down as best I could, and soon I was loading up my truck on a winning bid of eleven dollars. It was a memorable moment. Not until I got home and took inventory did I discover the true extent of my treasures. It was a good boost to my honey business and gave me many good hours of assembling and wiring frames in the winter months that followed.

Nothing, however, really equals the things you make up for yourself, particularly when they are the product of your own creative imagination. Most such inventions are utterly simple, requiring neither inventive power in their conception nor skill in their creation. A scrap of plywood, for example, is used to press lids onto pails, saving my hands, and it hangs on a nail to be used each year. A five-gallon can with a tiny can soldered on for a spout is used to refine beeswax to perfection. Labels need not be pasted one at a time and applied to containers. Instead, I paint paste onto a wide pine board, spread a couple dozen labels on this, then lift them from the board to containers in a rapid and orderly way. That is my labelling machine, which cost only the price of the paint brush—its only moving part. It never gets out of whack, unlike the labeling machine offered in the bee supply catalog for several hundred dollars.

Stacks of supers weighing several hundred pounds are rolled around in my honey house on little dollies. The dolly consists of a plywood piece with a rim tacked to the top and a ball bearing tacked under each corner. At first I screwed casters to the corners. This required drilling sixteen holes and turning sixteen screws. That was all right. But roller bearings, I have discovered, can be purchased for eighty-nine cents for a set of four and can be fixed to the dolly with only a few blows of a hammer, as each comes mounted in a casing with a nail. This simple improvement greatly enlarged my honey house, for with more than a dozen of these dollies on hand I can move things about and make space with little effort.

My hive stands, mentioned earlier, are another lesson in simplicity. Each is made by cutting a ten-foot two-by-four into two lengths of three and a half and two of one and a half and nailing these into a rectangle to hold two hives. These cost virtually nothing and completely meet the need.

Some beekeepers with a special skill for woodworking make all their hives and parts, including frames. Quite apart from my lack of skill to do this, it does not seem worthwhile. Frames are of precise construction, and the factories are able to turn them out accurately by the thousands. I have also found that hive bodies can usually be purchased second hand for less than the wood would cost to make them. Covers and bottom boards, on the other hand, are another matter, for they can be made out of scraps. A cover is made by nailing one or two pieces of plywood to a rectangular frame and covering it with an aluminum sheet. Such sheets can be had for almost nothing from most newspaper plants, where they are used once and discarded, a fact that seems to be unknown to most beekeepers. Bottom boards are just as simple. Factory-made ones are of complex construction and, for some unfathomable reason, reversible; that is, they provide a shallower space on one side than on the other. This reversibility is worthless, for no beekeeper is going to remove a whole hive in order to flip the bottom over. My own bottom boards are easily made by nailing rails to wide pine boards laid crosswise, then painting them on the outside with creosote.

It is always a challenge to invent ways of speeding operations in the honey house. The shed attached to mine for super storage also serves as a honey-warming room. Full supers from the yards are rolled in on their dollies on cool fall days and left there for a day or two while a small electric floor heater, controlled by a thermostat, brings them to the temperature of a warm summer day. This greatly speeds the job of spinning them out. Sometimes your inventions can save you not only time but much overhead expense as well. An example of this is the frame rack I just recently invented. I was about to buy a second extractor for several hundred dollars, so that my uncapping procedure could proceed without interruption, one extractor spinning the honey out while I filled the other. But just then I came across an enormous saucer-shaped reflector, about three feet across, which, with a bit of figuring and scheming, I was able to suspend from the ceiling by a pipe rigged with a roller bearing. I load this, turning it slowly as I go, while the extractor spins, thus solving my problem at almost no cost.

Invention and the exercise of creative genius mostly fills the winter months. The summer's work exposes the bottlenecks, the procedures where motions are wasted, and the winter's woolgathering supplies the means of overcoming them. On cold nights, warmed by my stove or bed, or sometimes when trips or other monotonous pursuits force me into the company of nothing but my own thoughts, I can concoct new schemes or devices. There is never a dearth of material for my thoughts, and I approach each season with the conviction that, however splendidly things worked for me last year, they are going to go even better this time.

TWELVE

Comb Honey

Raising comb honey is one of the most ancient of agricultural crafts. In fact, until fairly recently in human history all honey was either comb honey or honey that had been crudely crushed from the combs. Even what would now be called the modern methods of production have hardly changed in nearly a century.

Comb honey is what honey truly is. The honey we see in shops, in neat uniform jars, is not exactly what the bees made. Rather it is what people have taken from what the bees made, the "improvement" human beings have imposed. Here, however, it is almost incontestable that nothing has been improved, except in terms of convenience, that good comb honey represents a kind of perfection never found outside of nature and rarely equalled by nature itself. Nothing tastes better, and what is perhaps as important, nothing is more beautiful to the eye. Who has fully sampled life's joys who has not tasted clear, white comb honey on a biscuit? What beekeeper has really tasted gladness who has not taken comb honey from his own hives? And what is nearer pure fulfillment than garnering one's crop and seeing the sections of snow-white combs grow into a veritable mountain? It seems almost a pity to see them sold. No rich man gazing at his gold could be happier, for comb honey is more beautiful to look at and is the fruit, not of greed, but of hours of beekeeping under the clear sky.

I shall never forget the first time I saw comb honey, and how it fascinated me as a small boy. My mother brought it to our cottage and let me cut it from its little wooden box, explaining that the bees had made it for me. I have few memories that extend back so far. The construction—and of course the loveliness of the transparent honey that ran from the broken cells —must have charmed me. I do not remember. Perhaps it was at that moment I became a beekeeper in spirit. Raising comb honey does, in any case, seem to me the culmination of the art of apiculture.

Comb honey is simply the filled and finished honeycomb that the bees have constructed in little boxes supplied by their owner. These boxes of honey have come to be called "sections," from the manner in which they fit into supers. Some older people still refer to them as "cards," for some reason unknown to me. Comb honey is not essentially different from the fresh honeycomb one might take from a bee tree. It is, accordingly, the only genuinely natural honey there is and, by that token, the only natural sweet known to mankind. All other honey has had something done to it between harvest and use, has had its nature altered, however slightly. The change is usually not great, but it is perceptible to a beekeeper. Even honey that has been only spun from the combs and strained has lost something that is discernible to the taste. Therefore, comb honey is to me the specimen of perfection, the ideal from which one may depart for practical considerations, but which cannot be duplicated.

Despite all this, comb honey is not the first honey choice of most people. Partly this is due to widespread ignorance of what it is, even among people who love honey, and partly to its higher cost. No doubt some people also feel that eating comb honey involves eating beeswax, which they find difficult to think of as food. Actually, because the bees draw it out to such unbelievable tenuousness, there is little wax in high-quality comb honey. Those who are accustomed to it usually swear to its wholesome effects, and I certainly add my voice to theirs.

Virtually all the comb honey I raise, which is a considerable amount, is sold directly at my roadside stand. I have sometimes sold it to stores and roadside fruit stands, but never with the great success I have had at my own stand, where nothing is sold except honey. Many who stop pick it up out of sheer curiosity: they have never seen it before. Some express skepticism at my label, which declares that the bees themselves put it in the containers. Many others are elderly people who were familiar with comb honey long ago but seldom see it now. I sometimes feel that I am fighting a lonely battle for wider use of this loveliest of foods. Children, I have noticed, invariably love it, and having discovered it they will probably seek it out for the rest of their lives.

For the beekeeper the great advantage of raising comb honey, and one that seems insufficiently appreciated, is that no special equipment is needed. The only tools are the regular apiary tools—smoker, hive scraper and so on—plus a pocket knife. One does not even need a honey house. No one in his right mind would spin out honey in the kitchen, but there is no problem in putting up comb honey there. A prodigious amount of equipment is needed for strained honey—uncapping equipment, extractor, tanks, strainers, steam generators, the honey house itself, and so on. In addition, spinning out the honey and packing it is considerable work.

Nearly all of this is avoided by the comb honey apiarist. He simply takes the loaded comb supers to the kitchen or shop, empties them, scrapes unwanted beeswax or propolis from the sections, and they are ready. The two great advantages of producing strained honey are that the honeycombs can be returned to the bees year after year instead of being consumed as part of the crop, and honey that has granulated can be restored to a liquid by warming it. Nothing can be done to restore granulated comb honey, and while such granulation does not spoil its value as food, it does detract from its desirability. A beekeeper must, therefore, sell his comb honey crop promptly.

I believe the best of everything is achieved by raising both kinds of honey, unless one has only a few hives, in which case there is no need to raise anything but comb honey. My comb honey crop is the first to come off the hives, so I can begin selling it at my roadside stand at once, along with jars of honey saved from the previous season. Later, when the buckwheat fields bloom, I try for a second large harvest, blending the rare goodness of buckwheat to the natural goodness of comb honey.

The early honey, from the locust trees, clovers and basswoods, is light and beautiful in the white translucent comb. It is gathered rapidly at this time of the year, when both days and nights are warm, so the resulting sections are well capped over. I can also get this honey off my hives before the heavy work of harvesting the extracting honey commences, thereby adding pleasure to the summer days. Many aspects of beekeeping hold special joys, but this one is especially great—to sit out in my neat little honey house, with my ancient radio keeping me company, and in a leisurely fashion put up hundreds of sections of comb honey, using no tool other than my pocket knife. The honey then moves right from my honey house to my deep freezer (a step to be explained in due course) and then to my honey stand, where it is eagerly snapped up by passing motorists.

Beekeepers tend to think that comb honey getting requires extraordinary art and patience, perhaps more than they possess. Non-beekeepers, on the other hand, imagine that it must be relatively easy, that it differs from getting strained honey only in that the last step, removing the honey from the combs, is omitted. Actually, there are certain procedures and manipulations special to raising comb honey, but there is no special art beyond the basic understanding of bees that any beekeeper should possess.

Getting comb honey requires somewhat more attention to the hives. When extracting supers have been put on hives they can be disregarded for a while, sometimes for weeks, and it will not matter—they will fill up with honey sooner or later and the bee master can then garner it at his convenience. One must, however, keep a close eye on the comb supers, for they must be gotten off the hives almost as soon as they are filled. If they are not, then the honeycomb becomes darkened, or "travel stained," as it is called; that is, the cappings lose their whiteness as a result of the thousands of tiny bee feet continuously walking upon them. This does not hurt the honey in the least, but it detracts from its beauty.

It is important that comb honey supers be filled rapidly, during the early or midsummer honey flows when the weather is warm. The fall flows should not be used for comb honey, other than to complete the unfinished sections left over from the earlier flows, for comb honey made during cool weather is waxy, less delicate and, if it contains goldenrod, granulates quickly.

There are many ways to raise comb honey, some simple, some not so simple, and some, of course, better than others. I think I have tried them all, and I shall describe two that certainly work. One is exceedingly simple and requires virtually no skill; the other is more complex but, when properly done, produces stunning results.

The simple way is just to set comb supers over one's strongest colonies, with no more special attention than that. While this involves the least work, it is not the best system. Those strong colonies would produce more extracting honey than comb. They are also more likely to swarm with comb supers on them. Still, one who is raising comb honey for the first time cannot do better than to use this method, and it is still one I use each year on at least some of my hives. Sometimes, for example, when I run out of extracting supers and a good flow is on, I pile on comb supers rather than have hives in the yard with no supers at all.

The other method involves some radical manipulations. I have never seen it fail, however, provided the special manipulations are correctly done, so it is no doubt worth the extra time and work. The system is as follows. Early in the season, when the dandelions are blooming and before the main honey flows begin, remove a strong colony from its bottom board and set it down on a new bottom board immediately in back of where it was, facing in the opposite direction. On its original bottom board, still at the original stand, set an ordinary shallow extracting super fitted with nine frames of foundation—not drawn comb, but foundation *only*. Now find the queen in the original colony and set the frame she is on, queen and bees and all, to one side for a few minutes out of the way and in the shade. She will be safe there and will not fly away.

Next, *shake* most of the bees from most of the remaining frames of the original colony in front of the shallow super on the original hive stand. Do this until about two-thirds of the hive population has been shaken. This procedure has already been described as "shook" swarming, and it is a well-known method of swarm control. Before this "shook" operation is completed, remove the queen from her frame, snip off about half of one wing (or the tips of both wings if it is easier) and let her run into the shallow super, along with the other bees that have been shaken off there. She could, of course, simply be shaken off with the rest, but then one would not have a chance to clip her wing, and it would also be easy to lose track of her.

The bulk of the population, together with its queen, has now been transferred to the new shallow hive. Add a queen excluder, plus three comb supers, cover both hives in the usual way, with crown boards and hive covers, and give the bees the rest of the day to settle down. It is desirable, although not essential, to introduce a new laying queen to the original, depleted colony on the new stand, as this will enable the colony to rebuild its population with great speed and get in condition to gather a fine crop of honey itself.

Consider, now, the result of the foregoing manipulations.

The original hive, although otherwise intact, has lost its queen and most of its population and finds itself at a new location. Either it has a new queen, supplied by the beekeeper, or it immediately prepares to raise one. For a few days there will be little activity at the entrance of this hive, for nearly all the flying bees will either have been shaken at the old location, where the shallow hive now sits, or will have returned to it of their own choice, since this is what they consider to be their hive location. But in a couple of weeks this original hive will again be populous, for brood will have emerged in large numbers and bees will again be foraging. Meanwhile, there is no chance whatsoever that this colony will swarm, because it not only has a new queen, but more significantly, it has lost its flying bees. By the time this colony regains its strength it loses all interest in swarming.

On the original stand there now sits a shallow extracting super with nine frames of foundation, and over this the excluder and three comb supers. The shallow super becomes the new but temporary brood chamber for this colony. It is as if the bees had swarmed and taken over this shallow hive. They occupy the supers at once, since these, like the shallow hive below, contain foundation. This is the secret of the system's success. The bees immediately begin drawing the foundation and storing honey in the supers. If the beekeeper peers into the supers after a week has passed he will find comb honey being made in all three at once, and at an astonishing speed.

This new colony must be watched closely for the first day, however, for it is likely to swarm out either the day the shook operation was performed or the next morning. There, is, of course, no brood at all in the hive to hold the bees there, and it is as though they resented the whole procedure and were determined to begin afresh in a place of their own choosing. They will not go far, however, because their queen is clipped. If the bees swarm, the beekeeper need only find the queen in the grass in front of the hive, place her at its entrance and let her run back in. This done, the bees quickly return on their own. Then they settle down to establishing a new colony and, of course, making comb honey. There is not much room for them to store honey below, for there is only a shallow super that rapidly fills with brood as the queen resumes egg laying. Virtually all of it, therefore, goes up above, soon to be taken by the beekeeper.

When the heaviest early honey flows are over and most or all of the comb honey has been garnered, the two hives are reunited in the following manner. The hive that was moved, and which has by now grown to enormous strength under the new queen, is put back on its original stand, and the shallow hive, now without any comb supers but with a huge population of bees, is placed on top of it, where it becomes an extracting super like any other. All the brood in it hatches out and it becomes filled with honey. The flying bees from the moved colony soon find their way around to the new entrance and are accepted there. The colony has two queens for a while, of course, but one of them, most likely the younger one, soon deposes the other. This colony, uniting the populations of both, now produces a good crop of extracting honey from the fall flows, and of course it does not swarm, for the swarming season is long past.

The system is well worth the extra labor it involves, for, if done properly, it not only results in a great honey yield but also requeens the colony and puts it in excellent condition for winter. The one disadvantage is that it leaves the beekeeper at the end of the season with new extracting supers filled with darkened comb. This is a disadvantage unless one needs additional extracting supers. Thus, if you manipulate ten colonies each year in the manner described you add ten dark extracting supers to your collection each year, whether you need them or not.

There is however, a way of avoiding this, and that is to use a full-depth super instead of a shallow for the shook swarm. This of course results in additional full-depth supers every year, but you are likely to need these anyway for normal replacement and expansion, and it does not matter in the least that the combs are darkened. The result of using full-depth supers instead of shallows is not so spectacular in terms of production, but you are likely to have fewer headaches in the long run.

Those are the two best methods of getting comb honey. They are not described in the manuals of beekeeping. In fact, most manuals merely instruct you to reduce the colony to a single story, crowding the bees and thus "forcing" them up into the comb supers. Not one of them, so far as I know, describes just how this is to be done. Most beekeepers know, too, that bees are not easily forced to do anything, and that merely crowding them in a hive, with no other precautions, is the best way in the world to precipitate swarming.

I have tried the following system, however: divide a strong colony, leaving the queen with the *heaviest* of the two stories on the original hive stand, and add comb honey supers, one at a time, to that. Here the problem arises of what to do with the story that is moved. I have simply piled them up together, four high, on new stands, let them build up to strong skyscraper colonies, added supers as needed, and then in the fall distributed them back to the hives they had come from. But this was not a good system. The bees were slow in getting to work in the comb supers, the drawn comb in the single brood chamber attracted them more. A number of hives also swarmed, spoiling everything. And the four-story colonies made up of the stories left over were very inefficient honey producers. The bees had so much room to story honey that they were not interested in putting it into supers. On the basis of all this I do not recommend the method of hive reduction.

There has been one highly significant innovation in comb honey equipment in the last several years, and that is the substitution of round plastic sections for the traditional square sections made by folding strips of precut basswood. These round sections are superior in every way, but the equipment has, unfortunately, not been properly marketed and is no longer easy to get. For the past twenty years all of my comb honey has been produced in round sections.

A form of comb honey that has become increasingly popular in the past several years is the so-called *cut* comb honey. This is raised in regular shallow extracting frames, using special unwired comb honey foundation, then cut from the frames in uniform rectangular shapes. This comb honey is, of course, as good as any other and much cheaper to produce, although all the frames must be cleaned each year to be used again.

About the only special problem in producing comb honey, of whatever kind, is the damage caused by the so-called lesser wax moth. The tiny larvae of this small moth puncture the cappings of comb honey, riddling the surface of the comb with tiny holes in rather short time. Evidently, the parent moths lay their eggs in cracks around the outside of the hive and the minute worms then emerge and work their way into the supers. So long as the super is on the hive the little wax worms can do no significant damage, but the moment it is removed and the honey is no longer under the protection of the vigilant bees the worms can roam about undisturbed. They do no real damage to the honey, but they ruin its appearance, and this is serious enough.

Beekeepers once dealt with this problem by fumigating the comb honey with bisulfide while it was still in the supers. It would be hard to imagine a worse fumigant. Bisulfide is foul smelling, highly flammable, and toxic to the beekeeper himself if inhaled. Yet it did not affect wax worm eggs, so the supers had to be fumigated a second time to destroy newly hatched larvae.

Fortunately, this disagreeable procedure is no longer called for. It has been discovered that the wax worms are destroyed in every stage—egg, larval and adult—by extreme cold. Thus I pack my comb sections promptly after removing them from the supers, then wait about three days for any microscopic eggs to hatch. This wait is not essential, but it does guarantee the results of the cold treatment that follows: piling the sections into a deep freezer, about a hundred at a time, and letting the temperature drop to five or ten degrees below zero (F), which takes a day or so. This produces no change whatever in the honey, but it does destroy any vestige of wax moth life. The freezer is then turned off and the honey left inside for two or three days, by which time it has returned almost to room temperature. It it were removed while still cold, moisture would condense on the sections, perhaps to harmful effect. Using this simple operation, which is still not widely known, I can raise large crops of comb honey without any damage from wax worms.

Someday I shall be too old to maintain far-flung bee yards and to haul the tons of honey to my honey house, and too old to spin it all out, for this is heavy work. But it is hard to imagine being too old to raise comb honey. The work here is sometimes more time consuming, in relation to the amount of honey produced, but it is seldom arduous. So I can speak of someday retiring from commercial beekeeping, but it is not easy to entertain the idea of retiring altogether as long as the art of comb honey getting remains and as long as I can use a simple pocket knife. Considering that this art has been cultivated by men and women, and very often by elderly men and women, almost from the beginnings of agriculture, it is not likely to pass away.

THIRTEEN

My Honey House

The beekeeper's precious retreat is his honey house, but unlike a bee yard, this curious structure and its contents are a constant invitation to intrusion. People assume that its owner could not possibly be doing anything of importance in there and feel quite free to come and go as they please, some to ask questions, some to buy honey, but most just to talk. Sometimes, of course, they are welcome, but most of the time I want to be alone there. When I am in my honey house it is likely to be either the scene of intense activity, which I can ill afford to interrupt, or a place for puttering and pondering, which one can hardly do in concert with others. Beekeeping stimulates more profound woolgathering and concocting of schemes than any pursuit I know of. To do it properly and fruitfully, one must be solitary, developing a detached and serene spirit.

My own beloved honey house, unlike so many of the outbuildings that evolve to that use at the hands of beekeepers, was actually built to be a honey house, according to my own specifications and plans. It cost rather little, since it is no more than a neat frame structure erected on a concrete base, but over the years much has been added inside and out. It now wants very little either in beauty or utility. Flower boxes grace the windows, and each spring I put petunias in them. At the same windows green shutters, picked up at the village dump and repaired and repainted, give the structure a homey look. Morning glories climb to the roof each summer on one side, and just beyond these my herb and vegetable garden blooms and fruits. On the other side the birds nest in the now overgrown honeysuckles, and an aged clematis spreads itself over the side of the adjoining shed that I built onto the honey house for super storage. Of course the structure is too small—eighteen by twelve feet, with the attached shed for super storage measuring only six by twelve. But everything is compact and well organized, so that I am able to do what I want to do quite efficiently.

One end is my shop, where I repair hives, clean things up, make things, and in a word, putter. A beekeeper needs rather few woodworking tools, which for me is fortunate, as I have a limited skill with anything more complex than a hammer or saw. Still, necessity does enlarge one's creative powers, and I have sometimes stood in astonishment to see what my hands have wrought. There is, for example, a fine little buzz saw, made up from an arbor I picked up for two dollars, a blade, a discarded kitchen table and an old washing machine motor. It is adequate for whatever extensive sawing is required. In my shop there are cigar boxes by the dozen, odds and ends of other containers I have picked up, whose contents and accumulations of the years are known to me alone and would be unfathomable to the rest of the world. Old book shelves and cabinets provide storage for assorted tools and implements, soldering materials, and a fairly large collection of old smokers, most of which need repair.

It is a nice place to be. My friendly radio keeps me company when I feel the need of it, and can of course be silenced the moment that need ceases. My little potbelly stove is there, acquired as a luxury, I thought at the time, but it quickly proved its worth. It burns wood and banishes the chill of a fall day in minutes, not only warming the shop and its proprietor, but lifting my spirits as well.

The other end of my honey house, which takes up a bit more than half of the total space, is devoted entirely to equipment for spinning out, straining, storing and bottling honey, and to molding the beeswax resulting from this operation. As tanks fill with honey, small plastic pails fill from the drizzle of melted wax, resulting in neat stacks of wax blocks as the honey spinning progresses over the course of many days. The wax is worth far more than the honey, pound for pound, but the amount of it, although considerable, is small in comparison to the tons of honey.

The honey house goes through a regular cycle as the year advances, its operations harmonizing with the orderly stages of work in the yards, which is rather the same every season. The cycle begins in the spring, when the hundreds of supers stacked away in the shed are distributed over the course of several weeks to the hives. Each hive eventually receives three supers —perhaps only two for a few backward ones, but sometimes four for what I call the "busters." These do not go on all at once. The second super goes on when the bees have begun to fill the first in earnest, then the third when the second has begun to fill. Everything must be done in an orderly way, taking account of the development of the colonies and the waxing and waning of the early honey flows.

Not much planning is needed here, however. My truck and trailer are loaded up with supers and these are distributed to the yards each weekend, as weather permits, and at the same time I deal with spring cleaning and swarming. It all works out about right. The combs are restored to the care of the bees before the wax moths return. By the time they get filled with honey, spun out and returned to the shed the season for the destructive wax moths will have passed.

After supering comes time for tidying up, restoring everything to order after it has been used and more or less dismantled the previous fall. With all my equipment back in shape, clean and shiny as a new penny, tanks and other containers covered with clean white cloths, I can step back and contemplate my orderly little plant, all ready to go on a new crop. Of course not for another year are things going to look quite that neat and orderly again.

The interlude between supering up and harvest is the time for repairing equipment and getting together those things you need. Each summer sees innovations and improvements, largely the product of my woolgathering. Frames broken and other pieces of equipment are taken care of, and my inventive schemes are carried out. It is a pleaseant interlude, a relaxed one in which I can set my own schedule, and a valuable one.

I have always taken a deep satisfaction in putting to use something that has been broken or discarded as useless. Old frames salvaged from a hive whose combs have been riddled by wax worms or mice can be cleaned up with lye and put back to use as good as ever, thereby enlarging my honey crop without unnecessary expenditure. Old hives and supers, many showing the marks of considerable age, can be cleaned up and restored. Odds and ends can be fashioned to whatever purpose my imagination has conceived—a new idea for a strainer, perhaps, or a rack for extracting frames. The possibilities seem endless as the years come and go. Now too is when the comb honey is harvested and made ready, when accumulations of beeswax scraps are melted down, and when the crystallized honey saved from the previous season is reliquefied and bottled to get my roadside stand into business ahead of the harvest. There is no rush here, no pressure, and whenever my chief impulse is simply to sit out with my bees, watching them come and go, I can indulge that too.

The operations in my shop and honey house are governed by three rules. The first is: No bees. They are rigorously excluded as not belonging there. Bees that get in are promptly removed.

A few bees in the honey house are quite harmless, having no inclination to sting, but they nevertheless are a distraction.

The second rule is: No honey drippings on the floor. This rule requires special vigilance when combs are being spun out, but it is important, for general neatness as well as for ease of work. It is a constant distraction to step in honey, then track it about, stepping in it again. A couple of good big sponges and buckets of water solve this problem.

And the third rule is: No people. I think I love people almost as much as I love bees, but I do not love either species in my honey house. Under no circumstances may any caller be told, as was once common, "You'll find him down in the honey house." Instead, the visitor is announced to me there, and I decide whether to come or to have the caller sent on his way. It depends on how engrossed I am at the moment and also, of course, on who the caller is.

There had always been a tacit understanding to this effect. My dear wife, for example, had long ago learned to knock tentatively when she came to the honey house door, knowing that an intrusion there does not always produce a cheerful greeting. But the rule was only loosely enforced until one disastrous July afternoon.

I was at work spinning out honey. All was going along well until my friend Osmo, a recent convert to apiculture, appeared at the door bearing the single super of honey from his single hive. In an expansive moment I had offered to spin this out for him. My honey house set-up would inspire questions from anyone of normal curiosity, but in trying to attend to the flow of Osmo's questions, I became completely distracted. I apparently stepped on the gas hose that feeds the burner to my steam boiler, shutting it off, unnoticed, and thereby setting off an unbelievable chain of events, unknown to me until the discovery of their appalling consequences later on.

No sooner had Osmo left and my work resumed, than I was dumbfounded to behold in the doorway the smiling face of the president of the university where I occasionally teach. He had chosen just this moment to see whether I might like to go sailing. I nearly dropped a heavy super on my foot. My venerable president, coming upon me as extractor, honey pump and uncapping machine were all going at once, with a great whirring and clatter, remarked that I had a regular factory there. (I could not help wondering whether perhaps he was thinking that I could be using my time far better than at such folly as this.) (The next day, however, I got to thinking that harvesting a nice crop of honey is not half as frivolous as sailing around in boats.)

By the time I had shut down the motors to make conversation, chatted amiably, declined the sailing invitation and seen my second visitor on his way, the smell of gas led me to have a look under the steam boiler. Well! Because the burner had been inadvertently shut off when Osmo called, the boiler, in cooling, had sucked melted beeswax out of the pot into which the vented steam had been exhausting, drawn it all the way up the hose, through the uncapping machine, on through the rest of the hose and into the boiler itself! I could not believe my eyes! It took me a good hour to clear the system, and by this time I decided to leave the job for another day. Meanwhile, my third rule was delivered unto my family, with Mosaic finality and to the accompaniment of thunderbolts overhead: No people in my honey house—ever!

These are precious recollections. They bring a smile, even though the episode seemed horrendous at the time. Life is not always simple and easy—it would be monotonous if it were

—and perhaps the good memories one can store away, of varied kinds, are really more lasting and more genuine than bank notes. Certainly, the more they are used the brighter they get, and they do not ever really get spent.

FOURTEEN

Stings

A beekeeper worth the name develops a healthy contempt for stings. Indeed, he really should start out with that attitude before he has received his first one, so that this aspect of his craft can always be kept in proper perspective. Over the course of years I have woven a veritable philosophy around my attitude of sublime indifference to stings. I have needed the fortification of this philosophy, for a sting does still hurt, just as much, I think, as when I was a novice beekeeper. And it still brings from my lips the same sputtered oaths. In spite of this, I have to maintain a genuine and stoical lack of concern for them. I have to really believe, when I am working with the bees, that I am *not* going to be stung. This is the central requirement for the demeanor necessary in the presence of bees. I have to believe this even though I know, if I pause to think about it, that it is the exception rather than the rule if I conclude my work in a yard with no stings.

Bee work requires intense concentration. One has to keep one's mind on the task as hand, without distraction. Otherwise, blunders are made and the bees might, in fact, become antagonized, so that instead of facing the possibility of a sting or two one is suddenly met with the threat of hundreds of them. You can avoid such a sudden turn of events by keeping your mind on what you are doing. Success in dealing with bees demands a certain demeanor. What is called for is efficient and deliberate movement. It is not so much *slow* motion that is wanted but a controlled approach. Such control is a difficult thing to describe, or even to demonstrate, but nothing destroys it more quickly than anxiety and fretfulness. The moment you jump in alarm you abandon the temperament essential to beekeeping. Some people possess that temperament by birth, as a part of their nature. They somehow sense exactly what is called for and the bees do, in fact, tend to keep their peace with them. Others, although they may have kept bees for years, never develop a deliberate approach, and their hours in the bee yards are hectic and disorganized. Stings are their appropriate reward. These persons should never have taken up the craft, and few of this kind ever do. They belong in the wrestling ring rather than in the apiary.

The best description of the demeanor needed for beekeeping was conveyed to me years ago quite by accident. A sweet and saintly woman came upon me as I was working with some hives, and she was impressed by my bare hands and shirtsleeves. After watching from a safe distance for a while she remarked: "You just send love out to them, don't you?" That is it exactly. It is not just a matter of loving bees; I suppose every beekeeper loves bees in some sense or other. It is more a thing of spirit or attitude. However absurd it may sound to those of scientific orientation, a good beekeeper sends love out to the bees, without giving it any particular thought. In that frame of mind, the work goes well, smoothly, efficiently, without upsets and, in fact, usually without many stings.

Despite what most people believe, bees are not prone to sting. Cross bees are the exception, gentle bees the rule. Most wild things are gentle, and bees are too. They are among the gentlest things on earth, far superior to men in this respect. They have their own purpose, as all things do, and it is not to sting. They must be provoked into it. A beekeeper who stands in the midst of his apiary, perhaps clad in nothing but shorts and sandals as thousands of bees fill the air around him, is not

being courageous. His mere presence is no signal to the bees to attack. For years I kept a dozen hives on my garage roof in the heart of a city, with neighbors and children on every side, and there was never a single complaint of a sting. I was finally obliged to move them, not because anyone was stung, but because a new neighbor moved in down the street, and, noticing beehives, became alarmed at the thought of stings and complained. At that point, upon moving the bees, I moved myself as well; for although I loved my house, I loved my bees more.

The bee was given her sting for the defense of the colony and nothing else. Hence, bees attack almost entirely in proximity to the hive; elsewhere they can be goaded to sting only by extreme measures, such as being stepped on with a bare foot.

The same is true of hornets and wasps. The sting is a defense mechanism. Nature is indifferent to the loss of this or that individual insect and makes no provision for its survival, but the destruction of the colony threatens the species itself. It is there that the life of the species is carried forward. Of course, virtually every sting received by a member of the general populace, whether in proximity to a beehive or not, is called a *bee* sting, so bees, innocent of any involvement in 90 percent of such incidents, nevertheless suffer condemnation for them all. There is hardly a large lawn or meadow that does not harbor yellow jackets, which go peacefully along unnoticed, their nest concealed in the ground, until someone disturbs it. Then the report is spread of a vicious stinging by "bees," and the incident is likely to be so reported in the local newspaper if it is serious. Proper identification is rarely made. I have even seen large paper hornet nests referred to as "beehives," and more than once I have been summoned, in my capacity as beekeeper, to come deal with them.

It is in this manner, too, that bees have acquired the reputation of being more dangerous than rattle snakes, a comparison I have seen solemnly reported in newspapers. More persons, it has been discovered, die from insect stings than from snakebites. This is, in fact, true, because a minuscule part of the general population is hypersensitive to insect stings. For these few, a sting is a real threat to life. Despite precautions, these people are likely to receive a sting sooner or later. The likelihood of a given individual ever suffering a snakebite, on the other hand, is relatively small. Rather few people ever see a poisonous snake, much less receive a bite from one. These basic facts are then modified into the falsehood that more people die each year from bee stings than from snakebites. This, in turn, becomes the outrageous general statement that bees are more dangerous than rattle snakes, which makes splendid newspaper copy.

The misconception might be harmless enough if it did not also separate vast numbers of people from an appreciation of the most beautiful aspects of nature, not to mention the strange reputation it imparts to beekeepers. It does sometimes make life difficult. I have already mentioned my having to move the apiary from my garage roof, not as a result of mischief done, but simply mischief ignorantly feared. The same kind of fear nearly cost me my best apiary site. I found what seemed to me a very promising place to set up a yard and approached the farmhouse a quarter of a mile away to seek permission. The farmer assented at once, but his wife was alarmed at the thought of bees visiting her garden. My reassurance that bees, after all, fly for miles only alarmed her more. She evidently thought they would fly such distances only to seek her out and attack her in her garden. It is pathetic that such wedges of fear and ignorance should be driven between people and nature, for we shall always be part of that nature, whether we understand her or not.

A beekeeper soon learns that bees are subject to swings of mood and temperament just as people are, and generally from the same basic causes. This is no projection of human feelings into other animals. It is one of the most obvious facts of apiculture. The general formula is very simple. When all is going well and the bees are able to satisfy their ends, they are agreeable, but when their efforts are frustrated, they become cross. A beekeeper can work with his bees in his shirtsleeves on a warm spring day when the life of the colony is expanding and acres upon acres of flowers are quite suddenly opening, offering pollen and nectar in greater abundance than the bees can take advantage of. Hives can be taken apart, combs removed for inspection and the bottom boards cleaned with only the slightest notice from the happy and industrious bees. Sometimes on such a day even the veil can be discarded with little risk.

When, on the other hand, the sources of nectar have dried up, as is likely in August, and the bees sense a threat to their well-being, they respond angrily to the slightest disturbance to their hives. Again, when the beekeeper has harvested honey, leaving little on the hives, the bees are sometimes reduced to a very ugly mood until more nectar is gathered and the threat of starvation is banished. Their mood swings from one extreme to another even in a single day. Many beekeepers have wondered, for example, why the hives are so cross when buckwheat is in bloom. In fact, they are not then cross in the morning; only in the afternoon. The explanation lies in a peculiarity of buckwheat itself. It secretes nectar only in the morning.

A beekeeper, knowing the signs of these swings of temperament, is often credited with great courage when no credit is due. Swarming bees, for example, are notoriously gentle, at least for the first day or so. They have abandoned their hive, therefore have no hive to protect and no inducement to sting. So some beekeepers do not even bother with a veil when they deal with a swarm. This always makes a stunning impression upon onlookers, and I have awed many audiences this way.

And of course I always have beehives near my house. I would not want to live where I could not. It is one of my pleasures to present visitors with a comb just taken from a hive and covered with hundreds of bees, among which they are invited to pick out the queen. The bees have no reason to fly from the comb and sting, and virtually all of them are young nurse bees anyway, but this performance is invariably met with stiffened expressions on the faces of my guests. If people will not open their eyes to the wonders and loveliness of nature, if they insist upon closing them in fear and distrust, then I feel that I must, when I can, force their eyes open. I feel like Plato's philosopher, entering the dark caves of ignorance in which people immure themselves and dragging them into the sunlight.

It was discovered in antiquity that smoke instantly mollifies the mounting anger of bees, transforming them from a bold and threatening army into a passive and retreating throng. This is a very useful fact of their psychology. A beekeeper would usually be helpless without his bee smoker. A gentle puff or two gives him complete control of the situation under almost any circumstances. No one seems to know why this is so, and I am often asked what the smoke "does" to the bees. I am convinced it does nothing to them, in any ordinary sense. Certainly, it does not harm them in any way. My view is that they react to smoke in exactly the way we do—they turn away from it. Their defense is, in any case, an appropriate one, for they do what would be the best thing to do if threatened by a forest fire. They turn their attention to their stored honey and make ready to salvage that, at least, in case all else should go up in flames.

It is a widespread belief among beekeepers, even among those who have studied bees for years, that upon sensing smoke the bees all gorge themselves with honey. Sometimes this is even offered as the explanation for their gentleness in the presence of smoke—that they are so filled with honey they can no longer bend their bodies in the manner necessary for implanting a sting! Which only shows that there is probably nothing too absurd to be believed by someone, even sometimes by experts. When a puff of smoke wafts over an open hive one can, indeed, see bees soon drawing honey from open cells, but only a minute fraction of the total population is so engaged. The rest go about their activity much as before. Certainly the hive as a whole does not "gorge" itself, and authorities who have suggested this have substituted imagination for vision. A bee filled with honey, is, moreover, still perfectly capable of stinging. She has simply lost the inclination.

There are varieties of stingless bees, but they are not of much interest because they gather no significant quantities of honey. And I am, on the whole, glad that our honeybees do sting. I find something to admire in the way they can bear down on an intruder, even when I am the intruder. Beehives in gardens would probably be as common as tomato vines if their occupants did not sting, and while this would be nice, in a way , it would also rob the beekeeper of that specialness that I, at least, prize. And it would, it seems to me, be an imbalance in nature if anything as delicious as honey were obtainable with little effort. As things are, the bees hold their own against the virtually omnipotent human species, and I am glad it is so.

FIFTEEN

The Cross Hive

Everyone can recall certain moments that were turning points in life. The moment of my first bee sting was surely one of these—not just because I had been stung, even though the immediate consequences of this turned out to be rather horrendous, but because the fates had somehow put me in the proper frame of mind for it. From that moment my attitude toward bees, and their stings, has been essentially what is required for the art of beekeeping.

I was still young but had already sensed that the hostility people see in nature is born of ignorance. My love for nature had turned to awe and amazement when I had recently beheld my first beehives. Soon afterward I went out to the country to call on an ancient beekeeper I had heard of. About the only thing I knew about bees at that point was that they will not sting if you do not bother them; and this was less an item of knowledge than an article of faith derived from my general attitude toward living things.

I found the beekeeper, very old and crippled by arthritis, and he took me at once to his apiary. There must have been a dozen hives. I had never seen so many bees. Striding dauntlessly up to them, in the steps of the old man, and like him without any veil, I did not wince as I felt a sting on the very top of my head. I somehow had the faith that the bees would not attack me if I approached them in the right spirit and that this sting was some sort of accident. I was right about that, for there were no more, but within a half hour my entire body, to my toes, was covered with brilliant red blisters, and I hardly made it home and into a bathtub before my eyes refused to open. For several days I wore a face that rivaled that of the ape. The experience seems only to have reinforced my determination to become a beekeeper, and in any case, those miserable initial effects have never been repeated. A sting now, even to the eyelid or lip, produces the same sharp pain and the same expletives, but no swelling.

Every old-time beekeeper can tell about the cross colony he once had that no power of heaven or earth could subdue. Such a colony is not usual, but is encountered sometimes. It violates every principle of apiculture. A puff of smoke only rouses it to greater fury. It is invariably a colony under stress—one that has just lost its queen, for example, or one that has been robbed of most of its honey.

My own encounter with such a hive is unforgettable, although I have to admit now that the anger of these bees was provoked by my choosing an inappropriate time, during a dearth of nectar in the fields, to take their honey. This hive did in any case teach me a lesson about that, and it dispelled conceit that with skill and the right approach I could manage any colony of bees on earth.

I arrived at daybreak in the yard where this colony stood, thinking I could get my work done before the heat of the day. The deep red of the rising sun warned that the day would be hot and therefore ill-chosen for work in a bee yard. And indeed it was hot, even before the sun was very high. When I saw a grasshopper in front of my nose, *inside* my veil, I should have interpreted it as an omen and left the work for another day. Things went all right for a while. I was using a bee blower and had about forty supers off the hives and loaded when off came the cover of the cross hive, which had never been particularly cross before. It was as if they had been observing my approach for the past hour with mounting fury.

Every beekeeper can imagine the scene that followed. The bees rose from the open hive in a cloud. My shirt, already plastered to my back with perspiration, was quickly stitched down as if by a thousand needles. A few bees even managed, miraculously, to pass through the wire mesh of my veil. This unsettles the nerves of the most stoical beekeeper. I got the hive back together, gathered up my equipment, and with elephantine grace got myself away from there, observed with profound curiosity by a young field hand not far away. Glancing over my shoulder as I fled, I noticed that the field was suddenly empty, the field hand having evidently moved with approximately the speed of light from the center of the field to its periphery. And sure enough, there he was, off to the edge, his shirt off now and twirling slowly, like a windmill, in front of him. I didn't ask any questions. My faithful old dog, who always accompanies me on my bee trips and who has never failed to respond to my call, did not appear this time. I became convinced that her brave heart had finally given out, that a thousand bees were now stinging her lifeless body in some forsaken place where she had vainly sought safety. Actually, she was eventually found, stretched out comfortably by a cool spring in a darkened cow barn nearby, oblivious to the fierce bedlam of the world outside.

That evening my dear wife was shocked to count the stings I had received. I could have told her where she might have found a

few more. The prettiest twist to the whole episode came about a
week later, however, when I returned to find this same colony
now fairly good-natured, and to learn that the young field hand,
whose eyes, I was told, had been swollen shut for two days, had
decided he wanted to raise bees himself, was eager to learn more
about them, and wanted me to give him lessons! Well, he
seemed to have gotten through the hardest lesson with good
grades. He moved away soon after, however, and our paths have
not crossed again. Perhaps he is now keeping bees.

I wrote to the bee supply company that night for a complete bee suit with zip-on veil, an item that had always been considered the necessary uniform by female apiarists of my acquaintance. This brought to a full circle my own philosophy about stings. That philosophy had begun with a scorn for even a veil and with the conviction that stings are the reward of the clumsy beekeeper. Perhaps one gets less heroic with age, but I generally use my bee suit now, with its zipper veil that no bee can penetrate and the ventilated leather gloves I bought at the same time. Now I do sometimes spend an entire afternoon with the bees without a single sting. Cowardly or not, it seems good.

Still, I know that as long as the bees are such a part of my life, which will surely be to the end of my days, there will be plenty more stings. It is worth only so much to try to avoid them.

SIXTEEN

Garnering Honey

In most branches of agriculture harvesting is the most reward-ing phase. It is the time to taste the fruit of one's labor and measures one's success. It is not always so in beekeeping, for the gathering is not a straightforward matter of reaping and taking. The bees, never tamed, do not always yield up what they have gathered with the docility of domesticated flocks. Yet an ex-perienced apiarist has learned their ways and knows how to steal away with their precious honey before they are even aware that he has done it. If their resentment is roused by this, then their owner, if he knows what he is about, is miles away by the time it happens.

The commonest mistake of inept beekeepers is to try taking the honey on a hot day when the flowers have dried up and the bees, already in a sour mood, are ready to take out their frustration on whatever moving thing draws near their hive. Sometimes, too, a careless beekeeper permits sticky honey to become exposed in the yard under these already stressful condi-tions, by breaking bits of honeycomb or by using a mechanical bee blower which requires breaking the supers apart before blowing the bees out, creating drizzles of honey here and there. This can create a frenzy of excitement in the bees. The air becomes filled with them, and no veil or bee suit is total protection against them. What should be a joyous task becomes irksome, nerve-racking toil, tempting novice beekeepers to wish they had never gotten into such business.

I harvest my comb honey supers as they become filled throughout the season, beginning in July. Escape screens, which permit the bees to move downward a few at a time into the hive below, but do not allow them to return, are inserted under the supers. Cleverly arranged little wires spring nearly shut behind them as they pass through, permitting only a one-way passage. After a day or two the supers are empty or nearly empty of bees, and I simply walk away with my bounty. Any bees still remaining are sent flying with a few good huffs and puffs as I walk off, for a comb honey super is not so heavy that I cannot hold it in front of my face and blow into it. At the same time I can savor the sight of the lovely comb sections and make a preliminary assessment of their quality. I do not think of comb honey simply as good food; it is the distilled nectar of flowers sealed into snow-white waxen cells of the most exquisite beauty.

The means of harvest is about the same for the honey that will be spun from the combs in my extractor. It does not matter how long it has been on the hives, for even though the cappings of the combs may have become darkened by the thousands of bees moving over them day after day, this makes no difference whatever in the honey that will be spun from them. When there has been a heavy flow from the locusts or other early sources I try to make a preliminary harvest early in the season, mainly to have it on hand for the hundreds of people who are eager to buy it. But there is no need to do this. If the honey flows are slow and drawn out, so that it takes most of the summer for the supers to fill properly, then the harvest can be put off to September and the honey will be just as good. In that case, however, it is harder to keep the different honeys separate.

By early September, the time of the last and largest harvest, the days are usually bright, pleasant and cool. The hives are tall and loaded with honey. Those that have three shallow supers on them will give me nearly a hundred pounds. Some will give me more, some less, but when I average a hundred pounds overall for the season I am content. This adds up to a ton of honey from an average yard of twenty colonies.

A day for harvesting is at hand, then. There will be more harvest days in other yards, and another day to return and finish the work at the yard I have chosen for this day. Every such day will be pleasant if early snow does not overtake me. I have learned the pitfalls to avoid, learned how to avoid stings, how to avoid straining my back and limbs, and how to avoid excessive perspiration. There will be time, as I proceed with the work, to appreciate the crisp air and bright sun that only autumn provides, and to relish the sight of the goldenrod and wild asters on every side. Sometimes where the soil is very rich the goldenrod grows higher than my head and I must pick my way through it to find the hives it conceals.

The bees have an air of contentment. Their hives are filled and they feel secure for the winter—a state of being that has been the purpose of all their gathering. They would feel less secure if they knew what is about to happen, but it will take another million years of evolutionary change to teach them the meaning of the beekeeper who now approaches. They long since learned the significance of the bear, whose name in Slavic languages means "honeyeater," but the methods of a beekeeper are more deft and subtle than the rampaging bear's. Their brains are no match for mine.

Of course, I do not menace the bees. I am going to take most of their honey, but they will still have more than enough to carry them through until spring when their colony life will begin anew. And it is not unfair that I take it either, for it is because of my skill and the means I have provided that they have been able to gather so much more than they need in the first place. Left to themselves in the hollow of some tree they would gather much less. I have earned what I shall take.

I go about the work with my veil tied snugly, my bee suit zipped up securely and my trousers tucked into my boots. My bee gloves, with their long gauntlets, are there if I need them, but I probably will not. It is doubtful whether my bare hands will receive more than one or two stings, possibly none at all, and the greater dexterity of bare hands is worth this insignificant risk. My smoker is fueled, smoldering well, and my pockets bulge with spare twine, corn cobs and burlap scraps for occasional refueling. Another pocket holds a roll of masking tape and scraps of newspaper, which I shall need before long.

Now to begin. I approach the first hive from behind and pry up the top two supers, leaving them tightly stuck together by the propolis the bees have applied to every crack. Just a few cool and gentle puffs of smoke tell the bees they should stay where they are, and they do. They are in no way harmed, but an instinct tells them to guard their precious stores and be prepared to fly off with them in case fire, suggested to them by the smoke, really threatens. Raising the two supers and drawing them toward me an inch or so, I tilt them forward with one hand and hold them effortlessly at a near balance for a moment while my other hand slips the escape screen under them. The two supers are then lowered onto the screen and the whole business is shoved squarely into place. A generous piece of asphalt shingle, softened slightly by the warm sun, is laid over the crown board hole where it fits snugly, keeping any bees from entering by that route. Now the job is virtually done for that hive, but the hive cover is left off for the time being while exactly the same procedure is repeated for every other hive in the yard, perhaps twenty or so in all. By that time I have slipped escape screens under a thousand or more pounds or honey, and yet I have done no strenuous lifting at all, only a brief balancing act at each hive.

Next I return to the hive I began with and scrutinize the supers above the escape screen for any crack or opening through which bees could enter and rob out my crop, which they will almost certainly do if they can. That is why the hive covers were left off: I want to be able to see that all crown boards, as well as the supers themselves, are perfectly bee-tight. There are always a few that need a bit of chinking and taping over: That is why I have the newspaper scraps and masking tape in my pocket. Where there are holes and cracks large enough for a single bee to pass through there are by this time several bees clustered, bees that have emerged from the supers. They are a dead giveaway, drawing my attention instantly to the leaks I am looking for. If I had new equipment these precautions would not be needed, but most of my supers are old, some are very old and weathered and cracked and chipped here and there. When I am satisfied that all is tight and bee-proof I replace the covers and the brick that belongs on each and the work is done for the day.

There is time to count the supers and calculate roughly the wealth they will add to my pocket. Forty supers will yield well over a half-ton of honey and many hundreds of dollars. A day or two later, or a week later if I am busy with other things, I return to gather up the supers, heavy with honey but empty of bees. I load them one at a time onto my truck and my little trailer and

cover them well with cloths and crown boards, in order to keep temptation away from the bees. The loading up can sometimes be done without even wearing a veil, for the theft is so swiftly performed that the bees do not even know what is going on.

The last super having been loaded, it is now time to gather the escape screens still on the hives, and here smoker and veil will be needed again. A billowy puff of smoke goes right down through the escape screen before I even pry it loose. The screen is removed and replaced by the crown board and cover. Bees still clustered on the escape screens are dislodged with a single sharp blow in front of the hives, and I am then ready to drive off with my crop.

Thus is the harvest accomplished, a different yard each week, sometimes two at a time, always with at least two such procedures at each yard. Meanwhile, I spin out the combs in my honey house and store them away, emptied of honey, ready to be used again next year.

It is good work, and the tons and tons of honey that are spun out through the warm fall days between trips to the yards restore both my body and my mind. The sight and fragrance of a hundred or more gallons all ready to be drawn off into glass jars is by itself enough to ease whatever effort it took to get them.

SEVENTEEN

Honey Spinning

Autumn has come and I am deep into spinning out honey. These October days are incomparable to any others of the year. They seem laden with the sense of ending, and yet mingled in this is a heavenly beauty. They carry the sad feeling of bidding farewell to beloved friends, and yet one sees that this is but a phase in the eternal cycle. The period of fruiting is over, woods and fields are transformed, and what remains of my garden's harvest sprawls over the ground in the morning dampness. A few slugs take advantage of the sun's slow retreat. The occasional geese overhead, sometimes close, sometimes distantly honking, add to the sense of departure. But who can be blind to the sweetness of a quiet fall day?

The flowers have dried up and offer nothing to the occasional visiting bee except, here and there, some late pollen. Nature's activity is coming to a halt, well ahead of the first frost, but the hives are heavy with the late fall honey. They will winter well this time, no doubt of it, and I need not worry on cold winter nights that my bees will be hungry, as I sometimes do when a cruel early frost can rob some of my hives of their chief hope of survival. The bees now come and go, as always, but they are listless, their flight mostly pointless, the product of sheer habit, as the months until spring stretch out before them.

Autumn always creeps up on me and then pounces, threatening to trap me with an early blanket of snow before my honey is harvested. It has never caught me, but it sometimes comes close, and each year I am driven by anxiety that the first snowfall will find me with extracting supers still on the hives. I am not sure that this would be a disaster or why it always seems so threatening. The honey could still be garnered even with snow on the ground. But everything would seem out of harmony, the mood would be wrong, and an activity that is normally filled with satisfaction would instead have the quality of an anxious dream. I always press, then, to have everything done before the first of November—the honey all spun out, the beeswax stacked in uniform yellow blocks, and the honey house itself tidied up and the stickiness rinsed away. Then with the first snow and howling wind I can feel that another phase of my beekeeping year is completed, while a new one begins, and I feel in step with the cycles of nature.

A day for spinning out the honey begins as I pull myself from my warm bed in the chill early hours. Soon the sun begins to dye the eastern horizon red. Before long, it will drive the heavy fog from the lake and then dry the wet grass. A bit of tea helps stir me to life as I think of the stacks and stacks of supers filled with honey and waiting for me in the honey house. They have been kept warm through the night in my little heated super shed, so the honey will flow as nicely as on a hot summer day. As dawn brightens I contemplate, over breakfast, the thin column of smoke spiraling from my honey house chimney, rising from my potbelly stove that I kindled last night and ignited in the sleepiness of the early morning. The honey house will be toasty warm and smell of the apple wood cut from falling limbs of nearby ancient trees. Every year at this time a few crickets find their way in. I do not know how. The structure seems secure against ants. But the crickets respond to the potbelly stove in about the same way I do, and they are certainly welcome to share it with me. Their bright notes are just the spice that is needed on these sometimes somber days.

The honey spinning continues until after supper and into the night, but my fatigue is compensated by tanks of precious honey. Besides this, a bed feels better to tired limbs than to a body that has done nothing, and not many thoughts can equal those that culminate a day of achievement. It is a lot of work, sometimes monotonous work, and I am sure there are people in other pursuits who, without working this hard, end their day far richer. But I would not relinquish my small honey house with its devices and old motors and gadgets, its simple machinery, its stove and its crickets. Once one has tasted the sublimity of nature, heard the hum of the bees, beheld the migrating geese, absorbed the song of the cricket and felt the intimations of the glory of God, one has no great temptation to try burnishing one's own greatness. The world and the hours, these are enough.

My honey house setup borders on the fantastic, at least to the eye of the layman, although it is all perfectly intelligible to me, since I designed it. Every element in it is intended to save time and work. It has evolved gradually over the years as new ideas and inventions have been incorporated until now it seems nearly perfect. Perhaps it resembles nothing so much as a one-man band. The master of the apparatus stands at the center, operating various switches and motors with both hands and feet, and a great and orderly process revolves mysteriously around him.

Reconstructing the setup now in my imagination I find two
gas burners for the generation of steam, which I must keep an
eye on for proper adjustment, three motors salvaged from old
refrigerators and laundry appliances, a great quantity of
switches to activate motors and warmers, floats, a warning

buzzer, various levers, paddles, and some miscellaneous things for which it would be hard to find a name—these in addition, of course, to the usual spinner (or extractor), tanks, uncapper and so on. The instruments of my one-man band look something like this:

Of course items are represented in this picture as strung out in a line. It would be quite out of the question to try representing them as they really are, for the whole complex apparatus is arranged more or less in a circle. I operate from the center of this circle where the many things needing my attention are within reach. Here is how it all works.

The supers are stacked, eight to a pile, on dollies that are rolled about where needed, as described earlier. I never need to lift a full super once it is in the honey house. The combs are loosened by prying up one end of the super and slipping a special stick underneath, thereby raising all the frames for easy grasping when the super is lowered onto the stick. A steam-heated knife is kept in rapid vibration by a motor that is turned on and off by a special switch at my toe. This slices the cappings off with a single motion for each side of the comb. The uncapped combs go one by one into the spinner and, when this is filled and running, they go into what I call the merry-go-round. This is a revolving rack of my design that holds the combs until the spinner is again empty and ready to receive them. The cappings, meanwhile, fall stickily onto a hopper and flow from there into my melter. This is an ingenious device that imparts no heat to the honey that accumulates in it but melts the cappings that float on this honey by means of steam-filled copper grids on top. As the wax melts it drizzles off into plastic buckets that serve as molds. Other than to change the plastic bucket from time to time the melter requires no special attention once it is steamed up.

My honey spinner is made to hold twenty-four combs, but an additional twelve go in perfectly well. Even though some of the combs rest flat against each other the honey all spins out as it should—a fact that, I have found, is little known among beekeepers. They can greatly increase the capacity of their radial extractors by taking advantage of it. The slots of the spinner are marked with a pattern of colored dots, which enables me to distribute the combs of each super throughout the radius of the reel and then restore them, after spinning, to the supers from which they came. This not only insures that the combs do not get mixed up but, more important, that the reel is always balanced and will not wobble. There is a system to this. Each super is emptied beginning at the center, and the combs dropped into the spinner according to the colored dots—red for the first super, yellow for the next one, and so on. Thus, even though the combs are of different size and hence of different weight, and even though some may be partly granulated, the spinner remains balanced.

Ideally, two people should work together at spinning. The nature of the work is perfectly suited to such cooperation: one can uncap while the other loads, runs, and unloads the spinner. I nevertheless prefer to do the whole thing by myself. I can start and stop everything according to my own mood and convenience. While the spinner is whirling away, driven by its old faithful motor and belt, I turn to whatever needs attention —adjusting the flame under the steam generators, checking the beeswax drizzle, scraping burr comb where it has accumulated or, of course, uncapping more combs and loading the merry-go-round.

The honey pours forth with a rush the moment the spinner attains speed, then continues to flow at a decreasing rate as the combs rapidly empty. It is conveyed by gravity to a baffled sump, which retains most of the particles of beeswax that have been spun out. As the sump fills, it automatically raises a float activating the switch to my honey pump that is driven by the motor from a washing machine. The pump conveys the honey to an overhead tank, made by cutting an oil drum in two. This is the holding tank from which the honey flows at a constant rate into the warming pan beneath it. If the honey in this holding tank rises dangerously near to the top, so that it might overflow, a buzzer sounds, activated by a float in the tank, and then I need only to turn off the pump for a few minutes.

The warming pan that receives the honey from the holding tank is a long water-jacketed pan interlaced with baffle plates. An immersion heater and thermostat keep the water in it at a constant temperature. A temperature of 130° F. is usually sufficient to retard granulation for several weeks, but the device can be set above or below that as needed. The honey flows back and forth across this pan, guided by the baffles, then empties into a double-thickness nylon strainer consisting of two ladies' stockings, and then into the one-hundred-gallon storage tank. The next morning it is drawn from the tank into whatever jars or tins I have arranged for.

Thus everything is incorporated into a smooth operation with a minimum of separate steps, from uncapping combs at one end to filling jars and tins at the other, the blocks of beeswax meanwhile accumulating as a byproduct and requiring no separate operation. The whole thing takes a bit of time to set up and get into proper adjustment, its various parts harmonizing with each other and the motions of the operator, but it is well worth it.

Honey spinning is long and tiring work, as I uncap the combs one by one and start the honey through the system, and sometimes it seems endless. Yet it is the object of the whole enterprise and yields a sense of deep fulfillment when, at the very end, I uncap the last comb and roll the last stack of supers into storage, concluding another season.

EIGHTEEN

People

I have discovered a curious fact about beekeeping—if anyone pursues the craft then, in the eyes of his fellows, he forthwith ceases to pursue any other. No one seems able to picture a beekeeper in any other role. Perhaps the strangeness of the image in their minds, the image of someone keeping company with bees, simply overwhelms every other possible association.

I am a beekeeper, but I have in fact had other interests along the way, and even a few accomplishments. Yet these, though they may be known, are never the subject of comment when I enter a gathering. The question is always, "How are the bees?" There is nothing else to ask. I do not know exactly how it should be answered, if put seriously. What can one say? I do have an answer, intended more to halt further inquiry than to satisfy curiosity: "They're waxing." But it usually does not halt further inquiry. The questions that follow are likely to be more point-less than the first, even when concocted in the minds of persons learned, witty and scholarly. The next question, for instance, is usually, "Do you ever get bit?" To which the answer is, of course, that I never have yet. Sometimes it is worth adding that I receive my share of stings, but so far no bites. But usually I prefer to add no qualification that might remove the look of incredulity from my questioner's face.

Another question constantly asked, for reasons I have never fathomed, is, "What do the bees do in the winter?" And the answer to this is that they languish, like myself. And that seems to me not a purely flippant response. It fairly well describes what the bees actually do. A similarly common question of the same order is, "Who looks after the bees in the winter?" I could say "no one," but the more positive response is "the Almighty." It seems somehow to put everything in a better perspective.

Sometimes serious questions are no easier to answer. I do not know what to say, for example, in response to the question of whether my honey is "organic." Any answer that does not include a disquisition on the foraging behavior of bees is almost certain to mislead. The same is true with respect to the question of whether my honey has been "cooked." If I restore granulated honey to liquid by warming it, do I thereby cook it? The question arises from the practice of some honey-packing companies of adding the word "uncooked" to their labels—which makes as much sense as describing bananas as "boneless."

A beekeeper friend of mine was once asked how often a bee dies. This was evidently a way of asking how long a bee lives, which is a perfectly good question. But upon hearing this question, my friend was so seized by giggles that he had to withdraw and pull himself together before emerging to reply: "Just once!" It is seldom that I collect a swarm without having some bystander ask how many bees are in it. I generally produce an arbitrary answer to this—something like "seventeen thousand three hundred and sixty-two." Strangely enough, I have never been asked how I know. One of the more memorable questions I've been asked came from a lady who had for years been putting up with a nest of honeybees in the siding of her house. Her question was whether she might be able to rid herself of them by putting a dish of honey out in the yard and then, when all the bees were out drinking honey, plugging their entrance behind them. Perhaps one needs to be a beekeeper to appreciate this naiveté.

It remained, however, for my sister-in-law to ask the greatest bee question of all time. She asked me (I swear), "How much do you make on your honey business, *per bee?*" Now I suppose I could take an estimated average population of a hive, multiply this figure by the number of colonies I have, divide this into my net profit for a year (or would it be the other way around?) and get some sort of figure having maybe fifteen or twenty zeroes following the decimal point. But I do not think I ever will. I somehow feel that my life was made richer by my having received such a question, reminding me that the ways of men are sometimes, like those of God, wondrous indeed.

People, in addition to being a fertile source of questions, are also the consumers of my honey crops, so I could hardly do without them. Nor would I wish to, for I have formed many friendships among this class. For years I sold virtually my entire honey crop by mail, and even now I have customers I have never seen but whom I have come to know well from years of this association. I know their idiosyncrasies and preferences. One, for example, who orders huge quantities of honey, eats nothing but raw food. He therefore telephones each year for my renewed assurance that the honey I send him has not been warmed at all at any stage. He is even unhappy that my uncapping knife is warmed, although I have persuaded him to live with this fact.

Another of my customers, formerly a stock broker, has gained fame by achieving total economic independence for himself, his wife, and his two children through tilling a mere five acres. I have never met him, but I read about him from time to time, and we correspond each fall when he orders the year's supply of honey. Another customer is a musician and composer of fame who does his vast Christmas shopping each year by telephoning to me a long list of names and addresses.

For years honey customers were driving past my door by the hundreds, and I was not bothering to sell them honey because I did not know they were honey customers. The light began to dawn when the youngster across the road set up a card table in his driveway to offer surplus produce from his garden and, before long, from mine. Eventually, jars of my honey were set out, and I was astonished by the result. Here, it finally dawned on me, was a good outlet for honey.

Scrounging some sawhorses, wide boards and scrap lumber, and half of a Ping-Pong table for a roof, I was on my way to assembling a honey stand. My only purchases were four lengths of pipe and flanges to support the roof, a can of paint, and a tarpaulin. Altogether I spent $12.09 on this crude but service-able stand. With the other half of the Ping-Pong table I made a roadside sign, then found another large scrap to make a second one. Using the honor system of letting people leave payment and make their own change, I stocked the stand and awaited results.

No sooner did I get the first roadside sign erected than the next driver stopped for a purchase, while I watched with interest from behind the shrubs. He will never know that he was the first of a long line of happy customers. In no time my dear wife was busy keeping the stand supplied and the honor box emptied. Since then the business has grown steadily as old customers have returned and new ones have been added. The honor system still prevails, with seldom any significant discrepancies.

The stand has also been a rich source of friendships and of a unique status for its proprietor. Upon entering many gatherings I need only to mention the honey stand to be instantly identified, even by persons living some distance away. The roadside signs, which have grown in both number and size, mark my location in the world. Four large colleges are fairly near by, so my stand draws great numbers of students who offer me their assessments of the world's ills. Somehow they seem sure that anyone who raises bees will certainly share their appraisals of the world and its problems and they are almost entirely correct in this. Some have dreams of keeping bees themselves, a vocation that evidently seems to them in keeping with the nobility of their thinking, which they hope to sustain through their lives. It is my own fervent hope that they will sustain these ideals, and perhaps in some cases unite them with beekeeping.

Not everyone can be a beekeeper. The tiny but pesky sting will always keep the membership in this strange class to a proper number. But for one who can see beyond this, it is, indeed, an enviable life, opening one's eyes not only to nature, to philosophy, to that life of the spirit that is basic to religion, but also to the warmth and idealism that dwells in so many of the human beings who are brought within one's association.

NINETEEN

Keeping Bees for a Living

Can one make a living keeping bees? The question has always intrigued me. More than once I have been tempted to forsake everything else to prove it in the affirmative. Perhaps I shall yet. What I have done is to compromise, by neglecting my other gainful pursuits while not entirely repudiating them, for actually I love those pursuits too. It is not a perfect solution, but few things are. The bees have seldom been far from the center of my interests and, as I get older, they become more central.

But *can* one actually make a living keeping bees? Many have done it, many do it now, but the answer is not really as simple as those facts suggest. It depends on what one means by a living, what kind of person one is and, above all, how good a beekeeper one is. In my own thinking on this question I have decided that the ancient rule of the good life—"neither too much nor too little"—applies rather well here. Many of the rewards of beekeeping are intangible, and they are easily lost if one is dedicated single-mindedly to gain. Indeed, one can go further and say that, if one's sole aim is a livelihood, then almost any of the familiar ways of gaining it is better than beekeeping. It is not the proper spirit for beekeeping to begin with, and one had better turn to something simpler, easier and less at the mercy of capricious weather.

If, on the other hand, you can be content with a simple and modest life and with treasures that are sometimes invisible to the rest of humanity, and if, in addition, you are resourceful and have a sense for nature, then you can indeed make a modest living from beekeeping. At the same time you will have a very good chance at that elusive mode of existence that the philosophers try to define as happiness. It can be a good life and a self-subsistent one. It cannot be one of riches, nor one of leisure, yet its non-negotiable riches exceed those of any work I know.

Many persons see in beekeeping a possible fulfillment of their desire for simplicity and a life close to the earth. This is especially true of young people who are not inspired by the goals that lured their parents. They swarm to my honey stand and pile question upon question. Sometimes I have a chance to take them around to my yards with me. I am glad for the occasional help and the company of those who love nature as I do, and I do not care if some of them are a little sloppy. Anyone can put on a necktie.

It must be emphasized that in apiculture, as in the faith, many are called but few chosen. The world is full of people who have tried keeping bees and have stopped. The image of the bee master quietly going about his work, the hum of the bees over his head, the open air and the sunshine, the opening flowers, the quantities of sweet honey that reward this agreeable activity —this is a pleasant image but not a complete one. One must add the occasional sting on the eyelid or nose, the tank of honey that sooner or later runs over noiselessly, the hive that falls from the truck, the exhaustion of a day of swarm gathering, the truck hopelessly stuck in the mud, the aching limbs during the harvest, the numberless frustrations that, while they reinforce the determination of the few who were born to be beekeepers, totally defeat the vast majority who were not. All the skill in the world is of little use without the fortitude to cope with discouragement and the frequent threat of disaster. Beyond this is the plain fact that many lack even the skill or the temperament ever to acquire it.

I thought of this one day after I had been approached by a young man who told me he had just purchased several hives of bees and was now living in a tent not far away. I soon concluded that he was not among those chosen. As I worked with my bees he withdrew to a safe distance, his hands, bare like mine, safely hidden behind his back. He shortly left to get his bee veil and returned wearing it backward. He had no comprehension of what I was doing and was unwilling to approach close enough to find out. I never saw him again, but I doubt that he ever became a beekeeper.

Spring never arrives without someone asking me how he might go about becoming a beekeeper. Something about the season, of course, fuels enthusiasm. I encourage everyone I can, but most do not get beyond the initial steps of thinking and dreaming. It is just as well that they do not; it is the person who dreams of bees in the winter who has a chance of becoming a beekeeper.

Perhaps no agricultural pursuit is as flexible as apiculture or requires less of a permanent investment. Someone who produces maple syrup has to take what nature has provided; he cannot go out and buy up more maple trees and truck them around. But the beekeeper can buy up colonies of bees and cart them more or less where he pleases or, when the occasion arises, he can sell them, all or part. He does not need to own the land on which he puts them, and the bees forage over thousands of acres that he does not till or tend or pay taxes on.

The ease with which a beekeeping enterprise can be expanded has lured some into enormous holdings. There are beekeepers who own thousands of colonies spread over great areas. Their honey houses are large complexes of extracting machinery and their crops are sold in steel drums. But when I see the big commercial beekeepers with their heavy trucks and hoists and equipment I certainly do not envy them. It is no picture of a simple life. It is also a hard way to make a living, loaded with headaches. For me it would be self-defeating.

Apiculture is about the only branch of husbandry that the drive for size has not robbed of its joys. The modern poultry farm is nothing but an egg factory, bearing no resemblance to the chicken yards we knew as children, with their clucking and daybreak crowing, which we no longer hear. Perhaps I am too much given to nostalgia, but I sometimes wonder whether today's children will have much to look back on. The family farm has been replaced by huge commercial operations that have lost the heart and soul of farming. The baneful apparatus of the factory now spreads itself over the rural landscape, knocking down everything in its path in response to the demand for increased production, often just in response to greed. It is becoming rare to see farm buildings that are still used. Some houses and barns are kept up, but most are collapsing and others are taken over by people who spend the better part of their lives in the cities. The scene fills one with sadness.

Beekeeping, however, can still be carried on in the traditional manner, as a backlot or sideline operation, or even as the means to a modest but wholesome livelihood. It has the same charm and fascination as in the days of old. It has not changed much in the course of a century. It seems to be an almost incorruptible craft.

The bees themselves are no different from those our forefathers kept nor, indeed, from the inhabitants of the nearest bee tree. For decades specialists have been trying to breed superior strains of bees, to bring this tiny animal under the same domination to which other livestock has been subjected, but with only limited success. They have even artificially inseminated queens, but this too has had only limited significance. Bees revert to nature after only one generation, for the queens then mate high in the air and out of human control with whatever drones overtake them. I personally hope the bees will always win this tug of war, that they will never be subdued and corrupted by the human drive for greater production, that they will never become the stupid and denatured animals that chickens and pigs have become through domestication. When I see a bee tree I know its inhabitants are the evolutionary product of millions of years, and that what I call "my own" bees are but the smallest step from the bee tree. The forests still lure them back and always will. The bees go on from season to season, just as they have for millions of years, and as they did before the human race appeared on the earth. I find this thought deeply satisfying.

Many men and women have a deep, instinctive pull to the land and husbandry. It is no longer satisfied by modern methods of commercial farming, and not many persons in touch with reality are tempted to try earning a livelihood in gardening, however satisfying this may be in other ways. For some people, however, beekeeping can fill this need completely. With only a minimum of tools and investment, augmented by resourcefulness in the use of what comes to hand, a beekeeper can play his part in the great cycles of nature, find a satisfaction that few pursuits offer, augment his livelihood or even gain the whole of it from his bees.

The beginning can be made with a single colony, set down almost any place, even on a roof or porch. Unlike other livestock, bees do not need to be fed except under infrequent and unusual circumstances. There is no butchering or cleaning of pens, disposing of wastes or refuse, or other constant chores ordinarily associated with husbandry. One can come from the bee yard straight to the dinner table with no smell of the barnyard. There is no despoilment of the landscape or exploitation of the earth's resources. On the contrary, the bees make an essential contribution to ecological well-being. Equipment can be kept simple and much of it can be made up with only a few common tools even by persons who, like myself, have little talent in this area.

My own formula, so far as the size of my bee operation is concerned, is to draw the line at that point where I would need to hire help. That is where the headaches begin and the law of diminishing returns begins to be felt. It is the line that marks the difference between two quite different pursuits and two kinds of beekeeper. If one crosses that line, if one depends upon paid help, even though it may be seasonal and unskilled, then there is little choice but to increase holdings as much as strength and circumstances permit, just to offset the increased overhead that hired help represents. This, of course, sooner or later means the hiring of more help and the purchase of more heavy equipment. Economic return becomes the governing consideration once one has chosen this manner of commercial beekeeping. Having become big, one finds that the thrust of activity is to become even bigger.

As a one-person operation, on the other hand, or sometimes as a joint endeavor of husband and wife, beekeeping can be totally fulfilling. Every bee yard is a little kingdom and the honey house a little castle. One does not get rich at this life, but it can help substantially in the domestic economy. One can sell the honey directly, at the top price, instead of dealing with processors and taking what they are willing to offer. The beekeeper can take a special pride in his work and in its product, which will bear his own label.

How large, then, should such a beekeeping enterprise be? Where is that point at which one needs to hire help? Can one make a living with bees, just on his own?

This depends on many things. Someone who relies on other sources for his basic livelihood and will continue to do so—the teacher, the mail carrier, whatever—and who looks forward to a retirement income can become a sideline beekeeper, keeping perhaps one or two hundred hives in several locations. He will not need to hire help and his bees will be profitable, provided he has the qualities needed for keeping them.

But now let us consider something more definite. Consider a strong, intelligent and resourceful person who has the temperament and qualities that make an outstanding beekeeper. Can such a person, perhaps in concert with a willing wife or husband, make a living from bees?

I shall show that he can, but I shall need a few assumptions, which, though not unrealistic, will be helpful to my case. I shall assume that this person is already an expert beekeeper and has accumulated over the years the equipment necessary for about three hundred colonies of bees. I shall disregard how he came by this equipment or how it was paid for. I shall also assume that he has a small truck or a good car and a fair-sized utility trailer. Finally, I shall assume that he has an adequate honey house equipped with extractor, tanks and the rest.

It should be noted that I am not assuming that our beekeeper is going to have to finance the cost of all this equipment. I assume he has already done so, or that in any case he somehow now owns it. And the question is simply whether he can, thus equipped, make his whole living with it.

We now need only two more assumptions. These are, first, that our beekeeper lives in a primary honey region and that he lives near cities or near a well-traveled road where perhaps a third of his crop can be marketed at retail.

This person could manage three hundred colonies single-handedly. He would be busy in the spring and fall, but at other times the work would not be be heavy. In fact, he would have little to do through the winter except putter. His honey crop would average about thirty thousand pounds each year, sometimes less, sometimes more. About a third of this would be sold at retail for about $6,000 after the cost of packing it. For the rest he would receive about $10,000. These figures would change with time, of course, but over recent years the price of honey has tended to rise. Our beekeeper would thus have about $16,000 after deducting packing costs.

Needless to say, these would not be his only costs, for we would have to account for the cost of fuel and supplies, which we can estimate at about $2,000, leaving the beekeeper with about $14,000 to live on.

It must be pointed out that no account has been taken of investment in equipment, so the summary given is meaningless from the standpoint of standard methods of accounting. It is nevertheless meaningful from the standpoint of common sense, for a beekeeper can accumulate, and pay for, the equipment over time while depending upon some other source for his livelihood.

The pursuit of beekeeping, whether as a source of livelihood or, as is usually more practicable, as a sideline, is totally engrossing. It offers fulfillment for the golden years whose approach seems so relentless and filled with emptiness to those who have somehow become estranged from nature. Sometimes the world seems on the verge of insanity, and one wonders what limit there can be to greed, aggression, deception and the thirst for power or fame. When reflections of this sort threaten one's serenity one can be glad for the bees, for the riches they yield to the spirit of those who love nature and feel their kinship with everything that creeps and swims and flies, that spins and builds, to all living things that arise and perish, to the whole of creation of which we are only a part, like the bees.

MENTAL HEALTH
THROUGH
WILL-TRAINING

Abraham A. Low, M.D.
Founder of Recovery, Inc.

MENTAL HEALTH THROUGH WILL-TRAINING

A System of Self-Help in Psychotherapy as Practiced by Recovery, Incorporated

Abraham A. Low, M.D.
Founder of Recovery, Inc.

Willett Publishing Company
Glencoe, Illinois 60022

To Mae
The Mother of My Children
and
A Mother to My Patients

The National Headquarters of Recovery, Inc.
The Association of Nervous and Former Mental Patients
802 North Dearborn Street
Chicago, Illinois 60610

TABLE OF CONTENTS

PREFACE TO THE 1997 EDITION

This edition of *Mental Health Through Will Training* celebrates the 60th anniversary of the founding of Recovery, Inc., by Abraham A. Low, M.D. After Low's death in 1954, Recovery, Inc., expanded across North America and overseas. Weekly meetings here and abroad deliver Low's comprehensive system of self-help concepts and techniques to people suffering from mental and emotional conditions.

Abraham Low's method has stood the test of time. Tens of thousands of people in need, from those just discharged from hospitals to those beset only by tenseness and anxiety, have used this method to regain their mental health and rejoin their community. People who once were severely ill now lead productive lives; people hampered by fear and anger now enjoy the harmony of a balanced nervous system.

In 1950, Abraham Low wrote:

> The present volume is meant to give an account of the psychotherapy methods evolved by Recovery, Inc., a nonprofit group whose purpose it is to train post-psychotic and psychoneurotic persons in the practice of psychiatric self-help. . . . The contents of the book are, in the main, reproductions of panel discussions conducted by the ex-patients and group psychotherapy interviews held by the author with his private patients in the years 1944 to 1949.

Several essays on "sabotage" have been added, describing the manner in which patients offer resistance to the physician's instructions. . . .

Psychotherapy, individual or group, is invariably based (1) on a philosophy, (2) on techniques. . . . In point of philosophy, [the author] cannot share the view that human conduct is the result of unconscious drives, sexual or otherwise. To his way of thinking, adult life is not *driven* by instincts but *guided* by Will. In emphasizing the priority of Will over Drives, he is merely echoing the principles and teachings of the late Professor Emil Kraepelin, founder of modern psychiatry, and those of the late Professor Wilhelm Wundt, father of modern psychology.

Quite proudly, [the author] claims also to echo the voice of common experience and common sense. Whatever may be meant by drives, be they instinctual cravings. . . or emotional trends, desires, wishes, yearnings and leanings, they all eventuate in impulses, acting or ready for action. To the author, it is inconceivable that adult human life can be ordered without a Will holding down impulses. What precisely is meant by the term *Will* is amply demonstrated in the text.

In preparing this 60th Anniversary Edition, the editors have kept the original text of the chapters, introducing changes only in punctuation and paragraph breaks for easier reading. Aside from this new Preface, other revisions include the addition of an Index, a section titled "About Recovery, Inc.," and Appendices containing the Preface and Concise Outline of Recovery's Self-Help Techniques as they were originally written. The numbering of the chapters has been made consecutive, and the Concise Outline has been updated. We hope that the new typography will be welcomed by long-time students of the book.

In recent years, concern has been expressed about the reading level required by this book. The importance that Abraham Low placed on the role of language in his method, and his insistence that overcoming difficulty was a part of the training, means that simplification could risk the loss of the book's therapeutic value. Low knew that the greatest benefit of his method would come only through patient practice, the "will to effort" over the "will to comfort." Recovery, Inc., members know that the effort expended in studying this book will yield enormous long-term benefits.

The editors wish to thank Mary Spalding and Patricia L. Reband for their intelligent editorial contributions to this new edition; and the Board of Directors of Recovery, Inc., for its cooperation in this project.

Phyllis Low Berning
Marilyn Low Schmitt
EDITORS

Editors' Note: The Preface written by Abraham Low for the second edition in 1952 and containing material of historical interest can be found in Appendix A.

About Recovery, Inc.

Recovery, Inc., offers a systematic method of self-help developed by the late Abraham A. Low, M.D., to prevent relapses and chronic conditions in people suffering from mental or emotional problems. Recovery, Inc., is a nonprofit, community-based self-help organization governed, operated and supported by lay volunteers who have sought help from and been trained in the Recovery method. Recovery groups, located throughout North America and overseas, meet weekly to provide training in Recovery's systematic method of self-help.

The Recovery, Inc., principles provide simple yet very effective methods for reacquiring self-leadership; overcoming fears, anger and symptoms of nervous origin; and strengthening self-confidence. Low set forth the Recovery self-help principles and techniques clearly and concisely in this book and in his other writings and recordings. Through the meeting procedures established by Low, members see and hear the application of these principles. Examples given at meetings by members of Recovery–following a four-step outline–graphically illustrate the self-help method. The group members' comments on the examples given offer a wealth of suggestions on how to practice the Recovery method more effectively.

Recovery training consists of (1) regular attendance at Recovery meetings; (2) study of Low's book *Mental Health Through Will-Training* and other literature, plus tape-recorded lectures by Dr. Low; and (3) practice of Recovery principles in one's daily life. It should be understood that all three parts are essential.

Veteran members caution that Recovery training is not easy, nor is it quick. It requires sustained effort and persistence over a period of time.

WHO ATTENDS RECOVERY, INC., MEETINGS?

Recovery, Inc., meetings are open to the public and are made up of adults from all walks of life. Some have recently been discharged from hospitals; some are under the care of professionals but have never been hospitalized; some have been diagnosed by their physicians as suffering from a nervous rather than a physical disorder; others suffer almost constantly from tenseness, are painfully self-conscious and feel inadequate, or have difficulty with angry temper. All can benefit.

Professionals who have referred people to Recovery have observed that Recovery intentionally avoids making therapeutic distinctions based on diagnoses and instead focuses on helping members learn to cope more effectively with the symptoms that are common across many diagnostic groups. There are many nervous symptoms–some say symptoms of stress–which may interfere with one's life: tremors, fatigue, fears, panics, head pressure, head noises, vomiting, loss of appetite, overeating, dizziness, sweats, palpitations, difficulty in swallowing, light-headedness, obsessions, compulsions, jealousy, difficulty in making decisions, depression, self-consciousness, preoccupation, feelings of inadequacy, fear of handling sharp objects, feelings of persecution, fear of crowds, bizarre sensations, fear of being alone, fear of fainting, unreality and countless others.

WHAT HAPPENS AT A RECOVERY, INC., MEETING?

The Recovery meeting begins with listening to a tape recording by Dr. Low, or reading aloud from one of Low's books. Examples are then given by four or five members of the group, relating troubling events in their daily lives and how they applied Recovery techniques. The examples follow an outline developed by Low that guides the sequence in which the incident is reported. About five minutes are allowed for giving the example and ten minutes for comments by those familiar with the Recovery method. These examples and comments last approximately one hour.

After a free-will offering, a brief period is provided for questions and answers or additional comments on any of the examples that were given. This is followed by a "mutual-aid" period, when nonalcoholic refreshments may be served and the members break into smaller, informal groups to offer more help to each other.

The meetings of all authorized Recovery groups are open to the public and are held in public rooms of community centers, libraries, churches, synagogues and other suitable public buildings. A Recovery group ideally is small enough to allow each person the opportunity to participate. Any authorized Recovery, Inc., group, throughout North America and overseas, is expected to be conducted according to standard Recovery procedures.

What Does It Cost to Attend?

There is no charge for attendance at Recovery, Inc., meetings although a free-will offering is collected at each meeting. Recovery, Inc., is a tax-exempt, nonprofit charitable organization incorporated under the laws of the State of Illinois. It is supported financially by (1) free-will offerings, (2) voluntary membership fees, (3) income from the sale of Abraham Low's literature and recordings and (4) other contributions and bequests.

Who Leads the Groups?

The leader is an average member of the group, rather than an authority. Only lay volunteers who have sought help from Recovery, Inc., and have had training in its method are authorized as group leaders. All Recovery leaders receive ongoing leader training and annual authorization from the Board of Directors.

Leaders are expected to demonstrate their practice of the method and are responsible for reminding the other members of the structures of the meeting. Recovery, Inc., encourages each member to develop self-leadership, rather than to rely on the group leader.

WHAT IF HELP IS NEEDED BETWEEN MEETINGS?

When additional help is needed, a very important mutual-aid procedure established by Low is the five-minute telephone call between two members. He emphasized that it is necessary to limit such a mutual-aid call to approximately five minutes. If still more help is needed, the member may make another five-minute call later in the day. The person who telephones for help should be attending group meetings regularly.

DOES RECOVERY, INC., SPONSOR SOCIAL ACTIVITIES?

While Recovery, Inc., members often form friendships with each other, Low wanted them to become average citizens of their communities, once again participating in life with outside groups as well as with Recovery groups. For this reason, most Recovery groups hold only a few social events.

IS THERE A RELIGIOUS COMPONENT AT RECOVERY, INC., MEETINGS?

Recovery, Inc., concerns itself with a single aim: to prevent relapses and chronic conditions in people suffering from mental or emotional problems. A Recovery member who wants religious guidance is encouraged to seek counsel from the religious community.

WHAT IS THE RELATIONSHIP BETWEEN RECOVERY, INC., AND PROFESSIONALS?

Hundreds of psychiatrists, mental health professionals, physicians and clergy refer people to Recovery, Inc., for training in self-leadership, knowing that Recovery does not take the place of the professional. Recovery does not offer diagnosis, treatment, advice or counseling. Members are at all times expected to follow the authority of their own physician or other professional. While Recovery, Inc., encourages its members to consult professionals whenever such consultation is appropriate, Recovery leaders and members do not recommend particular professionals.

Physicians, psychotherapists and the clergy often participate as regular members in meetings if they are suffering from mental or emotional problems. Members of these professions who are not seeking help are welcome and encouraged to observe a meeting at any time, but not to participate. In order to maintain the status of the leader as an average member of the group, professionals may not become Recovery leaders.

What Is the Structure of Recovery, Inc.?

Abraham Low laid down the foundation on which the entire organizational structure of Recovery, Inc., has been built. Recovery, Inc., is governed by a Board of Directors made up of a cross-section of the organization's group leaders. The Board, meeting regularly in Chicago, formulates policy that is administered by a small Recovery, Inc., paid staff.

All Recovery group leaders, area leaders, committee members, officers and members of the Board of Directors serve without pay. They are lay volunteers who have sought help from and are trained in the Recovery method. At whatever level they serve in the organization, they maintain their group leadership at weekly meetings.

Recovery, Inc., is grateful to educators, mental health professionals, members of the clergy and other community leaders who aid Recovery members in securing meeting places, community endorsement, local publicity, etc. In this way, Recovery and the community cooperate to offer help to those who need it. But the operation of the Recovery groups, the management, control and support of the entire Recovery self-help organization is completely the responsibility of the

Recovery leaders and members. Recovery, Inc., is an independent organization dedicated to preserving and making available the self-help method of Abraham A. Low, M.D.

WHERE CAN ONE LEARN MORE?

All authorized Recovery, Inc., groups are registered with the organization's headquarters in Chicago. To learn the location of groups, or for any other information about the organization, contact Recovery, Inc., 802 North Dearborn Street, Chicago, Illinois 60610, (312) 337-5661. A local telephone number can be found in the white pages of many telephone directories.

A CONCISE OUTLINE OF RECOVERY'S SELF-HELP TECHNIQUES

Recovery, Inc., was founded, November 7, 1937, by thirty ex-patients who regained their health after receiving shock treatments and/or other therapies at the Psychiatric Institute of the University of Illinois Medical School. Dr. Abraham Low was, at the time, the assistant director of the Institute. Between 1937 and 1940 the organization limited its services to the patients admitted to the wards of the Psychiatric Institute. In the fall of 1940, it expanded its work to include the psychoneurotic patients of the outpatient department.

In September, 1941, the group severed its connection with the University of Illinois Medical School and established headquarters of its own in the Chicago Loop district*. After 1942, the bulk of its membership was recruited from Low's private practice. During its early years, as is evident from this brief description, Recovery, Inc., had the opportunity to try out its techniques (1) with an intramural patient population, (2) with an outpatient group, (3) with private patients.

The object of Recovery, Inc., apart from its tendency to save time for the professional and money for the patient, is to help prevent recurrences in mental diseases and to forestall chronicity in psychoneurotic conditions. Its techniques place the emphasis on self-help.

---

*The present address of Recovery, Inc., is 802 North Dearborn Street, Chicago, IL 60610.

THE "RESIDUAL SYMPTOM" OF THE RECOVERED MENTAL PATIENT

After leaving the hospital, the mental patient is supposed to be restored to health. This is true in most instances if by "mental health" is meant the absence of delusions and hallucinations, of violent impulsiveness and indifference to group standards. But returning to the community, the patient still suffers from restlessness, tenseness and preoccupation. His inability to relax is aggravated by the sense of being stigmatized. Many returned patients are so suspicious of being watched or mistrusted that even simple inquiries like, "How do you feel?" or "How are you today?" are likely to cause irritation. These innocent questions may suggest to the patient that the reality of the recovery is doubted.

Feeling stigmatized, the patient becomes self-conscious and introspective. On a given night, he might have difficulty falling asleep. This is apt to cause alarm. The alarm increases the difficulty of sleeping. Then more alarm, more sleeplessness and more alarm yet. A vicious cycle is thus set going which may keep the patient from properly resting night after night. Other vicious cycles may soon establish themselves. The patient notices a sense of fatigue which in itself may be as insignificant as any sensation of fatigue experienced by the average person. But feeling stigmatized, he correlates his tiredness with the possibility of a relapse. And the more he dreads the relapse, the more intense becomes the fatigue; the heavier the fatigue, the more haunting the fear of relapse.

One patient had a nocturnal itch after returning home, another complained of a twitch in one arm, a third felt a hair on the tongue. Experiences of this kind are distressing enough to conjure up the vision of an impending relapse. The experiences become far more terrifying when the patient observes, for instance, that the arm suddenly begins to shake in automatic motion or when "awful flashes" shoot across the eye. Patients reported an "electric buzz running through my muscles," that "my tongue lay stiff in my mouth," that "my own voice sounded strange," that "my ear felt pushed in," that "I can't seem to hear myself when I speak." Palpitations, numbness, head or chest pressures, dizziness, difficulty of concentration, dimness of vision, air-hunger, headaches, nausea and scores of other disturbances are typical reported symptoms.

Observations of this sort may give rise to the vicious cycle, which has the familiar character of the symptom increasing the fear and the fear intensifying and perpetuating the symptom. While there are no statistics to substantiate the claim, it is fair to assume that many recurrences of mental ailments are the direct result of these "residual symptoms" which, fanned by the fury of the vicious cycle, produce anxieties and panics which finally necessitate the much dreaded recommitment*.

The Defeatism of the Chronic Psychoneurotic Patient

Most residual symptoms from which the returned mental patient is likely to suffer are similar to, or identical with, the common complaints voiced by psychoneurotic patients. Hence, the possibility of treating both groups by the same method. The psychoneurotic patients treated by Dr. Low belonged mainly in the category of chronic, protracted cases. Most had a record of from two to twenty years of suffering.

Such "experienced sufferers" have made the rounds of physicians and clinics and have been assured on numerous occasions, explicitly or by implication, that some therapeutic measure would cure them. The assurance never materialized, with the result that they no longer believe a cure possible. They know, however, that some or most of the past therapies had a transient, palliative effect. The palpitations were milder after a reassuring talk; the dizziness yielded to a sedative. Hence, they treasure the "pep-talk" or the prescription.

---

*Recovery, Inc., group leaders are trained to remind members to consult their physician about their symptoms.

In order to secure these elusive aids, they must complain; they must convince the professional that they "really" suffer, that their pains are not imaginary, that they can positively "not stand" their fatigue. To get a hearing from a professional is all the more important because at home their complaints are likely to be met with impatience or ridicule. Complaining, then, becomes a vital part of their daily routine. In the course of years, they develop the consummate art of the "expert complainer." What these long-term patients crave is a sympathetic ear which, after years of griping, they can no longer secure from their relatives and friends. They delight in a lengthy discussion of their fears and frustrations. Their ideal is to be explored, analyzed, sounded and probed. Essentially, they have decided that their case is beyond repair. What they expect is a hearing, perhaps some temporary relief, but not a final cure. The "chronicity" of this group has little to do with the nature of the symptoms, with diagnosis or etiology; it is self-appointed defeatism.

Since Recovery places the emphasis on the self-help action of its members, it ignores investigations and explorations which are not within the province of inexperienced lay persons. Complexes, childhood memories, dream experiences and subconscious thought are entirely eliminated from the self-help effort. The psychoneurotic individual is considered a person who, for some reason, developed disturbing symptoms leading to ill-controlled behavior. The symptoms are in the nature of threatening sensations, "intolerable" feelings, "uncontrollable" impulses and obsessive "unbearable" thoughts. The very vocabulary, with its frenzied emphasis on the "killing" headache, the dizziness that "drives me frantic," the fatigue that "is beyond human endurance" is ominously expressive of defeatism.

The first step in the psychotherapeutic management of these "chronic" individuals must be to convince them that the sensation can be endured, the impulse controlled, the obsession checked. Unfortunately, the professional is far from convincing. Any attempt to "sell" the idea of mental health arouses the "sales resistance" of the patient. "The physician doesn't dare tell me the truth," muses the patient. "It would be against his ethics to declare me incurable." The resistance is easily overcome in the group. The fellow sufferer, who explains how she "licked" her frightful palpitations after years of invalidism, cannot possibly be suspected of trying to sell something. That "colleague" is convincing and convinces the novice that "chronic" conditions are not hopeless.

The "Setback"

Low required patients to attend Recovery, Inc., meetings for at least six months. The average member may experience a considerable initial improvement through participation in the Recovery program. But the improvement is, as a rule, as short-lived as was the relief which the patient used to gain from the visits to clinics and doctors' offices. Between meetings, the novice is apt to suffer a "setback." She is again tortured by "that awful fatigue" or has been unable "to sleep a wink for three nights in succession," or the fear of doing harm to the baby reappears after it was gone for a short while. Recovery warns its members to be on guard against the unavoidable setback. When difficulty is experienced, members may call a veteran member for assistance between meetings. The calls are limited to approximately five minutes, but additional five-minute calls can be made if needed.

The Symptomatic Idiom

If Recovery members are to help and teach one another, they must be instructed to use a language which is not confusing. This is particularly important because language, if used glibly, tends to be alarmist and defeatist. By dint of its defeatist insinuations, language frequently engenders tenseness, which reinforces and perpetuates symptoms. To avoid the fatalistic implications of the language used by the patient, an alternative terminology must be supplied in matters of mental health. There are many languages. Features and gestures speak. So do symptoms. Their language is a one-word idiom: DANGER. This is called the "symptomatic idiom." Accepting the suggestions of the symptomatic idiom, the patient considers violent palpitations as presaging sudden death. Pressure in the head is viewed as due to a brain tumor. Tenseness is experienced as so "terrific" that the patient fears she is going to "burst." Her fatigue does not let up "one single minute," and "how long can the body stand it?"

In these instances, the implications of the symptomatic idiom are those of an impending *physical collapse*. If phobias, compulsions and obsessions dominate the symptomatic scene, the resulting fear is that of *mental collapse*. After months and years of sustained suffering, the twin fears of physical and mental collapse may recede, giving way to apprehensions about the impossibility of a final cure. This is the fear of the *permanent handicap*. The three basic fears–of physical collapse, mental collapse and permanent handicap–are variations of the danger theme suggested by the symptomatic idiom.

TEMPER AND TEMPERMENTAL LINGO

Another source of defeatism is temper. Recovery members are taught that temper has two divisions. One comes into play when I persuade myself that a person has done me wrong. As a result I become angry. This is called *angry* or *aggressive temper,* which appears in various shades and nuances: resentment, impatience, indignation, disgust, hatred, etc. The other variety of temper is brought into action whenever I feel that I am wrong. This gives rise to moral, ethical and esthetic fears or to the fear of being a failure in pragmatic pursuits. I am afraid that I sinned, failed, blundered, in short, that I defaulted on a moral, ethical or esthetic standard or on the standard of average efficiency. This is called *fearful* or *retreating temper* which may express itself in many different qualities and intensities: discouragement, preoccupation, embarrassment, worry, sense of shame, feeling of inadequacy, hopelessness, despair, etc. Fearful temper is likely to lead either to a feeling of personal inferiority or to the sentiment of group stigmatization. Whether it be of the angry or fearful description, temper reinforces and intensifies the symptom which, in its turn, increases the temperamental reaction. In this manner, a vicious cycle is established between temper and symptom.

In telling a person that wrong was done to him or that he is wrong, his temper speaks to him. The language which it uses is called *temperamental lingo*. Its vocabulary is limited to the terms "right" and "wrong." Unless the person learns to ignore the threats, warnings and incitements of the temperamental lingo, he will be the victim of angry outbursts and fearful anticipations. His tenseness will be maintained and intensified; new symptoms will be precipitated and old ones fortified. Temper is most dangerous when it plays on the symptom itself. By labelling sensations as "intolerable," feelings as "terrible," impulses as "uncontrollable," the lingo discourages the patient from facing, tolerating and controlling the reaction.

The very sound of the labels ("intolerable," etc.) is apt to rouse fear and defeatism. All a patient has to do is to call a crying reaction by the name of "crying spell," and no effort will be made to check the burst of tears. The word *spell* suggests uncontrollability. Substitute "crying habit" for "crying spell," and the impossibility of stemming the flood at least will not be taken for granted. Similarly, if the patient raves about the "splitting" headache, the dizziness that "drives me mad," the pressure that "I can't stand any longer," the fatalism of diction is bound to breed a despondency of mood. In order to prevent the temperamental response, the patient must be trained to ignore the whisperings of temperamental lingo.

"RECOVERY LANGUAGE"

The combined effects of symptomatic idiom and temperamental lingo are checkmated if the patient uses the Recovery language only. Recovery members call it proudly the "Recovery language." The most important parts of its vocabulary are the words "sabotage" and "authority." The authority of the professional is sabotaged if the patient presumes to make a diagnostic, therapeutic or prognostic statement. The verbiage of temperamental lingo ("unbearable," "intolerable," "uncontrollable") constitutes sabotage because of the assumption that the condition is of a serious nature, which is a diagnosis; or that it is difficult to repair, which is a prognosis. It is a crass example of sabotage if the claim is advanced that, "My headache is there the very minute I wake up. I didn't have time to think about it. It came before I even had a chance to become emotional. How can that be nervous?" A statement of this kind throws a serious doubt on the validity of the diagnosis and sabotages the professional's authority. Likewise, it is a case of self-diagnosing and consequently sabotage to view palpitations as a sign of a heart ailment, of head pressure as meaning brain tumor, of sustained fatigue as leading to physical exhaustion.

Once the physician has made the diagnosis of a psychoneurotic or post-psychotic condition, the patient should not indulge in the pastime of self-diagnosing. If he does, he is practicing sabotage. If, after a reasonable length of time, the handicap persists in its original intensity, the indication is that sabotage is still in action. The Recovery member still listens to the suggestions of the symptomatic idiom, fearing impending collapse and permanent handicap. Or, she gives ear to the verbal vagaries of the temperamental lingo, feeling helpless in the face of suffering. Clinging to her own mode of thinking, she sabotages the professional's effort.

Contrary to expectation, it is comforting to the patient to be called a saboteur. Considering himself as such, he knows that he has "not yet" learned to avoid resisting the professional. The "not yet" is reassuring. It suggests that in time he will learn. The Recovery members encourage one another to wait until they get well. They warn one another against impatience. The most effective slogan handed down from veteran to novice is, "Wait till you learn to give up sabotaging."

THE "SPOTTING TECHNIQUE"

If the Recovery member is to check these sabotaging propensities, she must be trained to "spot" the inconsistencies and fallacies of her own language, whether it is merely conceived in silent thought or given formulation in vocal speech. To this end, a system of "spotting techniques" was evolved by means of which the members learn to reject the suggestions of the symptomatic idiom and temperamental lingo whenever a symptom or a temperamental reaction occur. An extensive, though necessarily incomplete, description of the spotting techniques is furnished in part III of this book.

Editors' Note: The original Concise Outline of Recovery's Self-Help Techniques, written by Abraham Low for the second edition in 1952 and containing material of historical interest, can be found in Appendix B.

PART I

PANEL DISCUSSIONS WITH
EXTENSIVE QUOTATION OF EXAMPLES
OFFERED BY PATIENTS

CHAPTER ONE

Imagination, Temper and Symptoms

A PANEL DISCUSSION CONDUCTED BY PATIENTS

FRANK (panel leader): The panel is ready to start, and we are taking our material from the lecture entitled "The Wrong-Fearing Temperament." What we are going to discuss is the dilemma, which means a difficulty of making decisions. Has anybody an example of having trouble making up his mind?

TILLIE: Some time ago, I went to Field's and wanted to get a dress for my little daughter Doris. I couldn't make up my mind between two dresses. I looked at both dresses and felt confused. And when I can't make up my mind, I get a tightness in my left side, and when I get this, I feel like letting everything go. But this time I just took one and felt comfortable.

Then I went to the socks department, and I thought I would get size nine. But I thought they were too big, and I was in a confusion again. The tightness came back, and I got flushed and felt I couldn't breathe. I was on the point of throwing the socks down and leaving the store, but Doris said if they didn't have size eight and a half, she was going to take size nine. So she made the decision for me. Then the tightness stopped immediately, and I felt comfortable. Six months ago, once the tightness had started, all kinds of other symptoms would have come on, and I would have been in a panic all day and maybe for several days. Today my panics last a short while, and they aren't a bit as severe as they used to be.

MAURICE: I used to make conflicts and dilemmas out of things the average person wouldn't think to make an issue of, for instance, going to a movie or getting a haircut. I would make a start, then I'd think, should I really go? Then I might pick up a book and read. After a few minutes, I would feel I should go to the barber's. Then I would put it off again, and so it would take me hours to make a simple decision. Months ago I remember I went to the library and I would be in a conflict about what books to take out, and for days I looked over books and never took one out. That made me tense and disgusted because I couldn't make up my mind. Today I can decide in a few minutes.

CAROL: My two children have been sick the past two weeks. I thought it would be nice if my husband would suggest eating out tonight. A year ago, I wouldn't have the nerve to make the suggestion. I would have been sore at my husband if he didn't make the suggestion himself. This time I said, "How about it," and he was agreeable. But even now I don't know whether it was right to ask him. I get so tense when I have to ask for things.

FRANK: All this tenseness derives from the fact that we don't want to make up our mind. We are afraid we'll have to blame ourselves. We'd rather pass the buck. But we have to learn to make decisions and to take chances that we may be wrong. You know, the doctor tells us we must have the courage to be wrong in the trivialities of everyday life.

CAROL: I have another example. I have to take my wash to the laundry to have it ironed. Several months ago, I used to be tense on the way home because I had to rush back to prepare lunch for the children, and I was afraid I wouldn't make it in time. So I used to put off making the trip to the laundry and let it go day after day till we were most out of laundry. Today I just do it, and if I feel tense on the way back, I say to myself, "What of it?" The tenseness isn't so bad anymore anyhow.

FRANK: These are examples of trivial conflicts, and the very fact they are so numerous keeps us in constant tension, and the tenseness, of course, produces symptoms. I will give you an example of my own. As you know, I am the editor of the "Recovery News,"* and there is an article I am planning on writing, but I keep putting it off. Monday night I was home and I thought I would start on the article but didn't feel like doing it. Suddenly it became important for me to read the daily paper. Ordinarily I don't read it more than twice a week. But now it seemed I had to read it immediately. And so I got myself the *Tribune* and read it thoroughly. After I was through with it, I noticed the Sunday *Tribune* was still on the table from the day before. I got a hold of that and read it, again very thoroughly. Ordinarily I hardly throw a look at it. This you can call procrastination. But the point is, I didn't make up my mind to do something that I didn't feel like doing. I haven't been able to lick this procrastination of mine as thoroughly as I would like to. But I am gradually getting it under control, and on that Monday evening when I kept putting off writing, I finally made up my mind and wrote and finished the article.

DON: I used to buy medicine from a drugstore in the neighborhood. The clerk there knows about my condition because I told him. Now I am sorry that I told him because I feel uncomfortable when I have to go there to buy medicine. Of course, it is the stigma. When I need the medicine, I put off going to the drugstore. On several occasions I was pretty sick with my asthma, but rather than talk to the clerk, I

---

*The "Recovery News" was a mimeographed sheet which was edited by Frank Rochford in 1945 and early 1946. It was the predecessor of the *Recovery Journal*.

endured sickness. Finally I needed the medicine badly, and my first thought was again to put it off. But then I said to myself, "No, sir. You know you will be tense all day if you don't make up your mind to face that clerk." And if I am tense, I get all kinds of symptoms, fatigue, sleeplessness and tremors. So I went and got the medicine, and after that I felt I had done something worthwhile. Otherwise I would have suffered all day.

IMAGINATION, TEMPER, SYMPTOMS

PHYSICIAN'S COMMENT ON A PANEL DISCUSSION

The central theme of today's panel was fear, more particularly, the fear of making a decision. Tillie feared deciding between two pairs of socks, Maurice feared taking a book from the library, and Carol, Frank and Don quoted similar fears of deciding, choosing, taking a stand and reaching a conclusion. Frank surmised that all the issues and problems, conflicts and dilemmas listed by the panel members were sheer trivialities. But the fact is that Tillie, while grappling with her difficulty, developed panics and confusions and all manner of frightening symptoms. To her, the danger of making a wrong decision did not appear at all trivial. It loomed in her mind as a matter of momentous importance. She thought of serious consequences and grave responsibilities; she anticipated failure and disaster. In other words, her imagination was on fire.

If there were no imagination, there would be few panics and anxieties. And without panics and anxieties, nervous symptoms would die away. No nervous patient would ever fear collapse unless his imagination told him that palpitations, air-hunger and chest pressure spell the danger of imminent death. Nobody would ever shiver at the thought of "another sleepless night" except that imagination paints a lurid picture of the fatal results that a mythical sleeplessness has on health. I may mention the fanciful notions which patients entertain about the dreadful effects of "nervous fatigue," and you will realize that the idea of danger created by your imagination can easily disrupt any of your functions. If this is true, it is clear that the nervous patient is served by an imagination which is out of bounds, rampant, unbalanced. If the balance is to be restored, the patient will have to acquire a working knowledge of how his imagination functions. Clearly, all I can offer in a brief address is a sketchy account of its mode of operation.

Imagination is either busy or idle. If idle, it is bored; if busy, it is interested and either stimulated or frustrated. Its business is to notice, observe and interpret events. Once the event is noticed, imagination is aroused or stirred. It may then evince rising concern or stirring excitement. The concern will lead to further investigation and deepened interest, finally yielding some important or trivial discovery. The excitement will give rise to feelings, sentiments and emotions. Note here that concern, excitement, interest, feelings are intimately associated with the function of imagination.

What imagination notices, observes and interprets are events, facts and situations occurring outside or inside the body. Those taking place outside the body, in external environment, "strike" the senses of vision, hearing or touch and are "grasped" by them. This is the *"sensory grasp" of outer experience.* The events occurring inside the body, in internal environment, "affect" our deep sensibility and are noticed by intuition. This is the *"intuitive grasp" of inner experience.* We may then say that imagination is busy interpreting the facts of outer and inner experience. In the one sphere it makes use of sense perception, in the other of intuitive understanding.

In interpreting the meaning of events, imagination classes them as either indifferent or significant to our welfare. The significant events are felt or thought of, that is, imagined as endangering or securing our welfare. In this manner, imagination produces the sense of security or insecurity. If behavior is to be adjusted, imagination must inter-

pret events in such a fashion that the sense of security mate-
rially overbalances the sense of insecurity. Once this is
accomplished, an *imaginative balance* establishes itself.

After interpreting an event, imagination renders an
opinion which is in the nature of a tentative suggestion or a
first guess. It suggests, for instance, or guesses, that the person approaching you is a friend. The opinion is, then, that
the situation is one of security. Under such simple circumstances, imagination is hardly likely to go astray. The situation is such that it calls for little or no imaginative appraisal.
The sensory grasp is sufficient for proper identification.
After the friend reaches you, his features may strike your eye
as being changed. You imagine they express anxiety. This is
another imaginative guess. If you accept it, you may be
inclined to offer sympathy or aid. Suppose now that your
guess was wrong. The offer of sympathy was then misplaced and may be resented. The tentative opinion rendered
by imagination misled you to an incorrect conclusion and an
equally unwise decision to act. In order to avoid premature
conclusions, decisions and acts of this kind, the opinion, suggestion or guess offered by imagination must be verified. I
may mention briefly that verification makes use of logic,
past experience and of that singular capacity of the mature
human mind to observe elements which contradict or support an opinion after it has been formed.

It is the tragedy of the nervous patient that, after years
of suffering, he develops an unbalanced imagination, the
first guesses of which tend distressingly and consistently to
interpret inner and outer experiences in terms of insecurity.
The greater tragedy is that the first guesses are accepted
sight unseen without an attempt at verification. Unable to
resist its suggestions, the patient becomes the victim of his
imagination. An incessant stream of insecurity suggestions
is poured forth with rapid-fire velocity, leading to a continuous succession of wrong opinions, conclusions and decisions. The final result is that the patient, realizing that his
first guesses tend to be either wrong or harmful, comes to
fear forming an opinion, reaching a conclusion, making a
decision.

In a sense, his fears are based on good logic. In most instances, imagination has misled and deceived him. On a hundred or thousand occasions, it told him that his sensations will lead to collapse. The suggestion never materialized. How can that imagination be trusted? Whenever a symptom made its appearance, whether palpitations or numbness or dizziness, imagination suggested invariably that this was the last gasp, that an emergency was on. The patient went into a panic, clamored for instant help, insisted that the doctor be summoned without delay. When the relatives, aware of the "nervous" nature of the spell, hesitated to call the physician, perhaps in the dead of the night, the patient passed into a violent burst of temper, and the wish had to be granted. But the moment the physician arrived, his mere presence or calm manner dispelled frequently both symptom and temper in a trice. The deceitfulness of his imagination was here clearly demonstrated to the patient. It lied to him, led him to wrong conclusions, to hasty decisions. It produced temper, caused unnecessary expense, created domestic friction. Worst of all, it undermined his self-respect and made him look ridiculous. Trusting an imagination of this kind, it would seem, is impossible.

There were other experiences that made for distrust. Neighbors mentioned a remedy, or the patient read about it in the daily paper or heard of it over the radio. No sooner was the drug called to his attention than his imagination was absurdly fired with hope and enthusiasm. In the course of years, he spent more money on pills and capsules than his meager finances warranted. Trusting the suggestions passed on by his ever lively imagination, he consulted numerous physicians, wandered from clinic to clinic. He made costly trips because a change of climate was supposed to be beneficial. He went to sanitariums, watering places. He even had himself "checked at Mayo Brothers." His record of inept conclusions and ludicrous decisions is impressive, indeed. That record was inspired by his imagination, whose erratic and capricious counsel has been the ruin of the patient's reputation. How can he ever base a decision on its dubious recommendations?

It happened at times that he was free from symptoms for a few days, sometimes for a week, rarely a longer period. Then this imagination spoke the language of security. It suggested that he was cured, that the symptoms were gone for good. On these occasions, he concluded he was well and decided to "do things." He resumed his social life, visited friends, played cards with them, went fishing and automobiling. Occasionally, he ventured to return to work. The result of these efforts was dismal disappointment. Without any warning, "out of a blue sky," the palpitations recurred "worse than ever," right while he was engaged in a "grand game of poker." Or, he suddenly fainted while he worked on the bench. There was no escape from these dreadful symptoms. His imagination, even when it preached security, invariably led him straight into insecurity. How can he ever trust it? How can he depend on its first guesses or final conclusions? And without dependence, how can there be deciding or acting? His life is doomed to be a stark tragedy, a bleak and barren existence, mechanical, tedious, lifeless.

We shall revert to the experience Tillie had in the store. When she was unable to make up her mind whether to buy a smaller size sock, her daughter Doris came to her assistance and made the decision for her. "Then the tightness stopped, and immediately I felt comfortable," Tillie said. But if a little child can guide the nervous patient out of confusion and bafflement, the solution for his difficulties seems to be close enough at hand. Every patient has either children or mothers or friends. It should be easy, or at least feasible, to assign to them the task of making decisions and reaching conclusions. Unfortunately, the device does not work. Men and women have pride, and that pride is readily shaken, wounded and challenged. The fact that Doris had to make the decision for her was a severe blow to the mother's self-respect. It served to emphasize her tragic inability to act, to decide, to be self-sufficient. It accentuated the helplessness and wretchedness of her existence. Doris' intervention, it is true, relieved the symptoms of tightness and discomfort. Now Tillie's physical person felt secure for the brief period of a few minutes. But her moral and intellectual personality was made to feel more insecure than before. The next decision to be made was certain to reveal an increased distrust of herself and of her imagination.

To trust imagination means to let it perform its functions of dreaming, hoping, anticipating. If Tillie had given free play to her fancy, she would have planned the purchase of Doris' dress days or weeks in advance. She would have pictured in her mind, that is, in her imagination, how beautiful the child would look in a dress of a certain style, cut or color. She would have anticipated flattering compliments from neighbors and friends. She would have beamed with joy at the thought of Doris' delight when finally presented with the garb. On an evening walk with her husband, she would have strolled along the show windows, viewing patterns, tentatively accepting some, rejecting others. All along, her thought would have dwelled fondly and proudly on the details of the situation when, a week or two ahead, she would arrive at home with the garment neatly wrapped in a box. The surprise, the breathless suspense, the ceremonial of unwrapping, the gasp of astonishment ringing from the child's lips, the kiss of gratitude, the eagerness to slip into the dress immediately and eye it in the mirror–all of this and many other dreams, hopes and anticipations would have currently crowded Tillie's brain, continually feeding and occupying her imagination.

This is precisely the point I meant to make. The acts of planning, dreaming, hoping and anticipating keep imagination busy and occupied, interested and stimulated. They prevent idleness and boredom. And if imagination is properly kept from being idle or bored, there is no or little occasion for restlessness or irritability. And without restlessness and irritability, symptoms do not stand much of a chance of being maintained or precipitated. Had Tillie permitted her imagination to be occupied with dreams and hopes, her chest would have currently swelled with pride, and her heart would have habitually expanded with joy. Instead, her chest became the seat of agonizing pressure, and her heart was rocked by wild palpitations because her imagination was allowed to busy itself with fears and anxieties mainly or solely.

What prevented her from keeping her imagination fruitfully occupied was her *preoccupation* with terrors and panics, with symptoms and distress, in short, with the idea of insecurity. And if an imagination is more or less constantly preoccupied with ideas of insecurity, it will be deprived of the opportunity to occupy itself with those dreams, hopes and visions from which ideas of security originate. If this happens, the imaginative balance will be disturbed, the thoughts of insecurity will drown out the ideas of security, and anxious preoccupation will cancel out the pleasurable occupations. The result will be a paralyzing fear of deciding, planning, initiating and acting. But without decisions, plans, action and initiative, there is no possibility of developing pride, self-reliance and self-sufficiency. It was the sustained preoccupation with ideas of insecurity that prevented Tillie from acquiring even that modicum of self-trust that prompts the trivial decisions of daily existence.

You will understand now that if the nervous patient is to regain his lost imaginative balance, his preoccupations with ideas of insecurity will have to give way to occupations with thoughts of security, that is, with hopes, dreams and pleasurable anticipations. You will also understand that hopes, dreams and joyful anticipations are the very warp and woof of decisions, plans and conclusions. And if you ask how you can manage to rout your preoccupations, my answer will be of the simplest kind: Stop listening to the threat of the symptomatic idiom and the imbecilities of the temperamental lingo, and your imagination will again be able to indulge in its stimulating occupations, and you will be in a position to make decisions, draw conclusions, formulate plans without fearing the dreadful consequences suggested to you by temper and symptom. Learn to use the Recovery language of self-confidence and fearlessness and your imagination will be freed of the deadweight of panics and anxieties. Thus delivered, it will once again occupy itself with thoughts of security and ideas of self-sufficiency.

CHAPTER TWO

Temper, Symptoms and Insight

A Panel Discussion Conducted by Patients

Frank (panel leader): We will discuss today the article on "Temper and Insight." It says there that in a temperamental deadlock, people are not quarreling over real issues but over whether one person is right and the other wrong. I shall give an example.

A number of times on the panel, I mentioned that my mother does not set the breakfast table. One item that is particularly irritating to me is the sugar bowl. It seems to me it is always empty. It is certainly not a matter of great moment whether it is filled or not; it only takes a few seconds to fill it. The fact is, I have to fill it practically every morning. Before I had my Recovery training, this used to irritate me no end. I felt I had the right, as a son, to have the sugar bowl filled, but I was denied that right. Ridiculous as it may sound, my mother and I were in a deadlock over this issue of the sugar bowl until I applied the Recovery language and knew that right and wrong are phony issues in domestic life. I now fill the sugar bowl every other day or so, and each time, it makes me feel good to know that I don't get worked up over trivialities any more. I think I now have insight into the phony nature of temper.

Tillie: Several months ago, I had an argument with the lady upstairs. I wanted to make a telephone call, and when I took off the receiver, she was talking, so I thought I'll wait a while. I waited fifteen minutes, and she was still talking. Then I heard her say to the party, "Somebody is trying to get on the phone." I said, "I would like to make a call, and I have been waiting fifteen minutes already." She said, "All right, go ahead," and hung up with a bang.

Soon after I was finished with the call, she came downstairs and asked, "What's the matter? Is something burning?" I said, "No, but I have to go shopping and had to make that call." She got very excited, so I said, "If you don't quiet down, I will not talk to you." That made her mad. She said, "You have no right to tell me to get off the line. I would never think of doing such a thing. I have too much character." I said, "Are you telling me I have no character?" I lost my temper then, and I gave it to her all right.

After she left, I called Gertrude, and she said, "You can't afford to lose your temper because of your health." I didn't just like that, and I still thought I was right. But I was awfully tense all that day, and I had my air-hunger again and that pressure around the chest, and the symptoms did not disappear for more than a week.

A couple of days ago, I met this lady again. The building is ours, and I asked her politely to please tell her boy to keep off the grass. Then she said my daughter Doris caused much more damage to the lawn than her son. This time I smiled and refused to get into an argument. I was sore, but the aftereffect lasted just a short time.

ADA: A few weeks ago, my husband suggested we go to the movies, and this particular movie was a mile from home. It was a nice Sunday, and he thought we should walk. One thing I can't stand is strolling. I want to walk fast and get there because I am tense. So I told him I wouldn't stroll. He said he rushes all week, and on Sundays he likes to take a slow walk and refuses to be rushed. This all happened within two blocks, and he said, "I am sick and tired of arguing, and we'll get on a street car." We did and I was angry. But when the show started, I forgot all about the argument, and I didn't work myself up as I should have done if that had happened a year ago. At that time, I wouldn't have talked to him for several days, or I would have thrown up to him that he was inconsiderate and selfish and didn't care whether I suffered.

FRANK: I think that what Tillie and Ada said illustrated what I brought out about right and wrong being a phony issue. Tillie talked for about five minutes, but I didn't hear one sentence that had to do with objective realities. And Ada didn't say a word about the actual facts of walking. She didn't bring out the fact that the distance was too far to walk or that it was necessary to walk faster to get there in time. All of this didn't matter. The issue was whether one person would get his way or the other.

ANN: Several months ago, my husband's sister came through Chicago and had to wait sixteen hours for her train east. So we invited her to spend the night with us. My son offered to let his aunt use his room, and he would sleep upstairs. I got flustered because I did not know whether I could clean the house in time. It seemed too much of a job for me to get my son's room ready. So I set about cleaning, and I was quite pleased with the effort I made. The room looked really like a guest room. To be sure that it remained clean, I asked my boy not to go into the room. But, lo and behold, before long Johnny was in the room, and his dog with him, and the boy was eating pretzels. I lost my temper and gave him a real tongue-lashing.

A few minutes later, when I was vacuuming the living room rug, I suddenly felt fatigued. It seemed I couldn't go on. It was such an effort. I wanted to lie down, but suddenly it dawned on me that the tired feeling had come on so suddenly that it was, of course, the result of my temper. I took up the work again, and the fatigue was gone in no time. I think that the insight that the fatigue was a mere feeling helped me get rid of it.

ADA: Something happened this morning where my Recovery training gave me insight into my temper. Our janitor dislikes children, and when he sees them on the sidewalk, he pushes them around. I used to argue with him about it but don't do it any more, as a rule. There is an empty lot near our house, and the boys and girls play there. This morning, my boy and five others were playing there, and the janitor came along and said he would call the police, and my boy came up crying. He was afraid he would go to jail. I was furious. The janitor has nothing to do with the empty yard, and it was none of his business to chase the children. I ran into the bedroom and pulled up the window. The janitor was there, and I was ready for him. Then I felt my palpitations and tenseness, and I decided I was doing wrong to show temper. I spoke to my boy and told him to go out and play and not to mind the janitor. Later, on my way to Recovery, I saw the janitor on the street, but I paid no attention to him and went my way and saved myself the palpitations and the discomfort.

TEMPER, SYMPTOMS AND INSIGHT

PHYSICIAN'S COMMENT ON A PANEL DISCUSSION

What the patients sitting on the panel presented so dramatically can be summed up in simple language. In former days, they said, we responded with temper to trivial irritations. There was a severe aftereffect with mounting tenseness, with symptoms and agonies of suffering. Today we still indulge our tempers, but the occasions are few, the aftereffect is short, and symptoms and suffering are transient and mild. Frank, with his flair for terse and compact expression, gave the proper phrasing to the change in reaction when he remarked that he has now "insight into the phony nature of temper." He made another thought-provoking statement when he surmised that "in a temperamental deadlock, people are not quarreling over real issues but over whether one person is right and the other wrong." But what precisely determines whether a person is wrong or right and whether an issue is real or unreal?

When Tillie cut in on the neighbor's telephone conversation, was she wrong? And when the woman at the other end of the line hung up with a bang, was she right? Frankly, neither you nor I nor anybody else can answer these questions intelligently. Tillie could easily marshal the most compelling reasons for proving that the intrusion was justified. She had been waiting a long time, and her call was important, while the "lady upstairs" was merely chatting, wasting her own time and imposing on other people who were busy and in a hurry. But the neighbor on the upper floor would have no difficulty arguing back that Tillie's interference was plainly an act of deliberate provocation, uncalled for and inexcusable. Are Tillie's arguments right and real? Are the lady's counter-arguments wrong and unreal? Where is the judge who could render a decision as to who is the villain and who the victim?

Let us take a closer look at the matter. Tillie interrupted the conversation of her neighbor. That neighbor gave every indication that she had not finished conversing. She clearly intended to continue but was forced by Tillie's intervention to cease speaking. Leaving the question of right and wrong to one side for the present, the situation seems to be clear: The will of one person conflicted with the will of another person. Force was pitted against force, power clashed with power. As it happened, the one person yielded, the other triumphed. This was a fight, a show of strength or weakness, a contention for the possession or use of an object (telephone wire). Why inject the issue of right and wrong? Why not rather speak the plain, unadorned, honest and sincere language of warfare, competition, constraint and compulsion? In that language, the thing was a tussle, a test of strength, a resort to force.

Tillie waited fifteen minutes before she finally broke in on the conversation. The impulse to use force was certainly operative during these long, drawn-out fifteen minutes. But it was kept in check. The inclination to exercise power was curbed during the period of hesitation. It was only after her patience snapped that Tillie released the impulse. Why did she wait? Why did she beat down her own pressing inclination? The answer is plain: Tillie knew that using force meant to disturb the peace among neighbors. She knew that the real and only issue was peace or power, force or friendship, not the wholly irrelevant question of right and wrong.

Tillie knew she was using force, but she claimed she exercised a right. The use of force was a fact, the claim to exercise a right was an opinion. You may say she thought or assumed or guessed she had a right to use force. But it was *merely* a thought, an assumption *only, nothing but* a guess; and thoughts, assumptions and guesses of this kind are imagined. The right which Tillie claimed was a figment of imagination, the force which she used was a fact of realistic experience. If Tillie's reaction is somehow typical of temperamental outbursts in general, then, we may conclude that *in temper, a right is subjectively claimed and force objectively used.*

A claim ought to be verified. An opinion ought to be tested, proved and substantiated. That calls for a judge. Who is to be the judge in matters of temper? And even if there were a judge, all he could do would be to hand down an opinion. His opinion may be final; it may compose and terminate the fight. But it would be nothing more than an opinion rendered by a duly constituted court instead of by the contending parties. True enough, the judge's opinion is supposed to be impartial, unbiased, based on evidence, testimony, records and documents. But no matter how heavily documented and how scrupulously unbiased the court decision may be, nevertheless, it is and remains an opinion. After the verdict is pronounced, one legal opinion has been substituted for two private opinions. The lawsuit may then be "settled" and "decided." But the question of who was right and who wrong still remains open. The loser may claim, with good logic, that the judge erred and justice miscarried. He may even contend that the law is wrong. You see here that the issue of right and wrong cannot be determined, not even by law. It can only be "decided" and "settled" by a court order. Right and wrong are always opinions, assumptions, suppositions, conjectures, speculations. That means, they are guesses, subjective, imaginative, unreal.

Opinions interpret facts. It ought to be clear to you by now that both the opinions and interpretations are guesses, hence, imaginations. It ought to be just as clear that facts are realities. Temper contains one opinion and many facts. The opinion is that of right and wrong. The facts are the sensations, feelings, impulses and acts (verbal and muscular) which are experienced or expressed in the temperamental sequence.

In Tillie's altercation with the neighbor, the facts were dynamic, impetuous, fierce. On the other hand, the opinion of right and wrong was pale, trite, hackneyed. In spite of that, Tillie's attention was almost exclusively focused on her temperamental opinion, while the facts of her sensations, impulses, feelings and acts went unobserved or unheeded. Yet, her sensations were pressing, her feelings boiling, her impulses overpowering and her acts menacing and stormy. Her heart palpitated, her knees shook, her throat contracted and her voice trembled; she was well nigh convulsed with rage, hostility and fury. But these facts received no or little mention in her report about the telephone conversation. All she claimed was that she was kept waiting, that her intentions were frustrated and her plans thwarted. She thought of the wrong only that was done her, of the rights that were denied her. She was certainly not concerned about the fact that she used force and that she disturbed the peace.

But force and peace are the outstanding facts of life. Force means that feelings, impulses and acts are given ruthless expression without regard for the rights of others. Peace means that these same elements are properly controlled in deference to the sensibilities, interests and claims of others. We may say: Tillie's thoughts were narrowly focused on one restricted opinion: that she was right and the neighbor was wrong. But of the facts of the situation, she was not at all aware. Her insight was warped. It centered on a personal opinion but ignored the objective facts.

You remember that after the telephone call was finished, the outraged neighbor appeared in Tillie's apartment. This was the occasion for another temperamental bout in the course of which Tillie says, "I lost my temper, and gave it to her all right." She then called Gertrude who told her, "You can't afford to lose your temper because of your health." This was an admonition to consider the realities of symptoms, sensations and feelings as matters of first importance and to ignore the "phony" theories of right and wrong. Tillie's reaction was defiant: "I didn't just like that," she said, "and I still thought I was right." The phrase, "I still thought. . ." is revealing. It reveals that Tillie refused to accept the insight offered by Gertrude. She obviously realized that Gertrude's counsel was sound and realistic but decided that she wanted temper and not health. The reason for the blunt refusal was that she "didn't just like that." You see here why our patients, prior to being trained in Recovery techniques, struggle against acquiring insight. They don't like it. They don't like insight because it deprives them of the excitement, drama and vitality of soul-stirring and heart-warming fights.

Fights provide the stir of action that is so sorely missing in the fears, confusion and helplessness that characterize the lives of our patients. Fights give them the sense of living that has fled from the boredom of their daily existence. They offer the opportunity to display vigor, strength, decision, eagerness, determination—all of them elements which are painfully lacking in a drab routine of hopelessness and paralysis of will. Our patients want agitation and stimulation, not equilibrium and peace. They want exhilarating theories, not balancing realities. They crave the use of force, not the adjustment of sensations, feelings and impulses. If you tell them that their unbridled tempers will upset health and disturb peace, their verbal or mental reply is: "I shall rather disturb peace and lose health than give up temper."

It is the crowning glory of Recovery that it was able to reverse this formula and to make patients adopt the principle that temper must be eliminated because it is the sworn enemy of peace and health. This radical change in attitude was beautifully demonstrated by Tillie in an encounter which she had with the same neighbor several months later when, challenged to a fight, she "smiled and refused to get into an argument." She "was sore, but the aftereffect lasted just a short time." Behavior was finally guided by the realities of peace and health, not by sentimental cravings for excitement and intellectual considerations for fictitious theories.

CHAPTER THREE

Temper, Sovereignty and Fellowship

A Panel Discussion Conducted by Patients

ANNETTE (panel leader): The subject for today's panel is taken from the article entitled "Temper As Craving for Symbolic Victories." Has anyone an example?

FRANK R: I can give an example that shows two sides of the story, that is, the difference in the results whether temper is or is not controlled. The other night, I walked home with Harriette and met my mother on the street. She had a letter to mail. I offered to let Harriette mail it so I could carry the bundles. But mother asked me to mail it. As usual, she had to have her own way. I lost my temper and grabbed Harriette and said, "Let's go," leaving mother to mail the letter. After that, I was pretty angry for a short while, but it was all over soon. In former years, I would have tried to justify myself; I would have been furious about the domineering ways of my mother, but this time I didn't do anything of the kind. The incident was closed as far as I was concerned.

Later on, when mother came home, I spoke to her, and she did not answer. A year ago or so, I would have got angry again, but that evening I simply kept quiet. At supper, mother hardly ate anything, and after the meal was over, she cried. Of course, I didn't like that. But since, as you all know, there is a deadlock between us, I couldn't do anything about it. As I said before, there is a difference in results between now and before. Before I had my Recovery training, the deadlock led to endless quarrels because neither of us would give in. Now I keep quiet, and while the deadlock persists, there is no argument. More than that, in former days I would have been angry and stayed angry for a long time. And, incidentally, I wouldn't have felt like eating, either, but on this particular night, I ate as usual.

ANNETTE: In other words, both you and your mother would have staged a contest as to who would starve most and say least. Well, you say that this time you faced the fact that the manner in which you acted might have been wrong and temperamental. You refused to prove that you were right. That is, of course, the best way for cutting short arguments.

TILLIE: I was in the subway last Saturday and sat down pretty close to the corner, and after I was seated, a woman entered the coach and wanted to squeeze in right between me and the corner. She persisted and made me move. I was provoked, but I moved, although there was plenty of room in the coach. I felt my temper going up, and I would have liked to tell the person a thing or two. But then I began to get tense, and I knew that I had to stop working myself up. So I thought, after all, this is a public conveyance, and anybody can sit where he wants to. So when I thought of that, my tenseness left, and I stopped working myself up.

ANNETTE: What was it that made you stop your temperamental reaction?

Tillie: I noticed the tightness in my side. When I get that, I feel choked. Then I can't stay in a closed room. That Saturday in the subway, if the tightness and choked feeling had kept up a few more minutes, I would have wanted to get off the train. So I stopped working myself up, and the sensations left.

SOPHIE: Before I had my Recovery training, when I called my children from the outside to come and eat, they usually didn't respond to the first or second call. Then I would get this tightening in my throat or a pressure in my head, and my temper would rise, and the symptoms would get more severe. After I got into Recovery, I learned I had to control my temper in order to check this irritation. Now I call the children a half dozen times, and I can call in the same level of voice, and my temper doesn't rise any more. In the past, when I used to work myself up, I always feared that something would burst in my head for sure.

ANNETTE: I will quote an example of my own. An elderly aunt of mine, we shall call her Aunt Jane, was the type of person who enjoyed temper tangles. She had never lived with anyone, but during the depression we had to take her into our home. When she came, I decided I'd make an effort to get along with her. I felt I could do that because she confessed to be fond of me. But what I actually did was to try to convince her that she was wrong. And that, of course, ended up in pretty terrific temperamental outbursts on both our sides. One time, after a rather heated argument, I awoke in the middle of the night with a very odd sensation in my abdomen. I felt as though something awful had happened and I was going to burst. I was frightened but did not know at that time that these were nervous symptoms. But the sensations followed so regularly on temperamental spats, I couldn't help realizing that they were closely associated with my temper.

Several years later, after I had undergone a good deal of Recovery training, I had occasion to get in contact with Aunt Jane again. A friend of mine let me use her car, and I invited Aunt Jane to join us on an automobile ride. This time I had a good opportunity to notice how I had changed while my aunt had not. Whenever I found myself wanting to prove her wrong and myself right, I knew at that very moment that all I was out to accomplish was a symbolic victory. I stopped short instantly, and instead of getting provoked myself or getting her worked up, I merely answered her remarks with "maybe" or "is that so?" The argument didn't even get started. On leaving the car, my aunt was obviously irritated and said, "I am just worn out. I never spent such a boring day in my life." And if that remark didn't provoke me into a sharper answer, I realized that I must have learned the technique of giving up the battling for trivial symbolic victories.

CAROL: About this temper. I think it is grand that we have been drilled to get rid of it. In my case, it is when I am with Pete, my husband, and I start to blow off steam. Pete, who knows Recovery, then says, "Temper!" and that puts me on the right track again. A year ago or so, I would be provoked with him when he would say, "Temper!" and I would snap back, "What of it if I have a temper." After that, I would usually let off a honey of temper. But now I know he helps me check it. And when I feel my temper rising, I cut the feeling down, and it doesn't have a chance at all.

ANNETTE: In conclusion, I would like to say that the panel members meant to bring out that we all got into temperamental situations. In former days, before we had our Recovery training, we would have exploded or fretted with a long, drawn-out aftereffect. During the explosion, we would have had the momentary satisfaction of letting off steam. That would give us a momentary sense of relief. Besides that, we would have had the pleasure of feeling ourselves in the right and the other person in the wrong. It is these two pleasures–letting off steam and feeling in the right–that our physician calls the "dual premium placed on temper." The trouble is that this "dual premium" is short-lived, lasting only a few moments. But then it is followed by an aftereffect which may last hours or even days. In that period of the aftereffect, we suffer many distressing symptoms. I know that I, for one, learned that the few moments of pleasure enjoyed during the immediate effects are not worth the hours and days of suffering I endured during the aftereffect.

TEMPER, SOVEREIGNTY AND FELLOWSHIP

PHYSICIAN'S COMMENT ON A PANEL DISCUSSION

A letter was to be mailed and, as a result, an ugly street scene developed, and a family group took their evening meal in the dead silence of a sullen mood. Tears were shed and feelings were crushed. And all the commotion, confusion and agony were caused by–a letter to be mailed. But a letter is a sheet of paper and, as such, utterly incapable of rousing tempers and offending feelings. No issue was involved. The contents of the letter were not challenged; the propriety, wisdom, advisability of its being mailed were not questioned. It was simply a fight about nothing, a struggle for a scrap of paper, a fight without an issue, a fight for the sake of fighting. How is it that men and women of mature age engage in fights "for nothing?" Obviously, mature years do not necessarily mean mature thinking or adult acting.

A fight is centered around an object and rooted in a motive. In the case of Frank and his mother, the object was the letter. What was the motive? A motive is a force that makes muscles move. Suppose the letter which the lady wanted to mail was addressed to a friend. Then the thought of the friend, the desire to communicate with her, the intention to please her supplied the motive that made Frank's mother walk into the street and move toward the mailbox. If Frank and his wife, Harriette, had not entered upon the scene, the letter would have been mailed without ado, and we would have no difficulty understanding the object of the walk, its motive and its successful execution. We would say that an act of behavior was manipulated correctly, or that its purpose aimed correctly at its proper goal. After Frank and Harriette made their appearance, the muscles of the letter-carrying lady suddenly deviated from the goal of the mailbox, the purpose of mailing was forgotten or neglected, and aiming was directed toward something that had essentially nothing to do with the original purpose. A new purpose intervened, changed the goal and redirected the aiming.

The original purpose was to communicate with another person, to give pleasure, to show consideration. The motive here was service. And service serves the end of peace; it creates good will and promotes the welfare of the group. This motive of service and group welfare was suddenly shelved after the arrival of Frank. A fight ensued, and its motive was hostility, competition, domination. What prompted that change in attitude? What is it that makes a person abruptly shift from a disposition to serve to a disposition to dominate?

Whenever you are alone in the privacy of your own home, you are master of your dispositions. You may do as you please and may release whatever disposition you wish to express, provided you keep within the bounds of law, morals and ethics. If your present disposition is to undress, you may disrobe at will. If you wish to rest, you may lie down on the couch; if you desire to sing, to whistle, to eat or read, to keep the eyes open or closed, there is nobody to check you, no standard to impose restrictions on your whim or caprice. Under conditions of privacy, you are in unquestioned control of your decisions and enjoy the exclusive and uncontested right to act as you choose. Being the master of your destiny and a law unto yourself, you are sovereign.

That sovereignty of yours is severely curtailed the moment you step out into the street. Now you are subject to rules which restrict your rights and put a check to your dispositions. You cannot, for instance, place a couch in the middle of the street and take your afternoon rest there. Even should the street be empty, you would not be permitted to use it as your private dwelling place. Outside your home, your conduct is required to conform to regulations, customs and traditions, even if no legal, moral or ethical issues are involved. The reason is that out in the street, you may meet other people, and once you are among people, you are the member of a group, and in a group you are rule-bound and lose your sovereignty, at least part of it.

In a group, the members are fellows with equal rights, demanding that their rights be respected by the fellow members. This is called *fellowship* and is opposed to sovereignty. Fellowship means service, self-restraint and respect for the rights of others. Sovereignty means, or may mean, the reverse: domination, unrestricted power and disregard for the needs, desires or rights of others. Fellowship is the principle of group action, sovereignty that of individualism. To the extent that a sovereign recognizes other persons as his fellows, he loses the prerogatives of sovereignty. To the extent that a group of fellows grants to any of its members the status of sovereignty, it weakens the principle of fellowship.

Groups are either loose assemblages, for instance, a crowd in the street, or a close-knit organization like the family. The closer a group is organized, the more is it pervaded by the spirit of fellowship. There is hardly a trace of fellowship in the street crowd; there should be a maximum of it in the family. All kinds of groups could be ranged between the street crowd and the family, with varying degrees of fellowship governing their mutual relations. On this scale, a group of friends ought to be held together by a far greater measure of fellowship than, let me say, a group of co-workers in a shop, and the group of co-workers should score a higher rating in fellowship than a group of voters attending a political meeting. The point that I wish to make is that the family ought to rank highest in point of fellowship among all closely organized groups. In a family, fellowship ought to be at its maximum, sovereignty at its lowest possible minimum. That this is not so is clearly evidenced by the almost universal prevalence of domestic temper.

When Frank met his mother, he offered to mail the letter. Behind this offer was a desire or determination to be helpful or courteous or considerate. The act expressed the motive of service, that is, the spirit of fellowship. Frank has frequently stated in panel discussions that he and his mother do not get along well together. They live in a more or less continuous temperamental deadlock, in an atmosphere of strife, spite and bitterness. You may conclude, therefore, that Frank's offer was a polite gesture rather than a genuine eagerness to be of help. But in group life, an insincere gesture of generosity and fellowship is far more valuable than an outspoken expression of enmity and a brutal assertion of one's sovereignty.

No doubt, the rebuff offered by Frank's mother was sincere. It was based on sincere bitterness and sincere hostility. Sincerity of this kind is anything but an asset. A group is interested in peace and order. And peace and order are destroyed or disrupted by the temperamental expressions of anger, vindictiveness and bitterness. A temperamental outburst is sincere, of course. So are murder and burglary. They are based on genuine and sincere desires to kill and rob. That the mother was sincere in her rude reaction to Frank's offer of fellowship was no credit to her. That reaction was dictated by the mother's will to have her own way, by her insistence on domination and her determination to assert her sovereign rights. As such, it served the ends of unrestricted individualism, not those of rule-bound group life. It was based on the principle of sovereignty, not of fellowship.

This is not an attempt to exonerate our friend Frank. He practiced his share of rudeness and sovereignty when, in a temperamental act of brusqueness, he "grabbed Harriette and said, 'Let's go.'" Both mother and son are currently disposed to display excesses of domestic temper, exercising their disposition to assert their sovereign rights and ignoring the needs for fellowship, mutuality and toleration. What interests us here is the close relation that exists between the workings of an aggressive temper, on the one hand, and the spirit of sovereignty and fellowship, on the other.

The members of the panel spoke of symbols and symbolic victories. One of the most pernicious symbols is that of sovereignty. Frank's mother imagined, perhaps unknown to herself, that she represented or symbolized sovereignty in her dealings with the members of her family. Her will to assert her sovereignty provoked the resistance of her son, with the result that family life was turned into a battlefield of temperamental dispositions in which both mother and son craved the glory of symbolic victories, and both effectively frustrated one another's ludicrous ambitions. In the end, a cruel implacable deadlock developed in which feelings and sensibilities were ruthlessly slaughtered and fellowship was made a shambles. The realistic objects of the incessant fights were invariably such trivialities as a letter to be mailed or a sugar bowl to be filled. The symbolic goal was the craving to assert sovereign rights. The inevitable results were tears, crushed feelings and refusals to eat or otherwise to share and to practice fellowship.

The deadlock between Frank and his mother is undoubtedly extreme. It is characterized by an extreme insistence on the exercise of unrestricted sovereignty and an equally extreme refusal to practice fellowship. Deadlocks of more moderate intensity were mentioned by the other members of the panel. Annette was in deadlock with her sour-dispositioned aunt, Sophie with her boisterous youngsters, Carol with her soft-spoken and well-intentioned husband. All of them were, in one way or another, embroiled in the tug-of-war of domestic temper. All of them had, in previous years, indulged in the cruel game of craving symbolic victories in the battle for their sovereign rights. And all of them had an unenvious record of tears shed, feelings crushed and meals taken in the dead silence of sullen moods.

But all of them told you, in unmistakable language, that for them, the concept of sovereignty has been finally exposed as an empty, silly and childish symbol and fellowship has become a living, mature and concrete reality. Even Frank, the helpless party to a relentless and apparently incurable deadlock, was able to state that before he had his Recovery training, "the deadlock led to endless quarrels because neither of us would give in. Now I keep quiet, and, while the deadlock persists, there is no argument." In his home, fellowship is not reestablished, but the peace-destroying symbolism of sovereignty has been routed and with it, Frank's symptoms of fatigue and sleeplessness. And if it is true that Recovery training is capable of laying the ghost of sovereignty, then we may be pardoned for claiming that our system of self-help is the sovereign means for promoting fellowship.

CHAPTER FOUR

Muscles and Mental Health

A PANEL DISCUSSION CONDUCTED BY PATIENTS

FRANK (panel leader): I will start off with an example. When I first came to Recovery, I had so many symptoms, I did not know where to start first. My symptoms were all pretty strong, and I did not know which was the weakest. My main symptom was nervous fatigue. Today I know it is not muscular fatigue but merely a sense of being tired. At that time, I had difficulty sleeping. It took me anywhere from an hour to three hours to get to sleep, and after I got to sleep, I would wake up every hour or so, and this went on practically every night. I also had practically no appetite and had to force myself to eat. I also had blurring of vision, numbness in the arms and legs and pressure in the head. A noise in the ears bothered me a lot. On top of it, I had difficulty making up my mind, and the simplest decision gave me trouble. Finally I had to give up my job and did not work for four years before I joined Recovery.

Even after I came to Recovery, it looked like a pretty hopeless job. Then I remember our doctor once saying in class that it is the minor symptoms that must be worked on first. But I couldn't tell a minor symptom when I saw one. Today, I know that it is not so much the weakest symptom that must be handled but the simplest method that must be used. And the simplest method is control of muscles. Ever since I used my muscles to walk on, fatigue or no fatigue, I am no longer troubled with that awful tiredness. And since I have been using my muscles not to toss in bed, I have no trouble sleeping.

HARRIETTE: Every now and then when I am talking with new patients, they are surprised when I tell them that I was pretty sick for over fifteen years and am now well. They say maybe you were not as sick as I am. Of course everyone thinks they were the sickest person in the world, but I think I was very sick all the time before I came to Recovery. I can remember in high school I got my famous headaches and nausea and fatigue and dizzy spells and weak spells and palpitations; my ears ached and my eyes blurred and my throat choked. And I would go to a doctor, and he would prescribe a tonic or say I needed a rest. And then maybe I'd be feeling better for a short while, and then another series of symptoms would come along. Each time the new series would come, they would be intensified, until, about six years ago, they got so bad, I decided to quit work.

For the next two years, I went around to doctors and clinics and had all sorts of X-rays taken and all kinds of medicine prescribed. But the trouble kept getting worse. So after I had gone all round to every place and even went to consult a doctor in Montana, I talked again to the family physician, and he recommended I should go to Chicago and consult our doctor who, my family physician said, treated his patients with a new method. He meant the classes and Recovery. Well, three weeks after I came to Chicago, I was working part time. After four months, I worked full time and have been working ever since, that is, over four years. I can say I feel better than I ever felt in my life, and no amount of money could ever pay for what I learned in Recovery.

FRANK: Can you say that you attacked your symptoms at their weakest point?

HARRIETTE: I don't know that. But the doctor told me to use my muscles. So I forced myself to eat when I felt nauseated and forced myself to walk when I felt exhausted. It wasn't easy, but what helped me was that I accepted the authoritative knowledge of our doctor. I know our doctor would not ask me to do these things if they could do harm.

CHRISTINE: My main trouble was a terrific feeling of depression and fatigue, which I thought was the hardest thing to overcome. When I got up in the morning, I thought I could hardly move and needed rest. But soon I learned that muscles could be commanded to move, but that didn't work the first few times. I had to practice a number of mornings, and what helped me most was the example of other patients when they were interviewed in classes. I thought what they can do, I should be able to do, too. And so I said to myself in the morning, you certainly can make your hands and feet work. What helped me was, like with Harriette, that I accepted the doctor's authoritative knowledge that my fatigue was in the mind and not in the muscles. My mildest symptom, I think, was that I had to force myself to eat. When I felt my throat was dry and I couldn't swallow a bite, I remembered that muscles can be commanded to work, and kept on eating. So I think I probably worked on the mildest symptom by the method which to me was the easiest to use.

In the further course of the panel, Phil recounted how he suffered from a lack of self-confidence after leaving the hospital, how he was afraid he made too many mistakes. "If I would get a wrong number on the telephone or forget to pick up a pencil, I thought I was going back to the Psychopathic Hospital." As a consequence, he kept out of the way of people and experienced great hesitancy doing simple jobs. Finally, he learned he could always "command the muscles no matter how weak the mind is."

He then reported a recent experience. He was driving his car, and on stopping, threw the door shut, leaving the ignition key inside. When some time later he reached into his pocket, he missed the key and knew he had left it in the car. He felt embarrassed. He knew he would have to phone his brother to ask for the reserve key. But then he would have to "admit I made a mistake and would have to look foolish." In former days, he would have thought of calling a towing service to have the car pulled in or would have considered some other foolish move, trying, by every desperate means, to cover up his inadequacy. This time, he simply forced himself to use his muscles, called his brother, got the reserve key and didn't feel embarrassed at all.

MUSCLES AND MENTAL HEALTH

PHYSICIAN'S COMMENT ON A PANEL DISCUSSION

When Harriette told recent members of Recovery that she recovered her health after fifteen years of futile search for a remedy, she met with skepticism. Had she told the doubters that her main means of recapturing health was the use of her muscles, their skepticism would have turned into outright cynicism. That the mind governs muscles is a truism, accepted even by the most sophisticated mentality. But that muscles can be made to mold and influence mental activity sounds incredible to the skeptic and laughable to the cynic. Fortunately, our patients do not belong to the group of "advanced thinkers," and to their plain common sense and unpolished way of viewing things, the humble muscle commands as much dignity as the pretentious brain cell. They know that if in a nervous ailment central management breaks down, the peripheral rank and file may be ready or can be trained to "take over."

And so, when in the lives of Harriette, Frank, Christine, Phil and many hundreds of Recovery members, the machinery of central management was thrown out of gear, the muscles were trained to hold the line until management could be reorganized and revitalized. After the muscles had demonstrated their ability to keep the concern going, the self-confidence of the brain was restored, and the body regained its capacity for concerted action and balanced adjustment. To the skeptic such "pinch-hitting" of the muscles for the brain may sound incredible, and to the cynic it may appear laughable. But skepticism and cynicism are off-shoots of intellectualism, and Recovery stands for realism, plain common sense and an unspoiled way of viewing life.

At the time when Harriette joined Recovery, she suffered from a condition in which her brain had almost ceased giving directions to the muscles. If any guidance was supplied, it was in the form of fearful anticipations, gloomy misgivings and dismal threats. The brain had retreated from active management of the body. It cowered away in abject defeatism, shivered at the thought of giving orders and trembled at the prospect of having to take the initiative and to shoulder responsibility. There were tasks to be finished, decisions to be made and actions to be planned, but the brain, paralyzed by fear, terrified the muscles into helpless inactivity and the inner organs into chaotic functioning. Harriette was tortured by "headaches and nausea and fatigue and dizzy spells, by weak spells and palpitations." Her ears ached and her eyes blurred and her throat choked, and for solid years, her brain warned her not to walk when she felt dizzy, not to work when she was fatigued, not to eat when she experienced her nausea. The sense of hopelessness in the brain created an attitude of helplessness in the muscles. Action was held in abeyance, life was suspended.

After fifteen years of unrelieved agony, Harriette learned in Recovery that if the brain defaulted on its managerial duties, the muscles can be made to "take over" and to "pinch-hit" for the cringing cerebral manager. At first she had her doubts. The method seemed too simple. When her nervous fatigue made her feel exhausted and her brain threatened that the next step meant unfailing collapse, how was she to force her muscles to venture into that next step that might lead to destruction? But then she heard a patient recite in a class interview how she had routed her fears by "commanding the muscles" to do what they dreaded to do. That patient had developed the habit of growing panicky at the mere sight of a knife, fearing to do harm to the baby. During the interview, I urged the patient to practice touching knives and assured her that the mere act of contacting or handling the "dangerous" object was certain to convince the jittery brain that there was no reason for jitters. The resolute-ness of the muscles would conquer the defeatism of the brain. The patient accepted my suggestion, practiced touch-ing knives and purged the brain of its fears. "I would have never believed," the patient exclaimed, "that such a simple method could cure my fears! But it did."

Other patients reported similar experiences. One of them was afraid of crossing the street. Stepping out of the house meant to set going a chain of frightening symptoms, palpitations, sweats, dizziness, muscular weakness and dimness of vision. The brain sounded the customary alarm, warning of a dire emergency. After due instruction, the patient learned to brave the empty threat of the sensations and the defeatist babble of the brain. He compelled his mus-cles to walk on and convinced his cowardly cerebral man-ager that no danger existed and that the warning signals flashed by the brain cells were false alarms, not to be taken seriously. After Harriette witnessed several class demonstra-tions of this kind, she decided to give the method a fair trial with the result that she worked part time after three weeks of practicing muscle control and engaged in full-time activ-ity after another four months. The brain had been convinced by the muscles that all that was required to shake off ner-vous fears was to make the muscles do what the brain feared to do.

That the brain receives the greater part of its knowl-edge from the muscles ought to be plain to anyone who is not blinded by the glamour of fanciful theories. Knowledge means experience, and the bulk of our experience stems from our actions, and our actions are carried out by our mus-cles, mainly. I do not wish to deny that a great deal of expe-rience is gathered from vision and hearing, touch, smell and taste. But the type of knowledge secured from these sources is chiefly informative. Practical knowledge, the knowledge of how to behave, of what to do at a certain time in a given situation, comes to you from acting and practicing, that is, from the activity of your muscles. With regard to that variety of knowledge and experience that tells you what to do and what not to do, there can be hardly any doubt that the *muscles are pre-eminently the teachers and educators of the brain.*

It is true that after the brain has received from the muscles its education about things practical, it stores, analyzes and codifies the items of knowledge which it has acquired. It sorts them according to their importance and value, their harmfulness and innocence, their promise of success and threat of failure. It formulates rules and standards, and elaborates an imposing system of logic and wisdom for the sound guidance of conduct. But the fundamental teaching and educating are done by the muscles. That a flame causes a burning pain, the child learns after the muscles have touched the burning object. Once the pain and burn have been experienced through muscular action, the brain forms the rule that the finger must be kept at a safe distance from flames. The relationship is clear: Muscles teach the brain, and the brain, enriched by knowledge, guides the muscles.

Before Harriette fell victim to a nervous ailment, her brain had acquired a generous store of useful knowledge from the countless muscular acts of behavior, which she had practiced in a busy childhood and active adolescence. From these endless series of muscular reactions, her brain derived a set of rules, principles and policies which regulated her daily activities. One rule was that headaches, nausea, dizziness, palpitations and symptoms of a similar kind are average happenings, not calling for emergency reactions. Another rule was that if doubts arose as to whether any of the symptoms were of an average or emergency character, a physician possessed of authoritative knowledge should be consulted. A third rule, we may assume, was that the dictum of the freely chosen physician was to be accepted as sound guide for thinking about and acting on the inner experience. These rules had served Harriette well. They told her what to worry about and what to ignore, and they settled her opinions, beliefs and convictions about health.

But after she developed her nervous incapacity, she forgot the previously well-established rules, indulged in self-diagnosing and produced sustained fears, panics and vicious cycles. Eating, sleeping, walking, conversing were now considered as acts fraught with danger. The brain was crammed with ideas of threatening collapse and impending disaster. All her opinions, beliefs and convictions gained from previous muscular behavior were drenched in a flood of defeatism. Fear ideas and emergency impulses poured forth from an intimidated brain down to the leaderless muscles, and action turned into inactivity, initiative into paralysis of will, self-confidence into helplessness and hopelessness. When, after fifteen years of an agonizing existence, Harriette decided to consult me, my problem was to convince her brain that eating could be done in spite of the threat of nausea, that nocturnal restlessness and brainstorms were no bar to normal sleep performance, that brisk walking was perfectly compatible with "nervous exhaustion" and that a lump in the throat was no impediment to well-articulated speech or to resolute swallowing. It was at that time that "commanding the muscles" was prescribed as the proper remedy.

As was mentioned, Harriette was at first skeptical. But when in classes and at Recovery meetings her skepticism melted, she commanded her muscles to lie quietly in bed when she was tense and restless, to walk on when she felt exhausted, to eat when the mere sight of food produced nausea and to speak forcefully when the throat felt choked. And after the muscles swung into action, disregarding the "symptomatic idiom" of the organs, Harriette's brain was instantly convinced that exhausted muscles can do a fine piece of walking, that a weary body can lie motionless in bed until sleep supervenes, that a stomach harried by the prospect of nausea can be made to take in food without sending it back, and that a throat drained of its moisture and contracted to a pinpoint could be induced to voice a well-modulated speech. With continued practice of systematic muscle training, the brain finally was rid of its defeatism and, invigorated by a newly gained conviction, mustered the courage to resume leadership and to reinstate the ancient set of rules, policies and principles for healthy conduct. Harriette's muscles had re-educated her brain.

Had Harriette retained her skepticism, she would have refrained from practicing muscle control, and defeatism would have nullified or retarded her cure. Unfortunately, too many patients persist in their skepticism, scorning the use of a method which appears "too simple" to promise results. One such patient recently tried to challenge my statements about the role of muscles in shaping conduct with the question, "But, Doctor, I don't suffer from palpitations or dizziness or fatigue. My trouble is an obsession. How can muscles cure an obsession?" The obsession from which the lady suffered was one of jealousy. The patient knew that her husband was a model of matrimonial loyalty but could not shake off the thought that he was unfaithful.

She was told: "I grant that yours is what is called an *obsession*. But if you ponder the meaning of the word, you will realize that what obsesses your brain is an idea. You know from experience that ideas come and go. How is it you cannot get rid of your idea? How is it that it 'obsesses' you and occupies your attention all the time? The reason is that the actions of your muscles feed this idea and reinforce it incessantly, preventing it from leaving the brain as ideas ordinarily do. Command your muscles not to act on the obsession, and it will die of inanition. What you do is to keep the thought of jealousy alive by means of your muscular action. You rummage in the pockets of your husband's clothes to find evidence of his philandering. When you arrive home, you search rooms, garret and basement to discover telltale objects left by an unwelcome visitor. You spy on your husband's activities, telephone his office numbers of times to check on his whereabouts, scrutinize his mail and notebooks, and keep a close watch on every one of his movements. When he arrives in the evening, you subject him to a relentless bombardment of quizzes, questions and suspicions. All of this is done by your muscles. Every search, every act of watching, every sequence of questioning intensifies your tenseness and keeps your attention forcefully riveted on the obsessive idea. That idea would die a natural death within a short time, as ideas commonly do, if you permitted it to expire. But the action of your muscles keeps it alive, prolonging your suffering and refusing to let your brain find its normal equilibrium. The surest way to make the obsession depart from your brain is to command your muscles not to ask questions, not to telephone your husband's office, not to launch into endless searches of rooms, pockets, drawers and notebooks. In your case, the muscles, if properly restrained, would not only re-educate the brain, they would also give it the much-needed breathing spell and would relieve it of the well nigh intolerable tenseness under which it is placed through the action of your muscles."

I could quote numerous other examples, illustrating the many uses to which the method of muscle control lends itself in its task of either convincing the brain that defiance of symptoms is possible and harmless, or relieving it of pressures caused by morbid preoccupation with disturbing ideas and impulses. But my time is up, and I shall close with the assurance that what Harriette did can be done by every nervous patient, and that the simplicity of the method which she used ought to be no occasion for skeptical shrugs and cynical sneers. Precisely because the method is simple, it is prompt, effective and–convincing.

CHAPTER FIVE

Realism, Romanticism, Intellectualism

A PANEL DISCUSSION CONDUCTED BY PATIENTS

ANNETTE (panel leader): The subject for today's panel is taken from the article "The Myth of Nervous Fatigue." When I became ill, I was always exhausted. When I came home after a day's work, I felt as though I had to crawl into bed. Many an evening I thought I was too tired to eat, and so I did not eat. I just crawled into bed and stayed there. The doctor prescribed a program of rest, and I followed it faithfully. Returning from work at about 4 o'clock in the afternoon, I went to bed, and sometimes I slept and sometimes I did not. I got up for supper and went right back to bed again. The first few days, I got a little relief, but very little. Very soon I felt just as tired lying in bed and resting. Of course, I thought the fatigue was physical. I thought I was gradually losing my vitality and resistance. But I went on with the program, spending more and more time in bed and doing fewer and fewer things. But I felt more exhausted than ever. Physicians had told me my condition was that of a nervous exhaustion, and I formed the idea that the nerves in my body were exhausted and shriveled and incapable of performing their job.

When I came to the Illinois Research Hospital, I was told in classes that my trouble was not fatigue but self-disgust and discouragement. I didn't like that very well because I knew how my muscles felt, and it didn't just sound right that disgust and discouragement should make them feel exhausted. But as I continued to attend classes, I became convinced that our physician was right, and I learned to be more objective about my symptoms.

After I returned home from the hospital, I wanted to move a large piece of furniture and did not want to wait until my husband came home. So I did the job and moved it, and then I decided to move the other pieces, and when my husband came home, instead of being in a state of exhaustion, I felt fine. After that experience, I was convinced that, as our doctor says, nervous fatigue is in the mind and not in the muscles. Any other example?

GERTRUDE: I have one. The other day, I got up early, about a quarter to six, and started my ironing. About eleven thirty, I felt tired and thought I couldn't go on another minute. I became quite dizzy and had the idea, "I've got to lie down because if not, I'll faint." I thought I was exhausted from being up so early. But in a second, I realized that what was really the matter was that I did not want to finish the ironing. I had a few shirts to do, which I don't enjoy doing. So I said to myself, this is a nervous fatigue, and lying down will not help any and also will not get the ironing done, and I kept right on. It did not take more than five minutes and the fatigue was gone, so I realized it was a mental fatigue.

ANNETTE: Did you have experience with this sense of fatigue in previous years?

GERTRUDE: I had it practically all the time when I was first sick. Even on days after I had a good night's sleep, I used to be so fatigued, I would lie down and rest. But then I felt just as fatigued no matter how long I rested. I could never figure out the reason till I got my Recovery training and learned that this nervous fatigue was nothing to worry about. Now I am interested in things and don't get bored so easily, and so I don't feel fatigued any more.

CHRISTINE: When I was ill, my strongest symptom was I would get up in the morning feeling so fatigued, I had all I could do to wash my face and put my clothes on. When I came to Recovery, I learned that was discouragement and self-disgust, but I still sabotaged at times, and whenever I did not feel well, I said I needed rest. Every doctor had told me I needed a rest cure. The other day, I felt miserable, and tense and tired, and I thought I just couldn't get dressed. But I made up my mind to go to the Recovery office to have a cup of coffee with the other girls.* But I felt so draggy, I didn't think I could make it. But I went, and when I left, I felt fine, and all fatigue was gone.

ANNETTE: Walking to the Recovery office involved a walk of about six blocks. Do you think you would have attempted a six-block walk, let me say a year ago, when you faced this intense feeling of fatigue?

CHRISTINE: No, my legs used to get weak and shaky, and they felt like they were going out from under me, and I really thought I couldn't walk. I was afraid I would collapse if I forced myself to walk. But last week, after my daughter's wedding, I felt plenty fatigued after all the activity and excitement. But I carried on. I said to myself, "If it is nothing but the sense of discouragement, it doesn't matter. And if it is a muscle fatigue, it will disappear."

MARCELLE: When I first got out of the hospital, I felt terribly fatigued in the morning. I had to get my husband's breakfast but went right back to bed the moment he left. I would stay there till eleven or twelve o'clock, and when I got up, I felt just as tired as if I had not rested at all. After I got my Recovery training, I knew that this was a feeling of discour-

---

*In former years, every afternoon between two and five, two members of Recovery volunteered their time to supervise activities at the Recovery headquarters. Members would drop in and spend the afternoon in the company of other patients. Coffee and cake were served on this occasion.

agement, and our doctor had told me I should take brisk walks, fatigued or not fatigued. And I did that and felt fine. At times, I still sabotage and stay in bed in the morning, but that is getting less and less.

FRANK R.: Before I had my training in Recovery, I was always tired. I always wanted to go to bed. But I couldn't sleep. I dreaded lying in bed struggling to sleep. So I put off going to bed till one or two o'clock. Finally, I would doze off, but I would be awake at five o'clock. When I joined Recovery and heard about nervous fatigue being just discouragement, I was very skeptical about that. I had had that fatigue so many years that I was convinced it was real muscle fatigue. But I listened to our doctor and practiced ignoring the fatigue. Today, I go to bed early and have no trouble sleeping and feeling refreshed in the morning.

ROSE E.: I used to hate to get up and make my husband's breakfast. But I did it anyhow. But the minute he left, I would just fly back to bed again. I would lie there for an hour or two and feel worse than before. Then I joined Recovery and learned that the tiredness is nothing but a sensation, and I can now ignore it and do my work even if I sometimes feel tired. I have practiced that and found it to be so. I found it is just nervous fatigue, and it leaves.

REALISM, ROMANTICISM, INTELLECTUALISM

PHYSICIAN'S COMMENT ON A PANEL DISCUSSION

Annette felt tired and thought the "fatigue was physical." She then formed the idea that her nerves were "exhausted and shriveled and incapable of performing their job." After she was told in classes that nervous fatigue has its source in the patient's sense of discouragement and self-disgust, she "didn't like that very well because I knew how my muscles felt." With this, she formulated the familiar philosophy of nervous patients which can be condensed in two sentences:

I *feel* tired; hence, I *am* tired, and I *think* my muscles are exhausted; hence, *they are.* On the basis of this philosophy, patients are convinced that what they feel is real and what they think is right. And it is the supposed reality of what they feel and the presumed rightness of what they think which keeps patients from ironing and dressing and preparing the breakfast. Protesting solemnly that their nerves are "incapable of performing their jobs," they do a perfect job at coddling their feelings and pampering their thoughts. Pronouncing their coddled feelings real and their pampered thoughts right, they prepare the groundwork for manufacturing a self-made incapacity.

I want you to know that this is a philosophy, confused and absurd it is true, but a philosophy nevertheless. My patients claim they suffer from frightening sensations, overpowering impulses, torturing thoughts and devitalized feelings. But I tell them that this is a half-truth at best; that what they actually suffer from is–their philosophy. And if their philosophy is based on the assumption that, in their spells and tantrums, their feelings are real and their thoughts are right, well, that is precisely the philosophy of temper. In the ordinary burst of temper, whether it be presymptomatic or postsymptomatic,* you *feel* the insult or injury was a "real" outrage and *think* you are "right" in considering it a deliberate hurt.

If I speak of a philosophy, I do not refer to a complex system of thought as described in textbooks. What I have in mind is what has been called *the philosophy of life.* Let me add immediately that I know three philosophies of this kind only: realism, romanticism and intellectualism. If, in the pursuit of your daily activities you coddle your feelings, you will act as a romantic; if you pamper your thoughts, your conduct will be that of an intellectual. Your behavior will then be governed by feelings whose telltale story has been hastily believed, or by thoughts whose immature suggestions were uncritically accepted. In either case, your action

---

*About presymptomatic and postsymptomatic see Part III, Chapter 39.

will be guided by the subjective promptings of your inner experiences instead of by the objective requirements of outer reality. If you were a realist, you would give first consideration to the actual facts of the prevailing situation and would not hesitate to suppress your thoughts or shelve your feelings if you found they conflicted with the realities of the situation. I shall illustrate the point presently.

You enter a bakery shop intent on buying a cake. The requirements of the situation are such that you must stand in line and wait. No doubt, you will not relish the prospect. You will be provoked and will experience irritation, discomfort and impatience. These are the *subjective feelings* with which you respond to the realistic facts of the situation. We shall call it the *feeling response*. Before long, your thought processes swing into action. You surmise that the saleslady could certainly move a trifle faster. And the customer who is just being served could indeed speed up her selection without insisting on being shown all varieties of cookies in the showcase. How inconsiderate people are! And what kind of government is this anyhow! A year after V-J Day, and still this nuisance of wartime restrictions, scarcities and rationing! This is your *thought response,* as intuitive, impulsive and spontaneous as was your feeling response.

I doubt whether any human being endowed with normal sensibilities will avoid the feeling of irritation and the thought of frustration in a situation of this kind. Be he realist, romantic or intellectual, he will respond with aroused feelings to an imposition and with critical thoughts to the persons who prolong or aggravate the frustration. He would not be "human" if he responded otherwise. In point of *inner responses,* men are alike. They differ only in their readiness to convert their inner responses into *open reactions.* The realist is inclined to control his feeling and thought responses; the romantic and intellectual tend to express them. It is all a matter of your philosophy (of life), and if your philosophy is realistic, you will exercise control; if it is romantic, your feelings may be expressed the moment they are aroused; if it is intellectual, your thoughts will tend to be voiced the very instant they are born.

A philosophy tells you which goals to choose and how to aim at them. You who are readers of our Recovery literature know that goals are of two kinds: group and individualistic. The realist aims at group goals, mainly. His ambition is to adjust his conduct to the requirements of group life. In the instance of the visit to the bakery shop, he considered himself a member of the group of shoppers. He knew that by expressing his feelings of irritation or his thoughts of resentment, he was bound to arouse the enmity of some members of that group. And antagonizing the group meant maladjustment. If his goal was to create good will in the group, he had to curb his individualistic inclinations to express his inner responses. He exercised control and remained adjusted. To the romantic and intellectual person, the good will of the group means little. Group standards are odious restrictions to their craving for individualistic expression.

In the episode at the bakery shop, the romantic would not have hesitated to voice his indignation with a candid and perhaps studied indifference to the sensibilities of others. He prides himself on being frank and aboveboard. "What is wrong about expressing a feeling?" asks the romantic enthusiast for frank expression. And forthwith, without scruple or hesitation, he rolls off a list of his likes and dislikes, regardless of whether they are offensive, tactless and out of place. He will tell you, without mincing words, that your furniture is not properly arranged; that if he had planned a house like yours, the rooms—or entrances or exits—would have been differently placed. If it is a woman romantic, she will intimate plainly that she has no taste for your jewelry and that her way of cooking a roast is different, and "if you want to get a real coat, let me take you to my tailor." It is all an expression of feelings, and if in the process, the feelings of others are hurt, well, it is about time they got used to language that "comes straight from the shoulder."

Presently, this unrestrained talker will steer the conversation into the channels of sickness, hospitalization, operations. She will revel in gruesome recollections of the "excruciating pains" she suffered without being able to convince her husband or physician that the pain was "real." What agonies she went through. She felt pain and tugging and pulling in the lower abdomen. "It was there, I felt it all the time. But they thought it was my imagination. Finally, I got my physician to take me to the hospital, and on the operating table they found adhesions all over." Her feelings had told her she had a tumor or something of the sort, and it was "really" there.

I could go on indefinitely describing the amusing, though by no means harmless, mouthings of these romantic souls. I could portray their lust for complaining, their zeal for being considered a martyr. But it would merely illustrate the fact that their philosophy is one of reckless expression of feelings. These feelings are coddled and treasured and magnified and thrust at every innocent listener who consents to be an audience.

I shall now give you a brief account of the intellectual mentality, the counterpart of the romantic soul. His stock in trade is the insistence, repeated tirelessly and ruthlessly, that he is right, that you better take his advice, that he could have told you how to avoid trouble if you had only cared to listen to him. Thinking that he is right, he promptly assumes that the others are wrong. Hence, he delights in correcting the statements and opinions of those about him. He is critical, aggressive, meddlesome. He not only knows things but knows them better than others. His views are advanced and modern, theirs are standpattish and outmoded. His supreme delight is to change things, to reform laws and institutions, to do away with the old and to create something new; hence, he is impatient with tradition, custom and standards. He knows how to arrange things, how to plan them, how to predict and prevent. Enjoying a self-appointed monopoly in correct thinking, he is eager to mend and "reform" the defective thought processes of others. These others are backward, benighted, reactionary. He is forward-looking, enlightened, progressive. The essence of his attitude is that he knows and is right and that the others are ignorant and wrong. And if they are wrong, it is his duty to tell them.

There is no reticence about this intellectual. He talks, and argues and fights for his opinions. His pet ideal is "free speech," not only in the political scene where it may have a legitimate place, but also in social and domestic contacts where it merely serves the purpose of shocking settled convictions and established views. Waiting in line at the bakery shop, the intellectual would, or might, let loose a stirring tirade of criticism against "that bunch of stuffed shirts" and their "red tape." He might inveigh against the greed of the "vested interests" and the oppression of the common people. Voicing their thoughts and opinions, particularly if they are shocking to the "lethargy" of the "standpatters," is a consuming passion with these right-thinking and enlightened intellectuals.

I do not wish to be misunderstood to imply that my patients are generally addicted to a romantic or intellectual philosophy of life. Presumably, some of them are, but so are some members of every group. At any rate, I am little concerned about the political, economic or social views of my patients. What interests me is their philosophy with regard to symptoms and temper. The fact is that my patients, prior to receiving training in Recovery, have been stubbornly romantic about their symptoms and emphatically intellectual about their temper. They coddled their defeatist feelings of "really" being exhausted and of "really" not having slept a wink for months, and pampered their thoughts of having the "right" to wail and complain and make extravagant demands on relatives and friends. What the panel members demonstrated convincingly is that persistent and systematic training in the realistic principles of Recovery is the superb means of ridding our patients of the pretentious pseudo-philosophies of decadent romanticism and arrogant intellectualism in their dealings with their common inner experiences.

CHAPTER SIX

Exceptionality and Averageness; Sentimentalism and Realism

A PANEL DISCUSSION CONDUCTED BY PATIENTS

ANNETTE (panel leader): The subject of today's panel discussion is taken from the interview entitled "Average Existence and Exceptionality." The doctor speaks there of desirable and undesirable exceptionality. Has anybody got an example?

ANN: I had a silly fear similar to the one described in the article. My sister told me something that had happened to a neighbor. He had been hurt in an accident. I got the idea I was responsible for that accident. But I knew immediately it was a delusion and was ready to wait till it would disappear. You know, I mentioned it on previous panels, that I get delusions of this kind, but I have learned to handle them. But this time, all of a sudden, I laughed hysterically. That frightened me. After I hung up, I had the fear that my sister would know my behavior was maladjusted. I called Rosalie, and she told me how she handled a similar story of an accident. I again got this idea that I was responsible. Rosalie said, "You know what you are doing? You are misinterpreting an event. You know that nobody in this world would think he is responsible for an accident he heard of. And if you think you are responsible, you think you are not like other people. You think of yourself as exceptional." That helped me. And last Saturday, when I had that feeling again that I was responsible for what somebody did, I had no fear in connection with it, and it just disappeared.

ANNETTE: Ann has learned in Recovery that even delusions can be controlled if you know how to eliminate the idea of danger. Such delusions are ideas. And our physician has told us repeatedly that ideas come and go if you do not add the thought of danger. Ann has proved that is correct.

ANN: Of course, I don't handle them right yet. Just thinking of these fears and bringing them out on the panel gives me tremors. I have some right now, but I can control them.

ANNETTE: Several weeks ago, I had a trying day, and I was quite tired and somewhat irritable. I had stayed up late, and when I went to bed, my feet were very cold. I mentioned it to my husband, but he did not reply. I resented that. A little while later, I got a cramp in my foot, but I didn't tell my husband, perhaps from fear that he might not be any more sympathetic than he was to my first complaint. I became tense and felt that I thought of danger but did not know exactly what kind of danger was in my mind. Later, the cramp went away, and it was then that I recalled that a very close friend of mine had died that week and that there had been a blood clot in the leg. Today, it is clear to me that the blood clot suggested to me that my cramp was dangerous. As I now know through my Recovery training, the patient likes to complain of something spectacular and exceptional. When I had the cramp, I should have thought of an innocent pain or muscle fatigue. But as our physician says, the nervous patient will not settle for anything less than a rare, incurable or hopeless ailment. I think that after that experience, I understand now why we think of the spectacular and exceptional.

GERTRUDE: One of the ideas I had was the thought of death. In Recovery, I learned that we cannot be exceptions, and if the average man and woman can think of death, we can, too.

But in the beginning, I was afraid of the thought. Now I can think of death as the average person does. I live only a short distance from three cemeteries, but most of the time, I am not even aware of their being there.

Carol: If I am among people, I feel I want to be tops, but I feel I am not genuine. Our physician has told me that means I hope to be exceptional but fear that I am not even average. On the train, I think the people are watching me. I know now that this is what our doctor calls the *sense of undesirable exceptionality*. I also want to be an exceptional mother, but I don't handle it right. I feel I have to watch Susie, my little daughter, every minute of the day. But the other day, when a neighbor girl came over and asked whether Susie could have lunch with her, I got objective about it and let her go.

ANNETTE: What happened when you went against your desire to keep an eye on Susie?

CAROL: At first, I had all kinds of wild thoughts of danger. But then I said, "All right, I am going to say 'no' to my sensations and feelings and be like my neighbor." I was tense, but I dropped the sense of exceptionality and was no longer afraid of being average.

SOPHIE: The other day, I went to the basement to do my washing. The children were home from school. I said, "I am going downstairs, and don't you make noise." As soon as I went, the noise started. I became furious. I shouted up to them to stop that noise. But they made such a racket, they didn't hear me. I felt so frustrated, I felt like crying. I dropped the linen, and I couldn't move for a few minutes. It seemed to me I was paralyzed. But then I stopped and looked into myself and said, "What are you doing?" I was setting an exceptional standard for my children not to make noise. When I recognized I had that standard, the tenseness left me, and I went on with my work.

FRANK: I can give an example. It is not so dramatic. It happens frequently that I have something to do, and I just don't want to do it, and I don't know why. I just can't get started. I am now working on the "Recovery News,"* and it is necessary to type up the stencil. It is a simple job, but it takes me a week or more to warm up to it. I think it is because I don't think it is good enough. I guess my standard is too high, and I still think in terms of exceptionality. When I realized that, I just made up my mind that I would type up the stencil, and I did it in no time. If I hadn't done the work, I would have condemned myself and got more tense. After I finished it, I felt quite proud of myself and there was no vicious cycle as there usually is when I procrastinate.

EXCEPTIONALITY AND AVERAGENESS; SENTIMENTALISM AND REALISM

PHYSICIAN'S COMMENT ON A PANEL DISCUSSION

When Ann, in distraction, turned for help to Rosalie, she was warned not to consider herself different from other people. If she did, she thought of herself as exceptional and not as being like other people. I shall ask: Do you really believe that anyone with a spark of vitality and ambition will content himself with being "like other people?" To have no other qualities than the ones found "in other people" means to be colorless, ordinary, dull, perhaps common and commonplace. Who would relish the reputation of being unimaginative, impersonal, nondescript? People wish and crave to have distinction, singularity, personality and character. They shudder at the thought of being just a cipher, one of many, nothing but average. What men and women actually hope, boast and pretend to be is–exceptional. And if my patients

---

*The "Recovery News" was a mimeographed sheet which was edited by Frank Rochford in 1945 and early 1946. It was the predecessor of the *Recovery Journal*.

think of themselves as being not just average, they do what everybody does. Why do I then urge them to shed their sense of exceptionality?

Exceptionality is a hope, a dream, an illusion, that means an imagination. Averageness is the reverse; it is a subtle fear, a sober fact, a disillusioned self-appraisal, that means a plain, uninspiring reality. People hope to be exceptional and fear to be nothing but average. If you choose to live in a world of hopes, dreams and illusions, you are a sentimentalist; if you prefer the realm of factual existence and everyday life, you are a realist. But you are not permitted to make a choice or to state your preference. You are what you are: sentimental and realistic, imaginative and matter-of-fact at the same time. What counts is the proportion, balance and ratio. Does your realism outweigh your sentimentalism? Or does the balance tilt in the opposite direction?

I am fond of believing that my patients represent a wholesome and desirable cross-section of the general population. If that is true, their personalities are as well or ill balanced between sentimentalism and realism as those of their relatives, neighbors and friends. They feel just as exceptional and are just as average as the social set to which they belong. When they deal with their children, their wives, mothers and fathers, they indulge in a pardonable sense of exceptionality, taking pride in the supposedly superior qualities of their family, clan, race. But I doubt whether my patients carry this sentimental bias into the regions of business, social activities and home management. There they are exactly as realistic and average-minded as the situation requires. The sentimental trend exhibited in one sphere of life is neatly balanced by a corresponding realistic attitude governing their activities in other spheres. There is solid balance, sound proportion, sane ratio.

If I ask my patients to be realistic instead of sentimental, if I insist that they renounce their romantic sense of exceptionality in favor of sober self-accounting in terms of averageness, I refer to the attitude they are supposed to take with regard to their symptoms. There they must not indulge in sentimental dreams of exceptionality; there they must plant themselves solidly on the ground of realistic averageness. If the average person experiences pressure in the head, he does not permit himself to be rushed into a hysterical panic. He suffers but remains calm. True, my patients suffer from conditions that are not average in intensity and duration. Nevertheless, I ask them to retain their balance, even in the face of extreme agonies.

Ann demonstrated, with singular clarity, how this can be done. She had a delusion and manipulated it as an average experience. How could she manage to think she was "like other people" at the very moment her brain was the seat of a delusion? Do people have delusions "on an average?" What Ann did *was* exceptional. It was the exact reverse of what could be expected "on an average." She turned realist and was calm and poised in a situation that was frightening, exceptional and extraordinary. With this, she carried the principle of averageness to the very limits of plausibility and possibility. Such feats are possible in Recovery, and in Recovery they are no feats. There they are average occurrences, the result of patient and systematic training. What Ann demonstrated was that under our system of training, sentimentalism can be so thoroughly overbalanced by realism that even under exceptional circumstances, the sense of averageness can be made to assert itself successfully.

Delusions are, of course, outside the domain of realism. And there can be no objection to ranging them among the sentimentalities of thoughts or wishes. If a patient claims to be Napoleon, if another thinks he is being observed and watched and spied on as if he were an important personage, you may call the one a *delusion of grandeur* and the other a *delusion of persecution.* But, in essence, it is romanticism and sentimentalism. Annette and Gertrude mentioned no delusions. They reported their experiences with the fear of a blood clot, the dread of dying. Is the fear of a blood clot sentimental? Average people certainly worry about death and vascular accidents. And if Carol worried about her daughter Susie, and Sophie became furious about the noise made by her children, and Frank couldn't get himself to warm up to a simple job, what is the warrant for calling these reactions sentimental or exceptional?

Take the case of Annette. Her feet felt cold and developed a cramp. This was an experience of discomfort and pain. The experience, as such, had all the earmarks of averageness. What could be more average and commonplace than cold feet and crampy muscles? There is no distinction, no glamour, no excitement in coldness and crampiness. The incident is so trivial that it cannot excite interest. It could certainly not be used as the subject for a telling story. But the moment Annette conceived the suspicion that the cold feet and crampy muscles might be the result of a blood clot, well, there was the plot for an exciting story that could stir the imagination. With a mere chilly skin and cramping muscle, her experiences were drab, trivial, uninteresting, uneventful. But with a clot, there was danger, excitement, drama. A blood clot is not everyday life; it is a dire emergency, a tragedy, perhaps a good story. To reach the dizzy heights of emergency and tragedy, Annette had to infuse the elements of temper and emotionality into an event that was otherwise plain, simple and devoid of thrill.

Take now the case of Carol. She was worried about the health of her daughter Susie. On the face of it, no sentimentalism seems to be involved in a mother's concern about the health of her child. A concern of this kind is realistic and average. Even if Carol felt she had to watch the daughter "every minute of the day," the sentiment was still within the scope of average anxiety, although decidedly overdone. But when Carol carried her apprehensiveness to the extent of refusing Susie to be watched by neighbors whom she knew to be responsible people, she displayed an unrealistic distrust in the reliability of the average person and indulged in what she calls herself a sense of "undesirable exceptionality." She set herself up as the only person to whom Susie's welfare could be entrusted. She alone had the requisite sense of responsibility. The others could not be relied on. Moreover, she conceived of Susie as a child that needed special watching, extraordinary care, exceptional supervision.

With this, she injected into everyday life concepts and senti-ments of exaggerated duties and responsibilities that have no place there. Suppose Susie, while attending a luncheon in a nearby home, hurt her leg or felt a "tummyache" or got involved in a fracas with the other children; the hostess could certainly be credited with ample sense of duty and responsibility to take proper care of the situation.

You see, Annette and Gertrude exaggerated the importance of their own bodily feelings and sensations and became *emotional*. Carol gave herself over to a vastly exag-gerated sentiment of duty and responsibility and became *sentimental*. You will now understand what the terms *emotionalism* and *sentimentalism* imply. Emotionalism means that plain and innocent sensations, impulses or feelings aroused by events of average intensity are conceived as so alarming that nothing short of an extraordinary fear reaction seems to suit the situation. Sentimentalism means that equally plain and average experiences are viewed as so exalted and valuable that nothing short of an excessive sense of duty and responsibility can meet the requirements of the momentous event.

Average life consists of trivialities, mainly. Average home life, for instance, calls for buttons to be sewed, dishes to be washed, children to be watched, pain and discomfort to be endured. All of this is routine, offering little stimulation or excitement and providing a great deal of irritation, a good measure of drudgery and some amount of suffering. Occasionally, there is a birth or wedding, sickness or death. Then the routine is interrupted by an exceptional event but is resumed, in all its deadly monotony, as soon as the event has passed. The irritation incidental to this sort of routine life is patiently borne by persons who are not too irritable.

But nervous patients are unfortunately blessed with an excess of irritability. As a result, the average irritations of routine existence are well nigh "unbearable" to them. They hate the routine chores. Routine, to them, is an infliction. It inflicts disturbing sensations, confusions, doubts and anxi-eties. To the average housewife, the breaking of a glass is a plain occurrence not to be fussed over. It causes a mild irritation that is easily disposed of by the consideration that the loss is trivial and replacement easy. But to the nervous housewife, the breakage may suggest that she is inadequate, that all effort is futile, that the inefficiency, incoordination and lack of attention revealed by the dropping of the glass are beyond hope. She may now become provoked at herself and work herself up to a pitch of excitement and emotionalism. Or, she may bring into play the sentiment of self-pity and condemn herself as a neglectful person, oblivious to duty and responsibility. The sentimentalism of self-blame may finally produce a panic. Then sentimentalism and emotionalism join hands to create exceptional fury in response to an event of average triviality.

The excessive irritability of my patients predisposes them to a grotesque hatred of routine. With the average housewife, sewing buttons and darning socks do not figure as exalted tasks or sources of great excitement. They are chores, devoid of thrill and inspiration. But the darning is done for the husband, the sewing for the son. Being meant for the ones she loves, the activity acquires a significant meaning in the eyes of the housewife. Every stitch and every patch has the meaning of doing something necessary, useful and valuable. Life is still a chore and unpleasant routine, but the routine is now meaningful, important, perhaps even vital. The inherent meaning of the work creates enjoyment. The enjoyment provides stimulation, gives a sense of living, a feeling of accomplishment. Added to the feeling of joy and satisfaction is the realization that the mending and patching constitute a duty performed and responsibility discharged. In this manner, the feeling of joy is supplemented by the sentiment of dutiful and responsible activity. Life of this kind is one of sustained feeling and sentiment. It is vibrant, stimulating, perfused with zest and interest.

We may draw the same picture of the average man working in a shop or at an office desk. The work itself may be a boring and dull routine, repetitious and tiring. But if done with an eye to its usefulness and meaningfulness in terms of maintaining the family, the otherwise uninteresting job assumes the aspect of importance, dignity, duty and responsibility. The shop or office routine, as such, may give no stimulation, but the thought of the ones for whom they are performed produces the feeling of joy and the sentiments of responsibility, dependability and consistency.

You will realize now that for routine to become palatable and acceptable, it must be capable of supplying a moderate amount of feelings and sentiments. The feelings are mainly those of joy, satisfaction and stimulation. The sentiments are those of duty and responsibility and their attendant sense of dependability, consistency, dignity and self-importance. Viewed against this background, the nervous patient is in a pitiable condition. When the housewife, incapacitated by a nervous ailment, sets out on her sewing performance, her fatigue interferes with the nimbleness of her movements. The muscles feel heavy; the fingers cramp; the lids droop wearily. Being determined to finish the job, she may continue the dreary occupation. But the work is done mechanically; every stitch requires the utmost in effort; the needle lies limp between the fingers, the garment flops to the floor. She picks it up, resumes the sewing, but she has to use every ounce of her flagging energy to perform the simplest movement of the hand. Finally, she gives up in despair. There is no use trying to do something for husband and child. This life of daily routine is an endless torture, squeezed dry of every drop of joy, drained of every semblance of importance, usefulness or value. There is no possibility of experiencing feelings or sentiments in this atmosphere of utter futility and helplessness.

Unable to infuse feelings and sentiments into the routine of daily activity, the nervous patient endeavors to eliminate routine from life altogether. The formula is simple: There must be nothing trivial, meaningless, unimportant in the sphere of daily existence. Everything must be drenched in a flood of feelings and sentiments. Plain conversations, questions and answers must not be tolerated. They must be converted into a stirring argument or an intense fight or a pathetic complaint. The fight makes room for feelings of

indignation, the complaint provides the setting for sentiments of self-pity or self-blame. All of it is absurdly exaggerated and morbidly intensified. But the illusion is created
that feelings and sentiments are again governing the daily
activities. That the feelings have degenerated into wild emotionalism and the sentiments into vapid and shallow sentimentalism does not count. Life is again pulsating, vital,
important. True, its vitality and importance have been
derived from an underhanded trick and falsifies feelings and
sentiments into something that only remotely resembles
them. But the fact is that the life-pulse, no matter how shaky,
has been restored, and vitality, no matter how empty, has
been recaptured. Trick or no trick, life is, or seems, worth living again.

CHAPTER SEVEN

Helplessness Is Not Hopelessness

A PANEL DISCUSSION CONDUCTED BY PATIENTS

ANNETTE (panel leader): Today we want to discuss a problem which most of us faced during our sickness or in the process of getting well. It is a problem closely akin to sabotage. Sabotage has many different forms, and one of them bears on a condition when we experience a general letdown, a feeling as though we had no interests, no feelings, no spontaneity. Everything we do during this condition requires a tremendous effort. This makes us unhappy and despondent. Any examples?

REGINA: You described my trouble; only I think the symptoms were much worse than you described them. I had that awful feeling of fatigue as if I couldn't even get out of bed. I didn't want to. I couldn't eat or sleep, and the household tasks I did before were such an ordeal. I couldn't even fill the sugar bowl. I almost got into a panic when I thought of it. I had a fatigue that seemed unbearable. I had to drag myself all the time. After I came to Recovery, our physician said, "You are not tired." If I went downtown, I would walk around for ten minutes and think I had to sit down. But the doctor told me that wasn't fatigue; it was just a feeling of fatigue. Now I walk for hours, and it doesn't bother me. I don't even have the feeling of fatigue any more.

ANNETTE: When you had to go through the movements of getting the sugar and filling the bowl, did that look like an impossible task to you?

REGINA: It certainly did. If I even looked at the sugar bowl, it made me nervous and tense. Every time I looked at it, I wondered, "Is that much sugar gone again? Will I have to fill it again?"

ANNETTE: When you had to go through this tremendous struggle, what conclusion did you draw about your illness?

REGINA: I felt hopeless and was sure there just wasn't any cure. I blamed myself for letting myself go like this, and the more I blamed myself, the worse I got. I know now that I set up a vicious cycle.

ANNETTE: After you got into Recovery, how did you handle that?

REGINA: The doctor told me to walk and do things regardless of the fatigue. And I learned that I slept even if I didn't know I did, and all of that helped me. But in the beginning, it was hard. For a few days I accepted the doctor's assurance. But then I sabotaged and thought that was good for others and not for me. I thought nobody felt like I did. But then I heard other patients describe the same difficulties in the interviews and panels. That gave me great relief. And I read the books and went to meetings, and finally I got well.

FRANCES: When I was sick, I had two small children, and I got so I didn't want to take care of them. The house was a mess, and the children were neglected, and I would run out of the house and go to my sister's. And I had the feeling I wanted to go back right away but didn't know how. I tried many times to do something, but I just couldn't. Frequently, I would just lie down and wouldn't get up. I remember how awfully hard it was for me to wash dishes. I would stand by the sink and felt I was going to topple over, and everything was going blank. When I was with people, I felt a sort of wave of darkness coming over me, and I felt like fainting. Finally, I avoided people and wouldn't see them. That was three years ago. But two weeks ago, an uncle came from California, and about thirty members of the family met at my sister's, and I remembered the feeling of self-consciousness I used to have with even two people. And here I was with thirty people, and I enjoyed myself and played cards with them all night and won eighteen dollars, and, I tell you, it was very comfortable.

ANNETTE: It seems to have been profitable, too.

FRANCES: Three years ago, they could have given me a million dollars, and I couldn't enjoy it.

ANNETTE: How did your illness affect your feelings toward your children, and your husband and other members of the family?

FRANCES: I can hardly understand it now. But at that time, I had no feelings for my children or for my husband or for anybody else. I had no interests, and nothing gave me enjoyment. Today it's different, and my husband often remarks about how enthusiastic I can be.

ANNETTE: I wish to mention an experience I had many times when I was ill at the hospital. Getting out of bed, as you described, was such an effort, and going to eat my meals seemed as though I couldn't get the food down. My husband brought me jigsaw puzzles, which I used to enjoy. I started to work one, picked up a piece, looked at it and thought, "This is too much for me." It seemed every time I picked up a piece, I had to make twice the effort to move it from place to place. When my husband visited me, the nurses would say, "Oh my, you have a nice husband," and one attendant said, "My, you must get well for such a nice husband." And I realized that was correct, but I had no feeling about it. During the first few months, I was indifferent to whether he came to see me or not. I certainly did not look forward to visiting days. But gradually my feelings returned but in a peculiar way. One day I still did not feel any particular enthusiasm about having visitors, but on another day, should my husband not arrive at the expected time, I got sore because he was late. I then realized that my indifference was lifting.

After returning home, my interests were not very active immediately. I did the simple tasks because I knew they had to be done. If I kept the place clean, it was not because I enjoyed it but because it was my duty. I assure you that today when I clean my apartment, I get a sense of pleasure seeing it clean. I get spontaneous feelings now. I didn't get them for a long time after leaving the hospital and did things "from duty and necessity," as our physician says. Had it not been for my Recovery training, I am afraid I would have gotten into a vicious cycle, watching myself and thinking I am not improving, noticing the sluggish feelings and worrying about them, seeing things neglected and blaming myself for it. The more I would have worried, the worse, I expect, would the condition have been; the worse the condition, the more worry. In those days, the most distressing thought was that I would never again have the capacity to feel, that I would never again be enthusiastic about things. Today I know this was a prognosis and sabotage.

FRANK B: A few months ago, everything looked hopeless to me. I had intense fatigue and would spend about three days a week in bed or take afternoon naps of about four hours. I wasn't working, and the worst thing was I still had the idea I was railroaded into the state hospital eight years ago when I first got sick. I was afraid to go to see a doctor because he might say I was nervous–and I thought I wasn't–and he would put me in the hospital again. But finally I went to see a doctor, and he said it was nervous fatigue and I should rest. But the more I rested, the more tired I felt. I watched my diet, and that didn't help either. I got worse and worse. I thought that when my nerves are fatigued, I'd better quit swimming, which I enjoy very much. I also stopped going out socially, and everything was an ordeal. But since I joined Recovery, I go swimming a few times a week and go out socially, and I am seriously considering going to work. A few weeks ago, if the doctor had told me I would be doing these things again, I would not have believed it.

ANNETTE: Did you find you got over these difficulties immediately after joining Recovery?

FRANK B.: No, I had to be satisfied with small gains. Going out socially was still a big problem. But after I learned to be sociable with the members of Recovery, I gradually enjoyed myself with outside groups. In Recovery I learned to throw off the stigma. That wasn't easy because I had been picked up by the police and brought to the hospital by them. Now I feel that's the past, and I think of the future. Of course, I am still sabotaging every once in a while. But I am just a rookie yet.

HELPLESSNESS IS NOT HOPELESSNESS

PHYSICIAN'S COMMENT ON A PANEL DISCUSSION

Regina had difficulty eating, walking, sleeping. Everything she did required effort, even the act of filling the sugar bowl. Annette had similar complaints and summed them up correctly as a "lack of spontaneity." When then Frances and Frank added their reminiscences of past ordeals, they merely contributed a new chapter to the old story. The story is that of having dragged along for months or years without initiative, zest or interest, i.e., without spontaneity, and having regained *spontaneity* through the self-help techniques practiced in Recovery.

To be spontaneous means to have no difficulty making up one's mind, to carry out one's plans and decisions, to feel like doing something and get it done, and all of this means *vitality*. The patients described a condition in which they lacked vitality when they were ill and regained vitality after they recovered. Previously, they felt lifeless and spiritless; now they live with spirited alertness. I grant that a person who does not feel the pulse of life, a person who has no affection, no anticipation, no sense of accomplishment, I grant that such a person is helpless. What more dramatic picture of helplessness can be drawn than the scenes in which Regina could not bear the thought of having to fill the sugar bowl or Annette could not command sufficient vitality to move a little piece of cardboard (jigsaw puzzle) from one place to another? At the time, they were certainly devoid even of a shred of vitality. Theirs was a mechanical existence, not a dynamic life.

When Annette lacked the strength to move a little scrap of paper, she had a right to feel weak, helpless and unhappy. She had also the right to feel distressed when she noticed that her feelings were low or gone. But when she became despondent and thought she "would never again have the capacity to feel" and "would never again be enthusiastic about things," she permitted herself to predict future developments, and this she had no authority to do. As she said herself, "Today I know this was a prognosis and sabotage."

A patient is competent to describe his present condition, his pains, pressures and palpitations, his lack of strength and vitality, his fears, panics and compulsions. If he wishes to place the label of "helplessness" on any of these experiences, I shall not quarrel with him. I have not seen a patient who was not helpless, totally or partially. Patients are helpless to stop their pressures, they are helpless when they find themselves seized with air-hunger or night terror. And if any patient claims to be helpless, I shall not challenge the correctness of his statement. But when a patient declares himself hopeless, I shall warn him that he has presumed to make a prognosis and has trespassed into my territory. The physician alone is capable of deciding whether a condition is hopeless or hopeful. The patient who assumes the diagnostic or prognostic function of the physician sabotages his authority. The patient can declare himself helpless, but he has no right to pronounce himself hopeless. Description is the domain of the patient, prediction is the province of the physician.

I well remember the time when Regina and Frances sat in my office reciting their tales of woe. There was a great deal of description, but most of it was prediction. They predicted that they could not get well, that they were doomed to lead a lifeless existence, that the hope I held out for them could never materialize. If I mentioned that she slept better and this was indication of a beginning improvement, Frances hastened to correct me, "But, Doctor, last night was terrible again. How long can I stand that?" If I ventured to suggest that my patients had to wait but got well in the end, the retort was, "But, Doctor, they are not as run-down as I am." All my reassuring statements were promptly swallowed up in a rebuttal sentence that invariably had the phrasing, "But, Doctor. . . ." Both Frances and Regina were confirmed "but-knockers." I had merely to voice a positive thought, and it was immediately knocked out by a negative answer. I presented them with a hopeful prognosis, and they swept it aside with a dire prediction of hopelessness.

I shall ask you to visualize the situation in my office when a depressed patient sits opposite me. We discuss a condition, but we never meet. Whatever I may say is instantly disputed or discarded by my opponent. But the patient is no opponent. He is a wretched creature begging for help. He insists on help, he clamors for it, protests he "would do anything to get it." If he is not my opponent, why does he oppose me so vehemently? If he is ready to "do anything to get help," why does he not do that "little something" I ask for: to drop his pessimistic and accept my optimistic view? Views are thoughts and can be dropped, other views can be adopted in their place. If that can be done, why does the patient refuse to do it?

I have given much thought and study to this absurdity of clinging to a harmful view when acceptance of a helpful view was certain to give relief. I have seen women who go through depressions each month before or during or after their menstrual periods. They are depressed and helpless but do not indulge in doom prophecies. The reason is clear: their depressions are of short duration, and a rich past experience has taught them to be optimistic about relief to be expected. My nervous patients come to me after months and years of suffering. Their pessimistic views have gained depth and strength. Their pessimism has become a habit, hardened and crystallized by continued practice. Such habits pervade the organism, color every move and thought of the person, and are not easily dislodged.

You can observe such habits of thought everywhere and at all times. These days particularly, it is not difficult to spot prophets of doom right at your elbow, at home, in the neighborhood, in the shop. You have heard all kinds of gruesome predictions in the past few years. Things, in general, were painted as utterly hopeless. The country is going to pot; inflation is certain to come, or it is here already to stay; democracy cannot survive. These gloom peddlers "knew" that our country could not possibly win the war, that industry would never catch up with the demands of the armed forces, that the end of the war would see an incurable rise in unemployment. The fact that their predictions fell flat did not discourage the soothsayers. Although promptly disavowed by actual developments, they nevertheless continued to roll off new gloom stories from their never-resting assembly lines. All these people had imbibed the view of pessimism; the view hardened and crystallized into a stubborn habit of thought, until finally the habit acquired such momentum that evidence to the contrary was powerless to shake it.

Everybody is pessimistic and optimistic at the same time. In the ordinary mature person, the two views are so balanced that optimism outstrips pessimism. This is true of every habit. Everybody is both generous and miserly, cautious and bold, loving and hating, forgiving and vengeful, appreciative and critical. It is in the very nature of human habits that they range themselves in pairs, the one member of which is antagonistic to the other. Pessimism and optimism are nothing but such a pair of mutually antagonistic features. Everybody is pessimistic and optimistic at the same time. Once a person has matured, the antagonistic habits have attained their balance. Then we have two varieties of persons, the ones mature and realistic in whom generosity, caution, love, forgiveness, appreciation and optimism overbalance miserliness, boldness, hate, vengefulness, criticism and pessimism; the others infantilistic and emotional in whom the negative features prevail. Before Frances and Regina came to consult me, they lived a life of balance in which the positive trends outweighed their negative antagonists. After they drifted into their depressions, the negative features took the lead and dominated their habit structures. They became extreme in their reactions and lost their balance.

The calamity is that when two traits join to form a pair of habits (pessimism–optimism, miserliness–generosity), the more undesirable trend (pessimism, miserliness) is pushy and aggressive and always ready to assert itself. It is easy to throw off a good habit. All you need is consistent poor example. A lifelong habit of honesty can be destroyed in short order by bad company or cajolery. Your well established habit of caution can be easily weakened or shattered by the ridicule of the "smart set." This is difficult with poor habits. If you are addicted to nail biting, you know how desirable it is to drop it; you know that it is harmful to your standing in your group; you are eager and determined to abandon it. And yet how difficult it is to discard it. I am not going to tell you the reason for this distressing tenaciousness with which bad habits cling to their useless existence. I merely mean to point out the fact that the more ugly or disturbing is a habit, the stronger is its hold on the individual. Pessimism is an ugly and upsetting habit of this kind. It disturbs balance and renders behavior ugly and melancholy to behold or endure. Were it necessary to fortify my argument with another example, it could easily be borrowed from the field of drinking. It is easy to induce a sober person to become an alcoholic. But try to steer a drinker back to sobriety, and you will realize the strength of poor habits and the weakness of good habits.

All my patients have acquired bad habits. The good habits, which used to balance them, have been swept aside. Previously, when the patient had a pain or pressure, he bore it with patience. Now he demands instant relief. The habit of endurance has given way to that of self-indulgence. In the same manner, habits of courage yielded to fearful anticipations; trust in one's body functions was replaced by an abysmal distrust of the organs. In the course of months and years, the undesirable habits acquired strength and cunning and tenacity. If the patient attempts to fight them off, he finds himself confronted with a ruthless, stubborn and obstinate force. He puts up some resistance but soon realizes that his good intentions are no match to the resourcefulness of his opponent. He feels helpless, despairs of ever being able to regain his balance and conceives the idea of hopelessness. If that happens, then the balance between the antagonistic habit traits of optimism and pessimism is destroyed, and the patient is reduced to an existence of mechanical action. Regina and Frances, Annette and Frank demonstrated how the balance can be restored and how life can be made to regain its vigor and vitality. All they did was to refrain from sabotaging the physician's authority. He alone knows which ailments are hopeless and which are hopeful. To cure a nervous illness means to rid the patient of his pernicious tendency to sabotage the physician's effort. Once this is done, the patient has learned that Helplessness does not mean Hopelessness.

CHAPTER EIGHT

External and Internal Environment

A PANEL DISCUSSION CONDUCTED BY PATIENTS

ANNETTE (panel leader): The subject of today's discussion is entitled, "Constitution, Environment and Temper." When I was sick, I did not know what was constitution and temper. About temper, I thought I knew something, but I did not. What I knew was the explosive temper, flying off the handle, perhaps throwing things, at least throwing words excitedly and viciously. In Recovery I learned that temper takes in everything that is an individualistic trend and opposes a group standard. For the patient, temper means, particularly, everything that goes against the standard set by his physician. Two factors disturbed me a great deal when I was sick. They were: what kind of a constitution I had, and what kind of environment I lived in and would return to after I left the hospital. In Recovery I learned that if I had a weak constitution, that did not mean I had to keep it that way. I learned how to strengthen my constitution. I was surprised to find that the way to strengthen my nervous constitution was to avoid tenseness and to handle it properly when it developed.

One Sunday, my husband called for me at the hospital, and we went to the Recovery meeting that was held at the hospital in those days. After the meeting, we went to the zoo. The streetcar was crowded, and someone jostled me, and I became irritated and at the same time fearful. I did not have enough Recovery training yet to know that this was a trivial incident over which I shouldn't work myself up. I felt hurt and stepped on. I interpreted the simple incident as meaning I was the type of person who would never be able to take care of herself in a crowd. I felt I did not know how to stand up for myself. Today, I know that I let myself drift into a vicious cycle between temper and tenseness, but I did not have enough training then to know just how to stop it. By the time I arrived at the zoo, I was extremely tense. I thought, how can I ever start out again in this world if I am going to be upset like this over every trivial instance? I am much too sensitive, perhaps because I have a nervous constitution. But if my constitution was weak, what could I do about it? Before long, I felt a blurring of vision, and a tightness in the abdomen, and worried about eating the dinner and was most uncomfortable.

About a year later, I was standing one evening with my husband in front of a show window, and a woman shouldered her way between us. My reaction was not to give an inch, to stand my ground and not permit anybody to push me around. But no sooner had I become aware of the impulse to stand on my rights, when I began to laugh. I instantly knew this was a trivial incident, and I was determined not to stand on my rights and to make myself uncomfortable and to produce tenseness and symptoms. As far as I am able to determine, that meant one thing to me, that during my Recovery training, I had learned to ignore that matter that I called my "constitutional sensitiveness," to be indifferent to my rising temper and to let my feelings rise and fall. I knew that both constitution and temper are nothing unchangeable.

PHIL: I told the folks here before that I had some sort of nervous trouble when I was about twelve years old. I was already in the eighth grade and was supposed to graduate, but for some silly reason, I did not want to go to high school and tried to flunk. But I was not successful, though I made a good effort to flunk, and graduated. All through high school, I had trouble with teachers and argued with father and mother, and when I was at college, I developed the habit of telling people where to get off. My father had made a very good fraternity, but I was not wanted by them because I was too cocky. So I made up my mind I was going to show these fellows a thing or two and demonstrate to them that I could lick them any time.

To make the story short, I studied hard to show them off; I got on the magazine staff and did a good job at writing. I joined the dramatic club and did well there. I was always busy flitting from one activity to the other. I was hardly ever in my room during the day. My roommate said, "You don't want a roommate, Phil, you just want somebody to help pay the rent." But finally it caught up with me. When the examination came, I was all exhausted. I would lie in bed for hours unable to sleep. That was the time I did not know yet that sleep has little to do with health. So I fretted over my insomnia, and that made matters worse. In the end, I broke and had to come back to Chicago. I can see now clearly that my nervous constitution was not equal to the strain and my sassy behavior was all a matter of temper.

ANNETTE: After your breakdown, did you stop trying to top everybody?

PHIL: That kept on. I did not learn from that experience till I came to Recovery. Then I learned to be average and humble and get along with people. I think it is getting into my blood to be average and plain.

ANNETTE: You have learned in Recovery that the sense of importance is perhaps stimulating but does not make for balance. And to preserve your health, you need balance. And the sense of averageness gives you balance.

PHIL: I have a pretty reasonable balance now. I am not tense any more. I gave up making a human dynamo of myself.

ANNA: My case is mostly one of temper. Until lately, I had quite a bit of trouble sleeping. I used to wake up in the middle of the night, felt tense and had all kinds of disturbing thoughts and sensations. The minute I woke up, I felt an electric current going through my body, and I got disgusted with myself and got sore at the doctor and everybody else. Then, while lying there, my mind would argue with the doctor, and I would say, "How long did I have to suffer like that?" And I would diagnose my own case and ask, "How does the doctor know I will get well?" And I would go on arguing that way back and forth.

Sometimes I would lie in bed till daybreak and work myself up to a vicious cycle. But lately, I thought I better start practicing what I learned in Recovery. So now when I wake up in the middle of the night, I just lie there and don't work myself up, and I relax and wait till I fall asleep. Sometimes it takes quite a while, but it is not as bad as it was when I used to work myself up. At times, I fall asleep in half an hour or sooner, and in the morning, I feel all right. I know now that working myself up makes the condition worse.

ANNETTE: When you woke up and it felt like an electric current, how did you handle that?

ANNA: Before I practiced Recovery, I would get sore at myself, and the longer I would argue with myself, the longer it would take before I could sleep. Now, I no longer work myself up, and I don't diagnose my own case. And I know the doctor said I will sleep if I don't worry about sleep, and if I lie in bed for hours, I will sleep part of the hours. I know now that it is true.

GEORGE: When I was little, I would get myself worked up so much that I would take my fists and hit myself on the head. All through public school and high school and college, I made life miserable for myself and my parents. I practiced the angry and fearful temper. Last December, shortly after I came to Chicago to join Recovery, I experienced a good example of what I think is fearful temper. I must mention, I could never hold a job before getting the Recovery training.

In December, I was working for a loan company, and again I felt like quitting because I didn't like the work. I stayed home and thought I should call the boss, but I didn't. Frankly, I don't think he missed me much. But the next day, I asked Frank to call the office and tell the boss I was too sick to work. But Frank talked me out of this. He said that is sabotage. And then it came to me that the doctor said if you fear to do something, you do not fear the thing but your sensations; you fear being embarrassed or self-conscious. And the cure is to do what you fear to do and to brave the sensation. So I phoned the office, and the boss just asked me to come back soon. That only proved that the doctor was right and that I was afraid of my own embarrassment. After that, I felt embarrassed on several occasions but faced it and did not try to ease out of it.

The other day, I went through an experience of angry temper. I was waiting for a train on the elevated platform, and I wanted to go to Evanston, and a train was just coming in. A motorman was standing on the platform, and I asked him whether it was an Evanston train. The fellow looked mean and did not answer and didn't even look at me. I asked him again, and he didn't answer. Finally I said, "I am talking to you," and he said, "I don't have to tell you anything, buddy." And I got angry and said, "You are nothing but a doggone conductor." But there was lots of noise, and I guess he didn't hear it. The good thing was, my temper didn't carry over, and in about two minutes, I was laughing at myself, and I had no aftereffect. Two or three years ago, I would have been proud that I had the nerve to tell him off, but this time, I felt a little ashamed.

ANNETTE: It seems a bit silly, but we do not prescribe perfect behavior. In Recovery we say we must learn a lot about temper, but we will not perform one hundred percent. If you have a temper outburst, be sure, if you immediately recognize that the explosion is silly and childish, then the possibility that you will be ready for another temper outburst at the slightest provocation is reduced greatly. And therefore you are not going around tense all the time like I used to be, ready to be on the defense and to stand on your rights in senseless trifles. If you can laugh at yourself immediately after the outburst, then you are relaxed. Any other example? If not, I will bring the panel to a close.

EXTERNAL AND INTERNAL ENVIRONMENT

PHYSICIAN'S COMMENT ON A PANEL DISCUSSION

Annette was jostled by a streetcar rider, and as a result felt irritated and tense for hours and ultimately developed blurred vision, tightness in the abdomen, disturbance of appetite and general discomfort. She recounted this example when dealing with the topics of constitution, environment and temper. Undoubtedly, the jostling man was her environment. But what he jostled was Annette's muscles. It was nothing but a jostle, a jar, perhaps a jolt. How is it possible that a mild encroachment of this sort produced serious derangements of vision, appetite, abdominal function and general well-being? Was Annette's constitution so weak that a trivial push from the outside could cause a violent upheaval of her inner organs? It does not seem at all likely that mild pressure against her muscles should occasion such a severe inner reaction.

The jostling streetcar rider was environment to Annette. But by the same token, Annette was environment to the jostling man. His muscles pushed her muscles. And it will be useful for you to know that men and women are environment to one another and that the one acts on the other by means of muscles. Even if they speak or merely look, the speaking and looking are done by the muscles of the mouth and the eyes. But if environmental effects proceed from muscle to muscle, how is it they reach down to the inner organs and even to the depths where the thoughts, moods, impulses and sensations of the personality are embedded? For Annette did not merely respond with organic distress (vision, digestion and tenseness); she was also irritated, fearful, "felt hurt and stepped on," doubted whether she "could ever start out again in this world." Her muscles were merely jostled, but her inner organs were profoundly upset, and her personality was thrown out of equilibrium. How was it possible for a trivial environmental event to release such widespread effects?

You who have gone through the process of Recovery training know that the careless streetcar rider did not merely jolt Annette's muscles; he also jolted her temper. And temper is the bridge over which environmental irritations can reach across the muscles to the inner organs and to the depth of the personality. Along this road, it penetrates to the domain which we call *internal environment.*

Roughly speaking, everything that exists or lives outside your muscles is external environment, everything that is inside your muscles is internal environment. Your home and its furniture, your father and mother, your friends and neighbors, your employers and employees, together with a host of innumerable things, conditions and persons, make up your outer environment. But inside you there is the inner environment, far more potent and vital, more readily disturbed and shaken than anything outside you. This inner environment is made up of your internal organs on the one hand, and your personality functions on the other. The latter are your feelings and moods, thoughts and decisions, sensations and impulses. Let your outer environment be disturbed by war, bereavement, fire or financial loss, and the chances are that you will bear the shock and emerge from it unscathed. But let your impulses be deranged, your sensations get out of control, your feelings become the seat of fear, envy and jealousy, your thoughts the prey of torturing obsessions, and the resulting commotion is likely to unsettle your nervous constitution.

Annette experienced another jostling episode a year later when a woman pushed her in front of a show window. She felt irritated again, but this time for a moment only. The next moment she laughed, and the irritation passed. There was no effect on the inner organs, no jolting of her personality functions. You will instantly realize the difference. In the first instance, in the streetcar, the environmental irritation was reacted to with temper; in the second instance, before the show window, the response was directed and mitigated by a sense of humor. The sense of humor, born of indifference to irritations, even if they are severe, prevented the emergence of temper which takes annoyances seriously, even if they are trivial.

We may conclude that the trivial irritations of external environment–they comprise the bulk of irritations in general–can be approached either with temper or with a sense of humor. If the approach is temperamental, the inner organs and the personality functions of the internal environment will be thrown into commotion; if the approach is humorous, the internal environment will be spared the anguish of frustration and the agony of disordered functions. The jostling or jolting will be felt by the muscles only; it will be prevented from spreading through the muscles to the inner confines of the personality, there to work havoc with emotions and sensibilities. But in order to prevent this spread, you must learn how to control your temper and to develop a sense of humor. In Recovery you have learned that temper is your worst enemy; humor, your best friend.

The experiences of Phil, Anna and George fit into the same pattern. Before they underwent Recovery training, their approach to environment was temperamental. It caused them no end of distress, unsettled their inner functions and unbalanced their personalities. Phil was, or felt, rejected by the men and women in his external environment. He took the rejection seriously and decided to demonstrate to his adversaries that he "could lick them any time." He became "cocky" and "was going to show these fellows a thing or two." This was temper. Instead of humorously ignoring external environment, he fretted over the rebuff and girded for a fight. The result was a disorder of inner functions and derangement of personality. His temper landed him in the hospital. Today he has acquired a sense of humor, and the rebuffs suffered at the hands of external environment hardly cause a ripple in his inner life.

Anna had difficulty of sleeping and was troubled with all kinds of disturbing thoughts and sensations. The electric current running through her body was a severe disturbance, indeed. She became disgusted with herself and "sore at the doctor and everybody else." The temperamental approach to environmental irritations reached here a climax. It engulfed the entire sweep of environmental existence. She was disgusted with and sore at her own person, her own personality and "everybody" outside her. How was it possible for Anna to reduce this torrential force of her temper to the level of calm detachment? In the face of electric currents shooting through her body, in the presence of threatening thoughts and violent sensations, how did she manage to drop her temperamental fears and angers and replace them with a sense of humor? For the present, I merely wish to state that she did and that it can be done. As Anna says, "I know now that is true."

The account which George gave of his temperamental exploits brings back to my mind the day, about six months ago, when I received a letter from him inquiring whether training in Recovery was likely to cure his condition. Since this involved moving from the West Coast to Chicago, I hesitated to encourage the move in view of his history of temperamental maladjustment since childhood. But here he is, and his temper is under control, although at times it still slips from under control as in his altercation with the "dog-gone conductor." Well, it is an instance of uncontrolled temper if such a remark is made, but it is an inspiring exhibit of a good sense of humor if the author of such unrestrained behavior can subsequently report the incident and laugh about it. Moreover, George experienced merely the immediate effect of his outburst but mastered the aftereffect when he laughed soon after the explosion. He laughed at himself and refused to take seriously the importance of his own dear self. With this, he practiced the Recovery system of self-discipline which insists that temper is the outcome of an inner arrogance which sets itself up as judge as to who is right and who is wrong. This arrogance is due to the sense of one's own importance and cannot be overcome unless the sense of humor is cultivated to the point where humility, plainness and averageness take the place of arrogance, exceptionality and self-importance.

Annette, Phil, Anna and George demonstrated that internal environment can be protected successfully against the dangers of emotional agitation if the patient learns to control his temper. This is an important enough accomplishment. But the abiding value of a demonstration of this kind is that it emphasizes a principle that has general application. We live in the age of technique and boast that we have conquered time and space and matter and nature. Perhaps it is true that we have accomplished all of this. But of what good are conquests if they play solely in the field of external environment, leaving internal environment prostrate and helpless to be ravaged by the onslaughts of unbridled tempers? Of what good is your automobile if all it has brought you is the possibility of experiencing your palpitation at a speed of fifty miles an hour? Are you interested in external speed or in inner peace? You hear it stated these days, on every street corner and in every newspaper column, that moral progress has not kept pace with technological advance. Well, it is truer to say that the emphasis on technological progress made us forget the importance of progressing in the domain of morale. Recovery has reversed the proportion, and the reversed position was given beautiful expression by the members of the panel. To us, at any rate, control of our internal environment is infinitely more important than all the possible triumphs we may be able to score over external environment.

CHAPTER NINE

Feelings Are Not Facts

A PANEL DISCUSSION CONDUCTED BY PATIENTS

ANNETTE (panel leader): I remember a distressing sensation which gave me no end of alarm. It was a severe cramping or pain in the side of my abdomen. It was so severe that when it hit me, I felt I could not walk. I had the same sensation on numerous occasions and was always afraid it would return. I know now that anticipating its return made matters worse. I was alarmed when I had the sensation and was perhaps more alarmed when I didn't have it but anticipated its return. After six years of almost constant suffering, I finally went to the hospital, but the doctor couldn't find anything wrong with me physically and sent me to the Illinois Research Hospital. It was then that I came under our physician's care and joined Recovery. It was only then that I realized that it was not the sensation that caused all the discomfort but the panicky feeling that something terrible was about to happen.

At the time, I felt like something would burst in my side. I was sure I wouldn't be able to stand it, that I would go to pieces. When the doctor told me, "Your sensation is distressing but not dangerous," it took me quite a while before I understood what he meant. I had to take his word for it, but I continued to feel something awful was going to happen. Today the sensation comes back occasionally. I have a slight twinge in my side even right now. In former days, I would have been concerned. Today I know, and know for sure, that the sensation is merely distressing and not at all dangerous. I no longer anticipate trouble. Any other example?

MARGARET: Recently, I had company from out of town. I hadn't seen them for two years, so I asked them to dinner. The cooking and the preparations were too much for me, and I got quite excited. I had again that pressure in my chest, and the palpitations were just awful. And I got a terrible pain in my head, and my eyes smarted, and every time I turned my head, it cracked. A year ago, I would have become panicky, and my husband would have called the family physician, and I would have fussed and stewed for days. This time, I knew they were symptoms and they were distressing but not dangerous.

ANNETTE: Did you go ahead with what you had to do?

MARGARET: I felt like giving up, but I didn't. I knew there was no danger.

MARY: Yesterday, I was invited to spend the afternoon with a friend. I took my little nephew along and had no trouble at all making the trip. I didn't feel nauseated as I used to feel on streetcar rides. By seven o'clock, I got ready to leave the party. As soon as I reached the street, my legs started to give in, and my heart pounded, and my stomach flew around, and I looked at my nephew and didn't know what to do. My first thought was to rush back to my friend's house and ask somebody to bring me home. But I knew these were symptoms, and the sensations were not dangerous, and I just stood there waiting till the symptoms would disappear. But I couldn't even wait because my nephew looked up at me and asked, "Aunt Mary, aren't we ever going home?" I was still very uncomfortable. But I took the next streetcar, and we got home without trouble.

ANNETTE: This is a beautiful example how you can be very uncomfortable and can manage to stand the discomfort if you keep in mind the physician's authoritative knowledge that you are not in danger. Any other example?

CAROLINE: I had a very gratifying experience this morning after my husband and I got up. He said, "What's the matter, don't you feel good today?" I asked, "Why?" He said, "You are very quiet today." Usually I am very talkative in the morning and, for that matter, all day. I have always a desire to talk about my symptoms, and I guess I drive people nuts. This constant talk about my symptoms is sabotage. I know that, but I haven't been able to check it so far. This morning, I decided to stop talking and complaining and kept quiet. So I said, "I have a pain in my head, but I know it will go away." We then talked of something else, and I couldn't help but realize how different it was than a year ago. A year ago, I would have said I have a terrible pain, and I would have been sure I had a brain tumor, and the doctor just won't tell me, and I don't know what to do, and if Recovery and our physician can't help, who can? But this morning, I stopped that.

Before I came to Recovery, when I had this particular pain in my head, I would give in and go back to bed, and my husband would bring me a hot water bottle, and it seemed that made the pain worse. And then he would bring me an ice bag, and, in the meantime, I would work myself up, and he would suggest I take an aspirin, but that did not help. After I came to Recovery regularly and talked to the other members of the group, I learned to handle this symptom. This morning, my husband offered to go to the store for me as he always does when I complain of my headache. Usually I become dramatic and say that the pain is so severe that I can't even think what I want from the store. This time I merely said, "Give me a few minutes, and I will write the list."

ANNETTE: Here we see Recovery training at its best. Not because Caroline did so much better this time and is improving, but because Caroline has learned to make fun of herself and her symptoms. She has gained insight and knows now that she dramatizes her symptoms. She knows she plays a game and plays for attention. She has learned not to take herself and her symptoms seriously. This is a great advance. Any other examples?

GERTRUDE: As most of you know, my husband has been discharged from the service. Before he went in, I was quite sick, and one of my difficulties was getting his breakfast. I would have a terrible feeling of helplessness when I would make it, and I would say I can't do it. I would then get a feeling of tightness in my throat and feel like crying. On these mornings, I used to have a feeling of unreality. I would feel alone, and things looked changed and distant, and I felt I was changing. When my husband was discharged and came home, I made up my mind I was going to do my job, and he gets up at five-thirty. I anticipated this feeling of helplessness, but even so, I got up, and I just felt fine. I discovered I was just looking for things, but they didn't happen. Really, I was only anticipating a danger, but there wasn't any if I didn't anticipate it.

ANNETTE: I had similar experiences with the feeling of unreality and with anticipating. You know our physician tells us that anticipation is nothing harmful, but it must be calm and not fearful. You may anticipate a palpitation. But don't think of it as dangerous. I remember one day I had to take some responsibility about a social function being given by Recovery, and I was the social chairman and had to arrange for a picnic grove. I didn't like being on the job, but I knew it was good for me. About a day before the picnic was scheduled, I became very uneasy. I thought I had to appear at my best at the picnic, and what will happen if I get some extremely distressing sensations? I may get this dizzy feeling and a sense of unreality. With me, this is a feeling as though I couldn't really feel things. I would handle them, and although I knew I touched them, I had the feeling I didn't touch them. I realized I had a fearful anticipation and knew I was not supposed to anticipate in fear.

But I had difficulty shaking off that fearful anticipation, so I called another member of Recovery. I said I know I shouldn't anticipate danger, and maybe I was merely tense as anybody might be preparing a picnic. This member then said, "You think you are merely tense, but I can tell by your tone of voice you are quite anxious about that symptom and the fact it may return." Then she said, "Why, you can handle that. You have handled it before." Then she told me how she used to be fearful, and she learned not to anticipate danger. I realized then how the older members of Recovery did things, and I was not experienced yet and didn't know yet how to handle that anticipating. But with months of practice, I soon learned how to anticipate calmly.

What helped me most to overcome this anticipating was the thought that I was average and not supposed to do an exceptional job. You know the doctor always tells you the average people you meet are not critical. If you make a mistake, they will know that people on an average do make mistakes. They will not condemn you. We must always keep in mind how we judge other people. If they commit a blunder, we think nothing of it. We do not think they are imbeciles. We simply notice the fact that somebody made a mistake and know that people do make mistakes. As the doctor says, "People are tolerant with others, but they may be intolerant with their own mistakes." We nervous and former mental patients must learn to become tolerant toward our own mistakes. We must not want to be exceptional. It is time now to bring the panel to a close.

FEELINGS ARE NOT FACTS

PHYSICIAN'S COMMENT ON A PANEL DISCUSSION

As I listened to the panel and heard one patient after another repeat that sensations are distressing but not dangerous, it occurred to me that nothing could symbolize more beautifully the close union that exists in Recovery between patient and physician than this fundamental Recovery principle that sensations are merely distressing but not dangerous. The patient alone knows how distressing is his sensation; the physician alone knows how harmless and devoid of danger it is. The patient knows his feelings, the physician knows the diagnosis.

Annette suffered cramps; Margaret had chest pressure and palpitations; Mary, Caroline and Gertrude were stricken with headaches, vomiting, tightness in the throat and feelings of unreality. Each had their own assortment of symptoms, and it would be absurd to assume that Annette felt Margaret's palpitations or Margaret experienced Annette's cramps. You see, sensations and feelings are intensely personal and subjective and are known to him only who happens to experience them. You may say that a feeling is known to the person only who feels it. To the outsider, it is unknown unless he is told about it. His knowledge of other people's feelings is hearsay knowledge. With regard to the patient's feelings, the physician is an outsider who cannot attain anything but hearsay knowledge of what the sufferer experiences. Without being told, he would not know that the patient has palpitations unless he counted the pulse. He could certainly not know how intense, threatening and tormenting they are.

Contrast now this highly personal and subjective quality, which we call *feeling*, with its celebrated counterpart—thought. If Margaret had the thought that the sun was shining or spring was in the air, she would have no difficulty communicating her idea to Annette. If Annette agreed to and accepted Margaret's idea, the two would share it, and there could be no doubt that both knew exactly what they meant by sunshine and spring and air. But suppose the two spoke of cramps. To the one, the word may convey the experience of a wild panic, to the other, that of a mild twinge. You see the difference: thoughts can be exchanged, accepted or rejected like an objective commodity. Feelings are strictly personal and singular, incapable of being exchanged or shared.

The basic distinction between feelings and thoughts is the physician's dilemma and the patient's calamity. It is the main reason why patient and physician have so much difficulty understanding one another. The physician speaks the language of thought, and the patient replies in the language of feeling. How can they meet? Take, for instance, the matter of sleep and sleeplessness. I know that patients who complain of insomnia get their due share of sleep. But after the patient awakens, he feels for certain he has "not slept a wink." My thought about sleeplessness is founded on expert studies and thorough knowledge and can be communicated to any patient. But will he accept it? Will he consent to share it with me? I tell him he slept, but being fagged out and listless, he is told by his feelings that he has not slept. Will he listen to the language of the physician or to that of his feelings? You know the answer given in Recovery. If the patient is inclined to cooperate, he will be guided by the physician's thought. If he is ready to sabotage, he will consult his feelings. Whether he does the one or the other means all the difference between health and suffering.

Another example of the clash between the patient's feelings and the physician's thoughts: My thoughts about "nervous fatigue" and "nervous exhaustion" are known to you. The patient merely feels fatigued but is not. His "fatigue" is a psychological feeling and not a physiological condition. Being discouraged and "having nothing to live for" or to "look forward to," he arises in the morning with the dreadful anticipation of one of those drab and depressing days in which he will have to perform a deadly routine without zest or inspiration. The monotony and lifelessness of that day stares him in the face. Being discouraged and "sick and tired of it all," he cannot relax; his muscles feel heavy and limp. The physician knows it is discouragement and self-disgust, but the feelings of the patient speak forcibly and persuasively of a real, physiological fatigue. Who will the patient listen to? To his physician or to his feelings? The answer is the same as with sleep: the patient is inclined to accept the verdict of his feelings and to sabotage the physician's authority.

I want you to know that your feelings are not facts. They merely pretend to reveal facts. Your feelings deceive you. They tell you of danger when there is no hazard, of wakefulness when sleep was adequate, of exhaustion when the body is merely weary and the mind discouraged. In speaking of your symptoms, your feelings lie to you. If you trust them, you are certain to be betrayed into panics and vicious cycles.

I said that your feelings lie to you, that they deceive and betray you. How can that be? How can feelings be true or false? If you are sad, what has that to do with truth, deception or treachery? Feelings are either experienced or they are not. They are present or absent but never true or false. Thoughts alone possess the quality of truth and falseness. And if the patient's feelings tell lies, they do so because an incorrect and deceptive thought is attached to them. The deception is accomplished by the thought, not by the feeling. The panel members expressed this relation between thought and feeling with convincing plainness. One after another they stated that before joining Recovery they *thought* of their panics as dangerous, but now they *think* of them as merely distressing. You see, a panic is a feeling of extreme distress which annexes either the thought of danger or that of harmlessness. The panics experienced by patients are not pure feelings, they are overlaid and modified and taken captive by a thought. If the annexed thought is that of danger, a vicious cycle will develop, and the panic will be prolonged. If the thought is that of security, the panic will be stopped abruptly. It all depends on whether the patient will accept the physician's thought of security or his own thought of danger. If this be so, then, it is no longer a question whether the physician's thought ought to prevail or the patient's feelings. It is no longer the problem of thought versus feeling but of one thought versus the other. The patient is not asked to change his feelings or to discard them or to disavow them. He is merely asked to substitute the physician's thought for his own.

You will now understand the meaning of my introductory statement that the Recovery slogan "Sensations are distressing but not dangerous" symbolizes the close union between patient and physician. If it is assumed that the physician approaches the patient with an objective thought and the patient reciprocates with a subjective feeling, the two could never meet. Feelings cannot be exchanged or shared. If the patient were nothing but distressed or sad or despondent, the physician's thought could hardly reach him. Communication and mutual understanding would be blocked effectively. But if the feeling experienced by the patient is reduced to a "quarter-feeling" of despair, associated with a "three-quarter-thought" of danger, then, the physician's thought of security can easily meet the patient's thought of danger. It can modify or eliminate it. In Recovery this has been done with singular success. As the panel members quoted themselves: In former years, they entertained their own thoughts that the panic was dangerous. Now they accept the physician's thought that it is merely distressing.

CHAPTER TEN

Objectivity As Means for Terminating Panics

ANNETTE (panel leader): The subject for today's panel is "The Vicious Cycle of Panic." We all had to deal with panics and may have to deal with them occasionally even after we have improved. I remember the first panic I experienced. Shortly before I went to the hospital, I awoke at night with a numbness in my arm. I looked in the mirror, and it seemed to me I saw a slight swelling in the side of my nose. Looking on the swelling in the nose, I became more painfully aware of the numbness in the arm. Suddenly, I was gripped with fear. I rushed into the bedroom where my aunt was sleeping and said, "I feel my arms are paralyzed." The moment I said this, the numbness seemed to spread all over my face. My aunt offered to call a doctor. That scared me more. I felt as though I couldn't get my breath, as if each breath was the last. While my aunt called the doctor, I began to tremble. The numbness disappeared now, but the trembling continued. Then the tremor went, and the numbness returned. Then the numbness passed, and the tremor came back. By that time, the doctor arrived, and after examining me carefully, said he could not find anything wrong. He prescribed a sedative and rest. The next morning, I was tired, but I dragged myself to go to work. After that, I dreaded the thought of numbness. I was always in fear of it. I developed the vicious cycle. If I

120

only thought of the numbness, it was there. And each time, I thought I was going to die.

Then I went to the hospital, and came in contact with Recovery and attended the physician's classes. There I learned that sensations are distressing but not dangerous. It took me a long time to understand that fully. I remember once I had a slight numbness and kept repeating, "A sensation is not dangerous; it is not dangerous." I repeated that again and again, but finally I got sore and decided it didn't help. Then I thought, "What else can I do?" I started out again chanting, "It isn't dangerous; it isn't dangerous." And I did not work myself up to a vicious cycle. One night, I awoke with a sensation that I felt in every muscle of my body, something like you feel when the elevator drops slightly. I got tense and weak and felt like waking my husband to ask him for a glass of water. But I remembered my Recovery training and knew that if I gave way to the impulse to awaken him, that meant I was helpless and needed help. And that meant that I was on the way to establish a vicious cycle. I knew if I was to control the vicious cycle, I must not act on the impulse. It was difficult to restrain myself. So I lay quietly, but then I got mad because there my husband slept peacefully while I was so uncomfortable. I was provoked at the idea that I had to curb my desire to call for help. But I didn't give in.

Suddenly, I remembered the doctor had told us the best way to calm down is to do something absolutely unemotional, something that has definitely nothing to do with excitement and temper, something that is utterly objective. So I said to myself, "I am going now to view this sensation objectively and without fear. I shall look at my sensation as I would look at an object." I asked, "Where is that sensation? Where do I feel it most? In my arms or in my stomach or legs? Just exactly what kind of a sensation is it? Could I describe it?" I had by now become objective, indeed. And then something extraordinary happened. When I set out to look at the sensation and to describe it, it was gone the very moment I started to look at it, and I fell asleep. In the morning, I felt refreshed and proud of my accomplishment. Has anyone else got an example?

GERTRUDE: One of my most distressing symptoms when I was sick were palpitations. One night, shortly after I joined Recovery, the palpitations were just terrifying. I remembered that all the doctors I had visited had told me my heart was in good condition. Our Recovery physician had given me the same assurance. But when I had the palpitations, I felt that was my last minute, and I was going to collapse. The more I became alarmed, the faster did the heart beat, and the faster it beat, the greater was my alarm. I know now I worked myself up into a glorious panic. The palpitations seemed intolerable. I got tremors, and my hands perspired. I felt weak and shaky and was positive something dreadful was going to happen. Like Annette, I thought of waking my husband, and when I saw him lying there, I was tense and irritated because I thought, "There he is sound asleep, and I almost dying from agony." I jumped out of bed and jumped quite heavily, hoping the noise would wake him. But he continued to sleep. I slipped back into bed, giving loud sobs and breathing heavily, but he slept on.

Finally, it occurred to me that that was all sabotage. I remembered the doctor asked us to do nothing about sensations, that they were distressing but not dangerous. So I tried to lie in bed quietly. But then it seemed I did not sleep all night. Now I recalled what the doctor told us about sleep: not to toss and to know that sleep has little to do with health, and if you lie in bed for hours, you sleep part of these hours even if you feel you haven't slept at all. Finally, I fell asleep. On the following nights, it got better and better. I felt more secure because gradually I accepted the doctor's authoritative knowledge that sensations are distressing but not dangerous.

ANNETTE: The point is that you kept practicing night after night till it produced results. This continuous practicing is not easy, but it can be made easier if you talk to others in Recovery and find they have gone through the same experiences and got their sensations under control. Any other example?

ADA: When I first broke, I was terribly afraid I lost my mind. Later, when I joined Recovery, the doctor assured me it was a case of nerves, but I couldn't believe it. One Saturday afternoon, I was to come to the panel discussion, and my sister made some remark about my condition, and I misinterpreted it as doubting my mentality. I thought they all knew I was mentally ill, but they are not going to tell me. The more fearful I got, the more tense I was, and the more tense, the more fearful. One of my symptoms was vomiting. It had improved, but now I vomited again. That scared me more, and I called Rosalie. I told her I was positive something was wrong with my mind. But she said, "Did the doctor say so?" I said, "No." Then she said, "That's your own diagnosis, and you know we must not diagnose." That reassured me, and I went to the panel and got more assurance.

Several months later, I met my mother-in-law, and she asked me how I was. I said I felt fine, and she said, "One thing I can tell you; that sickness you have doesn't run in my family." At this I developed a temper, and it took me some time to check the vicious cycle. A month ago, I saw my sister-in-law, the daughter of the mother-in-law that made that remark about "in our family." She told me she had seen her doctor because she had pains and felt run down and irritable. He told her he couldn't find anything wrong with her, and it was a case of nerves. "The idea of that doctor," she said, "to call my condition a case of nerves." It so happened that I saw her mother about the same time. I inquired about her daughter, and she let loose against that doctor who had the crust to say that her daughter was a "case of nerves." "My daughter," she said, "is very sick and has extreme pain and can hardly drag herself to work, and that doctor, mind you, calls that nerves." I remarked that I had a case of nerves and got well and suggested that her daughter come to see my nerve doctor. That is all right for you, she said, but not for my daughter. This time I smiled, and there was no temper and no panic.

ANNETTE: What Ada wanted to explain is that in the first encounter with her mother-in-law, she had a flare of temper which developed a strong immediate effect. To this she added an aftereffect that lasted for hours and maybe days because it was aggravated by a vicious cycle. When she met the mother-in-law the second time, the temperamental flare was slight, the immediate effect was mild, and the aftereffect did not come off. As a consequence, the whole flare blew over quickly, and no vicious cycle developed. Ada was able to do that because of her Recovery training. If these terms of the temperamental flare, immediate-effect and aftereffect are not clear to some of our listeners, I shall advise you to read volume 3 of *The System of Self-Help.** Any other example?

SOPHIE: I don t know what would have happened to me if Recovery had not come my way. One day an idea got stuck in my brain, the idea of losing my mind. With that, I developed a pain in my head, and the stronger the idea became, the stronger got the pain, and I worked myself up into a vicious cycle. Finally, I landed in the hospital where I got three months of shock treatment. When I came home, I had a battle on my hands. I wasn t well at all and still had the pain and the fear of losing my mind, and then I got all kinds of other symptoms. My husband was impatient, and I don t blame him, either. I complained all the time, and of course he couldn t stand it. Then I met Gertie, and she told me about Recovery. But my husband had by this time got sick of it all, and he wouldn t listen. He said he was all through, and he wouldn t let me go to see another doctor. But from what Gertie told me, I knew Recovery was my real chance. At first

---

*Editors Note: This title was published as *The Techniques of Self-Help in Psychiatric After-Care*. Please see Other Books by Abraham A. Low, M.D., on pages 417-418.

I didn't believe what I heard at the meetings. But when I noticed others getting well, I decided to stick to Recovery whether my husband wanted it or not. And now I can truthfully say I never felt better in my life.

ANNETTE: What is your husband's attitude now?

SOPHIE: He knows I am well, and he rather likes to come to meetings himself. His family is now won back, too. They used to say there was no hope for me, and for him to put me away somewhere. Now they don't say that anymore.

ANNETTE: Is there any other example?

TED: It appears that the vicious cycles I get into are relatively mild ones. I have no panics or excessive fears. But to me they appear extremely distressing, and they last a long time. I form an idea of danger, that I am helpless and a sissy, that is, that I am a weak fellow that won't show gumption. I think I have been in this sort of mild vicious cycle for many, many years.

ANNETTE: How does it affect you?

TED: In the presence of other people, I have the sensation of fatigue and a heaviness in my muscles, like I would rather sit still in one position for a long time instead of moving and looking around me. Since I have joined Recovery, I have learned to reject the idea I am a sissy. I am now a member of a young people's group at church, and before I joined Recovery, I couldn't do that.

ANNETTE: It is late now, and we will bring this excellent panel discussion to a close.

Objectivity as Means For Terminating Panics

Physician's Comment on a Panel Discussion

I shall limit myself to discussing the remark about objectivity made by Annette in the later part of her example when she said she remembered the physician had told her, "The best way to calm down is to do something absolutely unemotional, something that has definitely nothing to do with excitement and temper, something that is utterly objective." She then proceeded to look at the sensation as she might look at an object. "I asked," she continued, "where is that sensation? Where do I feel it most? In my arms, or in my stomach or legs? Just exactly what kind of a sensation is it? Could I describe it?" But when she thus transported herself into a mood of objectivity, the sensation "was gone the very moment I started to look at it, and I fell asleep." With the simplicity characteristic of Annette, she added that when she awoke in the morning, she felt proud of her accomplishment.

Annette had indeed reason for feeling proud. What she had accomplished was to demonstrate the fundamental principle of Recovery that symptoms can be conquered by means of simple and innocent procedures initiated by the patient, i.e., through self-help. The particular principle of self-help mentioned by Annette was formulated several years ago when one day our friend Frank Rochford recounted a simple and innocent experience he had while thinking about and observing his fatigue sensation. Frank's account was approximately as follows: "You tell us we have to have patience. We have to wait patiently till the sensation disappears. Well, the other day, I felt fatigued again. I knew I had to wait, so I pulled out my watch to see how long I would have to wait. While I was looking at the watch, counting the minutes and seconds, I suddenly noticed that I no longer felt this fatigue. Next time, I tried that stunt with the watch again, but I couldn't count the time because before I could look at the hands of the dial, the tired feeling was gone."

Frank conquered an intractable sensation through objectivity, and Annette stopped a blazing panic with the same simple means. And I told you repeatedly that the wildest temper outburst can be checked instantly if you take the objective attitude that you are not the judge as to who is right or wrong. I could extend indefinitely the list of occasions in which disturbances can be disposed of, without much ado, by adopting an objective view. You have pressure in the head and shudder at the thought of a tumor. Then you substitute my objective diagnosis for your fanciful imaginings, and the pressure is relieved.

What, then, is objectivity? And what is the reason for its magical effect on nervous symptoms? I shall ask you to view this conference table where I am just now delivering my address. I shall describe it as being about one yard and two inches in height, having a brown color, four legs, two drawers, adding a few other items of a similar nature. This mode of description deals with height, color, number of legs and drawers, and I could mention, as further descriptive details, the position of the table relative to walls and windows, the number of chairs it will accommodate, and the hardness or softness of its wood. If this is all I say, then every one of you could easily verify my statements simply by using a tape measure or by touching and looking at the table, i.e., by the use of your senses. You will now agree that one criterion of objectivity is the possibility of verifying a statement, either by measurement or by sense perception.

Suppose now that while speaking of this conference table, I display feeling. I dwell tenderly on the moments of great inspiration which I experience when I behold this eager audience of patients rapturously listening to my remarks. I may go on in the same emotional vein, extolling the singular value of Recovery activities of which this table is a symbol, or the great deeds of human salvation which have been performed right here from this table. If I continue in this exalted style, you will realize that what I say has nothing to do with measurements and sense perception. It is an account, flowery and exaggerated, of my personal and *subjective feelings,* not a description, plain and unadorned, of the unemotional and *objective qualities* of the table. My first report (of color, height, distance, hardness and softness) was objective because, employing measurement and sense perception, I steered clear of emotion. My second report was subjective because, eliminating measure and sense, I emphasized feeling. Objectivity, then, means (1) employment of measurement and sense perception, (2) elimination of feeling and emotion.

I have answered my first question which asked: What is objectivity? I shall now try to give the answer to my second question: What is the reason for its magical effect on nervous symptoms? One thing ought to be clear to you by now. If the patient is to be objective, he must rid himself of emotion. But why should he do that? What is wrong with having emotions? What is wrong even with having fears, angers, indignations? Eliminate fear, and you lose the valuable qualities of caution, foresight and premeditation. Throw out your anger, and you will deprive your personality of its capacity to be aroused to action by personal insults and group crises. Without emotion, you are chilly, unresponsive, uninspired and uninspiring. Emotions are values, and I do not think of inveighing against them, except in regard to nervous patients and nervous symptoms.

Emotions have their rightful place in the family, in religion, civic life, business and politics. Moreover, emotions are of two kinds. On the one hand, there are love, devotion and affection, enthusiasm and sympathy, the sense of fellowship and the spirit of self-effacement. These are the *emotions of stimulation.* They stimulate the organs of the body into more vigorous breathing, digesting and heart action. They operate to raise and harmonize the functions of the organism. On the other hand, there are fear and consternation, anger and indignation, envy, jealousy and disgust. These are the *emotions of frustration.* They lower the functions of the body and throw them out of equilibrium. The emotions of stimulation create *stimulating tenseness;* the emotions of frustration create *frustrating tenseness.* I do not have to tell you that you cannot go far enough in cultivating stimulating emotions and their attending stimulating tenseness. You cannot go wrong if you do your utmost to dwell on them, to enhance and coddle them to your heart's delight. Should you be "gripped" by any of these stimulating emotions, just permit yourself to become warm and responsive, emotional and subjective. But if you are seized, as is the case in a panic, with the frustrating emotions of fear, anger and despair, with jealousy and envy, with indignation and disgust, then you must bend all your energies to becoming and remaining cool, chilly, unemotional and objective.

Annette demonstrated how this can be done. She was in the throes of a panic and passed through the whole gamut of frustrating emotions. Fear, anger, indignation, self-disgust and despair rocked her body down to every cell and fiber. An overwhelming amount of frustrating tenseness was produced, pressing on the nervous system and creating symptoms which caused more fear and therefore more tenseness, till the vicious cycle swept her organism to a climax of agony. This vicious cycle was maintained only as long as she allowed herself to be emotional, i.e., subjective. The moment she began to ask the objective questions, "Where is that sensation? Where do I feel it most? Could I describe it?" she changed subjectivity into objectivity, became unemotional and calmed down almost instantly. What she did was essentially to apply measurements and sense observation to processes of inner experience and to eliminate emotionality from the field of bodily functions. The remedy was simple and innocent and represented the most consummate technique of psychiatric self-help.

You remember I meant to say a word or two about the magical effect of objectivity on nervous symptoms. But if I called Annette's performance "simple and innocent," how is it possible to consider it magical? Magic may be innocent, but is it simple? Well, if you conceive of a task as utterly complex and impossible of accomplishment, then you will think it miraculous and magical if a simple move "does the trick" of accomplishing it. You see, patients have a way of viewing their panics as uncontrollable, i.e., they consider control of emotionalism as a task "impossible of accomplishment." Annette demonstrated that objectivity wipes out emotionalism. Once she established an objective, unemotional attitude, "it was no trick" to quash the panic in an instant. But that emotionalism can be removed instantly, once you have become unemotional, ought to be considered perfectly natural and not at all magical.

Annette forgot to mention one item that may sound casual but is of great significance. She forgot to state that she practiced the method of objectivity on numerous occasions prior to the panic which she described during the panel discussion. She had frequently tried to be objective but failed. Success came to her after many unsuccessful trials. Credit is due to her not so much for the final triumph but rather for her refusal to be discouraged by so many previous failures. What she did was to practice faithfully and untiringly the method of trial and failure till finally she acquired an amazing skill of handling the method of trial and success. Many of our patients have made an effort to apply the self-help method of objectivity but met with initial failure and gave up. Annette persisted after many failures and finally scored a signal success.

PART II

PANEL DISCUSSIONS WITH ABBREVIATED QUOTATION OF EXAMPLES OFFERED BY PATIENTS

CHAPTER ELEVEN

The Will Says Yes or No

Claire, on the Saturday panel, recounted how several weeks ago her husband told her he had to leave town for a number of days. She knew it was a business trip which could not be postponed. Nevertheless, she was thrown into a panic at the prospect of being left alone. She felt a heat wave sweeping over her body, her throat choked, the heart raced, and the entire body felt limp. She was tense and dizzy and weak. She said nothing and could hardly have said anything because she was terror stricken. But her husband noticed the disturbed feelings and upbraided her for being selfish and inconsiderate. In the course of the panel discussion, she stated that her husband "obviously didn't care how I felt." Later, she added that she was able to stop her feelings by applying her Recovery training. She spotted the panic as an instance of temper and self-pity, hence, as sabotage. The spotting produced instant relaxation. "I was surprised," she said, "that I was able to control my feelings as quickly as I did. I think I am learning how to handle my feelings."

Claire became terrified at the thought of her husband leaving town. The terror meant to her that her *feelings* were disturbed. The disturbed *feelings* were noticed by the husband who upbraided her presumably for failing to control her *feelings*. That suggested to Claire that her *feelings* were not properly appreciated. Recovering her composure, she was surprised to find that control of *feelings* was easy. In the end, she concluded that her Recovery training had served her well in the matter of handling her *feelings*. After listening to this report of an incident in which feelings fairly leaped over one another, I must confess that the dexterity with which Claire manipulated feelings is surprising, indeed. And I shall ask: did Claire deal with feelings? Or did she play on something which she merely called by that name?

What happened to Claire was that she suffered a scare. Previous to the scare, she was reasonably calm. Being calm, her condition was that of relaxation. Her *thoughts* were relaxed. They were focused on the little household cares of cooking and shopping, or they reviewed the trivial happenings of the preceding day or dwelt on the funny dream she had the night before. There was no stewing over issues, no worry about problems, no conflict of ideas, no confusion of plans. The *feelings* were in the same state of relaxation, and she experienced neither fear nor anger nor excessive joy nor immoderate grief. The relaxed thoughts produced a serene spirit, the relaxed feelings gave rise to a mood of comfort. Whenever a person is serene and comfortable, his inner organs tend placidly and peacefully to their functions of circulation, respiration, digestion and elimination. Hence, no violent sensations, no choking, air-hunger or nausea. We may say that when Claire was serene and comfortable, her *sensations* were just as relaxed as were her thoughts and feelings. With no disturbance rocking the body, there was no occasion for the *impulses* to become turbulent and impetuous, so that the total of her experience (thoughts, feelings, sensations and impulses) was that of calm, rest and composure. We conclude that prior to being struck with terror, Claire's *total experience* was that of security, producing a state of relaxation.

I want you to understand what is meant by the word *total experience*. Our body has only two ways of experiencing a situation. No matter what is the nature of the situation, it is approached either with a sense of security or one of insecurity. If your attitude happens to be that of security, your entire body will partake of that experience. Your thoughts, feelings, sensations and impulses, your inner organs, outer muscles and skin, even your tiniest fibers and most minute particles of tissues will share in the total experience of security which now governs your body. Experiencing security, they will all be largely devoid of strain, tenseness, commotion and excitement. Barring certain organic diseases, no human experience is possible, even thinkable, in which thoughts express security and impulses are restless and erratic. Nor is it feasible that at one and the same time, feelings should be relaxed and sensations disturbed and muscles taut. The just prevailing sense of security may be mild or exalted; the experience of insecurity may be moderate or severe. But whatever may be its degree or intensity, the entire body is affected. It is a total experience.

A total has parts, and the total experience has its part experiences. I have mentioned them already. They are thoughts, feelings, sensations, impulses. These are the *dominant parts of the total experience.* If any of them become disturbed, the disturbance will spread to the other members of the team. If any of them is pacified, the entire team will regain calm and peace, and the disturbance will be stopped. This calming and stopping of disturbances is what is generally referred to as "control" (of disturbances). You will now understand that if you wish to control the total experience of insecurity, you must use a method which will control, that is, stop and calm any one of the dominant parts of that experience. Control one dominant part, for instance the confused thoughts, and the rest of the team (feelings, sensations and impulses) will follow suit.

The dominant part which Claire chose for control was her feeling of terror and despair. She claims that after this feeling was calmed and stopped, the sensations, thoughts and impulses quieted down, and she relaxed. But I shall ask: how can feelings be stopped, calmed or controlled? Which method did Claire use for controlling them? Feelings are spontaneous; they rise and fall and run their course, and no deliberate effort will ever put a halt to their spontaneous progression. Obviously, Claire did not control her feelings but some other dominant part of her total experience of insecurity.

That feelings and sensations cannot be stopped, calmed or controlled by deliberate effort ought to be familiar to you because I have emphasized the fact on numerous occasions. I told you repeatedly that thoughts and impulses alone are subject to control. Evidently, when Claire "applied her Recovery training," she applied it to her thoughts and impulses, not to her feelings or sensations. I shall repeat: two inner experiences only are subject to control: thoughts and impulses. I shall add that one factor only is capable of controlling them: the Will. The inference is that when Claire put a check to her total experience of insecurity, the feat was accomplished through the intervention of her Will. It was her Will which exercised control over her thoughts, perhaps also over her impulses, perhaps over both. Emphatically, it did not and could not control feelings and sensations.

You remember I mentioned frequently that the Will has one function only: it rejects or accepts ideas, and stops or releases impulses. In either case, it says either yes or no to the idea or the impulse. Suppose an idea lodges itself in the brain, suggesting danger. It is then for the Will to judge and decide whether or not danger exists. If the Will accepts (says yes to) the idea of danger, then, the thought of danger will mobilize feelings of insecurity and will release in their wake rebellious sensations and vehement impulses. The total experience will then be that of insecurity. Conversely, if the Will decrees that no danger threatens, the thought of insecurity will be discounted, and feelings, sensations and impulses will retain their customary equilibrium. You will understand now that ideas rising in the mind offer suggestions to which the Will replies with yes or no. This has been called the *denying and affirming function of the Will*. The same function may be exercised by the Will in response to impulses, releasing them with a yes and restraining them with a no.

How is it that this process of denying and affirming can be used for thoughts and impulses only and not for feelings and sensations? You will grasp that readily if you will consider what precisely the words yes and no mean when employed in connection with an inner experience. When the Will disposes of the thought of danger by rendering the verdict no, the denial can be expressed as saying, "No, there is no truth to this suggestion of danger. Perhaps there is not even a probability or possibility of it." Similarly, when an impulse presses for action and the Will interposes its veto, it says, in essence, "No, this impulse is undesirable, and its action will prove unwise and harmful."

No such ratings, in terms of truth and falseness, desirability and harmfulness, wisdom or folly, are possible in the instance of feelings and sensations. If a person is seized with grief or stimulated by joy, it would be senseless for the Will to claim that the joy is false or the grief impossible. Feelings are either experienced or not experienced. Their existence, wisdom and probability cannot be denied or affirmed. The same holds for sensations. If the head aches, it would be absurd for the Will to object that, "No, this is no headache. It is unwise, untrue or improbable." Clearly, if the Will is to intervene in order to control the total experience of insecurity, its no cannot be directed to feelings and sensations. Instead, it must address itself to thoughts and impulses.

We can now sum up our analysis of Claire's reaction. When her husband announced his planned trip, the idea of danger leaped into Claire's brain. The thought of danger mobilized feelings of insecurity, threw sensations into violent uproar and released a host of turbulent impulses (to cry out in despair or shout in anger, to argue, protest, run). When this happened, Claire's Will was inactive, and the thought of insecurity was accepted. The result was that the body was thrown into the total experience of insecurity. Suddenly she remembered her Recovery training and presumably recalled the Recovery motto that sensations are distressing but not dangerous. Now the thought of "no danger" dominated her brain, and she decided to ignore or deny the existence of danger. Her Will had been alerted and said no. The no calmed her thought processes, and the calm communicated itself to sensations, feelings and impulses. The total experience was now one of security.

When Claire noticed that her body had relaxed so miraculously, she felt the need for explaining the miracle, and in doing so, she employed the clumsy and incorrect language of the man in the street. According to this language, feelings are subject to control. Had she used the Recovery language, she would have surmised that her total experience of insecurity had been remedied by the intervention of the Will which said no to the idea of danger, with the result that one dominant part of the experience was brought under control and spread the effect to the other parts. Claire had done the right thing but, trying to explain it, called it by the wrong name.

CHAPTER TWELVE

Will, Beliefs and Muscles

The Saturday panel discussed the subject of "Real Sensations and Fantastic Interpretations." Phil, as one of the discussants, mentioned how in previous days, when he was not yet "sold on Recovery," his pressures, dizzy spells and confusions made him neglect his work till finally hospitalization was the only way out of trouble. "These symptoms," he said, "have not disappeared altogether. They still bother me every once in a while. But now when I have them, I remember what Dr. Low has told us frequently: 'You can throw off any nervous symptom at any time for a few seconds or minutes if you spot them as distressing but not dangerous. The symptom will come back in the next minute or so. But you can get rid of it again for a short while, and then again and again. And before long, you will be rid of the trouble for hours or for days. The symptom will return and keep returning, but in the end, you will bring it under control by plugging away at it.' Phil then continued, "That was hard for me to believe. It just didn't seem to make sense that an awful head pressure would disappear if I made an effort to spot it. But I can tell you that when I have these symptoms now, all I have to do is to practice Dr. Low's rule, and before long, they are gone."

When Phil set out to practice my rule, why was it hard for him to believe it would work? Why did he feel it made no sense? Nervous symptoms are the result of tenseness, and if you "spot them as distressing but not dangerous," you dismiss the idea of danger; and without the thought of danger in your brain, you feel safe; and if you feel safe, you relax; and if you relax, you lose your tenseness; and with tenseness gone, the symptom disappears. What can be more simple, what more easy to believe and more thoroughly in accord with sense? And if this is so, why did my rule appear senseless and unbelievable to Phil?

Clearly, Phil thought of nervous symptoms as afflictions which require complex and elaborate means for conquering them. He obviously shared the current view that in order to deal effectively with a nervous complaint, the patient must be subjected to a searching investigation for the purpose of unravelling hidden mysteries of thought and tracking down the crafty maneuvers of mischief-brewing emotions. If this were true, my rule would be naive, unsophisticated, unbelievable and decidedly unsuited to the purpose. But it may be that what is really naive and unbelievable is the modern trend to view thought as mysterious and emotion as mischievous. And I shall advise you to reject this contemporary superstition that your thoughts are forever scheming against your welfare and your feelings continually plotting against your health. I shall grant that in our present-day setting, leadership is lacking and confusion rampant. And with the amount of confusion governing this world of ours, it is easy to get thoughts muddled and feelings confounded. But Recovery refuses to be modern, and the leadership which it supplies aims precisely at teaching you how to conquer confused ideas and perturbed emotions through simplicity of thinking and humility of feeling.

I instructed Phil to stop thinking of danger and to command his muscles to relax. His head pressure suggested to him that he was losing his mind. I told him he will not lose it. Two ideas were presented to him. Of these, he chose one. There was nothing to prevent him from choosing the other.

Get it into your heads that a human being has the power to choose what to believe and what not to believe. This power to choose is called the *Will*. The main beliefs between which the Will must choose are that, in a given condition, you are either secure or insecure. If you accept the thought that your head pressure is the result of a brain tumor, you have formed the belief of insecurity. If, instead, you choose to think of a mere nervous headache, you have rejected the belief of insecurity and put in its place that of security.

Why did Phil think he was unable to swap thoughts? He had been swapping them all his life. For upward of thirty years, he had practiced the game of accepting ideas, rejecting them, exchanging the one for another, dropping them and picking them up just as he wished, wanted and chose. The swap was usually effected with facility and rapidity; sometimes it required hard work and long pull. But whether easy or difficult, the wanting was practiced and the choice made. What made Phil believe that all of a sudden he had lost the capacity for wanting and choosing? And as to commanding your muscles to do your bidding? This is done every second of your daily activity. You want to sit down and do it. You wish to stand and rise from your seat. You decide to make a trip, to enter business, to marry, to save a life or sacrifice your own, and you carry out your decision either instantly or after hesitation and deliberation. Nothing is needed for the successful execution of these acts and plans but Will and choice. And thoughts and muscles are made to obey the dictates of Will and choice. Why did Phil assume he could not choose "at will" to direct his thoughts and to command his muscles?

Beliefs are frequently stubborn and obstinate. They may become fixed, offering resistance to the summons of the Will. This is particularly the case if the belief has persisted for years. You know how difficult it is for me to shake your beliefs that you are doomed, that your heart will give out, that your fatigue will lead to exhaustion. Muscles are just as likely to develop obstinacy. They tend to acquire set patterns of behavior, preferring certain well grooved acts and avoiding others. Just think of the habits of procrastination, of twitches and spasms, of restlessness and sluggishness, and you will realize that muscles are not always pliant tools in the hands of the Will. In order to pry loose the resisting beliefs and rebellious muscles, attempt after attempt must be made to dislodge them from their comfortable berth and to force them to give up resistance. The resistance may be so strong that the attempts to break it must be repeated in innumerable trials before success is achieved. This requires the Will to use a great deal of power in continued strenuous practice, hence, the terms *will power* and *will practice*. By exercising its power, the Will masters its task and learns how to rearrange beliefs and redirect muscles. Having gone through the *learning process,* the Will gains experience and becomes an *expert Will.*

In our days of modern progress, this learning process, with its inherent will practice, has been largely abandoned. Children are seldom taught to exercise will power for the mastery of reading and writing. Things are made easy for them. The schools supply all manner of "aids" to help them avoid exertion. The same holds true for work done in the fields of commerce and industry. A person entrusted with a commercial or industrial job is not likely to be subjected to the grinding procedure (learning process) of apprenticeship. Instead, he is "broken in" by the expedient of accelerated courses in which a number of manipulations are demonstrated to him.

This method of giving hurried demonstrations (to the senses) and facile explanations (to the intellect) instead of thorough training (to the Will) has permeated most spheres of our daily existence. A few flimsy explanatory phrases, and the housewife "learns" how to use a machine for sewing, cooking, washing, cleaning. A few perfunctory demonstrations "teach" the buyer of an automobile how to run it. In all of this, modern men and women imbibe the lasting impression that technique has eliminated the necessity for learning, patient application and practice of will. Most devastating to the learning process and to the exercise of will power has been the contemporary trend to spoon-feed information. In radio forums, newspaper columns, popular magazines and sundry other vehicles of public "education," brief discussions are offered by obscure persons of doubtful authority in which weighty issues are hurriedly "explored" and speedily solved by versatile analysts, columnists and essayists. The learning process is scrapped and replaced by a growing habit of passive listening and easy acceptance.

Without the benefit of a Will trained to choose beliefs and direct muscles, the men and women of our generation have lost faith in the correctness of their decisions and the relevancy of their plans. They drift along in the shifting currents of a rushing existence with little knowledge of how to approach issues or tackle problems. Having neglected or evaded the discipline of the learning process, they lack the "know-how" of pursuing tasks, of aiming at goals and accomplishing purposes. Faced with difficult situations, they feel helpless. As a result, the modern tendency has been to shy away from responsible pursuits and to entrust their proper execution to "experts." These go by the name of "specialists" who are supposed to possess the requisite "know-how" for solving problems. The specialist is expected to formulate plans for the rearing of children, to make decisions for marriage and divorce, to determine the degree of vocational fitness, to advise in matters of dieting, budgeting, housekeeping, love making, reading selections and what not.

With the spread of specialism, self-help and self-management have ceased to play a significant part in the present-day domestic, marital and social scene. The habit of rushing to the expert for advice has resulted in a vicious cycle of helplessness: the more the expert's aid is solicited, the more helpless is the applicant bound to feel; the greater the helplessness, the more urgent the need for further consultations; the more frequent the consultations, the more poignant the sense of helplessness. In the end, an individual emerges who has a stunted Will, a meager "know-how," and a famished sense of resourcefulness, in short, Modern Man, the pathetic creature of an extraneous Will, without plans or directions of

143

his own and in abject dependence on forces outside his inner self.

I am not a reformer and have no intention to crusade against the modern mania for undisciplined "self-expression" in a life of senseless speed and meaningless change. My duty is to treat patients, not to cure the ills of the age. But my patients are unfortunately exposed to the detrimental influence of the spirit of the age. That spirit is inimical to the process of learning, to patient striving and persistent willing. If I am to teach my patients to dismiss their settled beliefs of insecurity, if I am to direct them to give orders to their muscles and have them properly executed, if I am to train them to practice self-help and not to depend on the questionable expertness of outsiders, if I am to accomplish all of this, I must first divest their minds of the modern fallacy that being shown a method means learning it, that witnessing the demonstration of a skill means acquiring it. With machines, this may be feasible; with life tasks, it is impossible. My patients will have to realize what former generations always knew: that a life task can be mastered only through a gruelling, exacting learning process in which all the resources of the Will must combine to achieve final fulfillment. Health is a task of this kind. It can be secured only if the patient's Will initiates a system of ceaseless trials and trials and trials until, in the end, the task is accomplished. If this is done, even the most stubborn belief will yield to the influence of the learning process, and the most sluggish muscle will obey the dictates of the Will.

CHAPTER THIRTEEN

The Will to Bear Discomfort

In a recent panel discussion, Phil stated: "All my life I have had difficulty with my handwriting. When I had to write anything or sign a paper, I became tense, and the strain made it impossible for me to write clearly. I always thought I just couldn't help it. I get nervous and can't write, that's all. . . . In Recovery I have learned that everybody can command his muscles to move. And now when my hand tenses up while I am writing, I know I can make the muscles of my hand to move calmly instead of racing ahead with the scribbling, and then the tenseness will pass. . . ."

Phil, in his pre-Recovery days, had the conviction he could not write and the certainty he could not help it. His credo was, "I can't do it, that's all." After joining Recovery, he discovered that convictions and certainties can be discarded and credos can be changed. When he changed his belief and dropped his conviction, which method did he employ?

Phil's fingers were never paralyzed. Hence, he was able to write. But for some reason he developed a sense of embarrassment and self-consciousness about the act of writing. The self-consciousness produced tenseness which caused the fingers to go into a mild spasm whenever they were made to wield the pen. The spasm may have given rise to some sort of a cramping sensation. That created discomfort. In order to avoid discomfort, he avoided writing. He feared to write because he dreaded the discomfort it entailed. But the more he feared it, the more annoying grew the discomfort; the greater the discomfort, the more intense the fear. In the end, the vicious cycle, relentlessly fanning both fear and discomfort into extremes of agonies, made Phil believe that smooth, effective and painless writing was impossible.

What seemed impossible to Phil was not the act of writing but rather the necessity to face, tolerate and endure the discomfort connected with it. This is an important conclusion because it describes the pattern which applies to *every* nervous fear. Some of my patients go to bed with the fear of not sleeping. They think they fear sleeplessness because it ruins health. But what actually frightens them is the torture, that is, the discomfort of lying awake in the dreadful stillness of the night. Or, a patient becomes panicky on entering a streetcar. He thinks his fear is that of threatening collapse. But what actually scares him is the prospect of being tormented during the ride by palpitations, choking sensations, dizziness and sweats. Again, it is the anticipation of discomfort and nothing else that causes the apprehension. I could easily quote hundreds of situations in which nervous patients are convinced that what they fear are certain acts or certain occurrences while, in point of fact, the only fear they experience is that of a discomfort which they conceive of as "unendurable" or "intolerable" or "unbearable." To put it bluntly: nervous fear is the fear of discomfort.

Phil disposed of his fear of writing by commanding the muscles to carry out the requisite movements. In Recovery, he said, he learned that everybody can do that. But a command is not a method. I shall ask: How did Phil learn to make his muscles obey his command? Long before he knew of Recovery, long before Recovery existed, he had issued commands to his muscles to write, but they balked. On a thousand occasions, he had made his fingers pick up the pen and run it across the paper, but the order miscarried.

The fingers shook, and the pen tottered. The product of his painful effort was an illegible scribble, not a clear script. Why did his muscles defy his command in pre-Recovery days and heeded it promptly after he passed through Recovery training? Which is the Recovery method of making muscles obey directions?

In his pre-Recovery days, Phil issued orders to his muscles to perform the act of writing. Had he done nothing else, there can be no doubt that the writing would have been accomplished. But while giving directions to his fingers, his mind was obsessed with the thought that writing was an "unendurable" torture and that he could not go through with the task. Your muscles will not move, of course, if you suggest to them the fear that the movement will lead to disaster. The very thought of disaster ("unendurable" torture) will block motion. Fear, even if mild, makes muscles tremble, and the trepidation thwarts proper execution. If you want your muscles to carry out your commands, you must not scare them into anxiety and hesitation. To strike the muscles with fear and then to ask them to act with precision is absurd. My patients are guilty of this absurdity. Gripped with a grotesque fear of discomfort, they first tell the muscles that the contemplated action is impossible or fraught with danger and then command them to act. The muscles, with a better logic, release a tremor and bungle the job.

Whenever that happened to Phil in his pre-Recovery days, he felt hopeless and concluded, "I cannot write. That's all." But that is not all by any means. The "I cannot" ought to read more correctly "I care not." Phil could write very well but did not care to bear the discomfort of a painful and difficult writing, with fingers scared into fumbling and trembling. In Recovery he was trained to face, tolerate and endure discomfort. And once he learned to be uncomfortable without wincing, he gained confidence and passed on to his muscles the assurance that writing was possible, though uncomfortable. The muscles, then, swung into action without tremor or delay. The method which was here at work was plainly and simply THE WILL TO BEAR DIS-

COMFORT. It is the only and authentic Recovery method of making recalcitrant muscles obey directions.

If the nervous patient is to rid himself of his disturbing symptoms, he will have to cultivate the Will to bear discomfort. Time was when bearing discomfort was considered part of life, a part accepted by everybody and practiced everywhere. Children were reared with an eye to making them stand up under hardship. Heavy labor, sustained exertion, privations and drudgery were regarded as incidental to the sweat and toil of daily existence and were borne with patience, resignation and humility. But in our days, comfort is hailed as something in the nature of a supreme achievement. It is cherished, worshiped, idolized. When we catalogue the accomplishments of our age, the first item we are likely to point to with mounting pride is the fact that our modern technique has eliminated drudgery from the daily routine. We boast, self-complacently, of the labor-saving devices which a busy industry rolls off its assembly lines in bewildering profusion. The housewife is daily assailed by the advertiser's exhortation to escape the "backbreaking" drudgery of homework. Billboards flatter you that "electricity is your servant." Your kitchen and bathroom are choked with gadgets meant to do away with the discomfort of effort and exertion. Educators rack their weary brains to ease the "uncomfortable" task of acquiring school knowledge. Mothers and fathers have learned to shun the discomfort of staying home with their babies. Youngsters, resenting the discomfort of rules and conventions, are in feverish haste to cast off age-old restraints. I shall ignore the fact that automobiles have abolished the effort of walking, that typewriters have disposed of the inconvenience of writing and that an elaborate push-button system prevents us effectively from working off our unspent energies on household chores and office jobs.

All of this may be rated as an unavoidable development, perhaps even desirable in a limited sense. What is more important is that this process of removing effort and creating mechanical comforts is being acclaimed as a value and cultural achievement. We take a childish pride in our "modern progress," extol with boyish conceit our "high standard of living." We class as "backward" and "unprogressive" countries which lack the mechanical comforts which we enjoy. In all of this, the cult of comfort is recommended as the royal road to superior culture. The pursuit of comfort is glorified and the facing of discomfort discouraged. In this modern scheme of life, the Will to bear discomfort has no place. If comfort is raised to the level of a value or ideal, discomfort is necessarily looked upon as something not to be tolerated and endured, as something that is definitely not part of life, certainly no necessary part of our "modern life."

I do not wish to convey the impression that I am opposed to the use of such mechanical conveniences as refrigeration, electricity and gasoline. If anyone wishes to introduce these or kindred comforts into home or shop, he has my blessing. But he will have to know that this type of legitimate comfort is merely useful and not at all valuable. In those departments of life which are governed by valuations, the cult of comfort is decidedly misplaced. If you want to maintain the values of health and self-respect, of initiative and determination, of character and self-discipline, what you will have to learn is to bear the discomfort of controlling your impulses, of steeling your Will, of curbing your temper. This calls for an attitude which, far from exalting the virtues of comfort, places the emphasis where it belongs: on THE WILL TO BEAR DISCOMFORT. When Phil embraced the Recovery doctrine that discomfort, even in our "advanced" days, is a thing to be patiently borne, bravely faced and humbly tolerated, he discovered forthwith that his "I cannot" write was nothing but an "I care not" to be uncomfortable. He then revised his distorted valuations, braced himself against that part of life which means discomfort and realized, to his amazement, that with the emphasis properly shifted, things were done more efficiently and life was quite comfortable again.

CHAPTER FOURTEEN

Realistic and Romantic Ambition

Frances, on the Saturday afternoon panel, reported that when her sister got married not so long ago, she was asked to help with the arrangements for the wedding. "I knew that I have a strong desire to run things. So I decided I was going to check that desire because I didn't want to get tense and develop symptoms. But things went wrong at the reception, and I got tense anyhow. I felt I had to take a hand and began to run around and gave orders and told everybody what to do. Right then, I felt my temples got tightened, and my neck was painful. Suddenly, I remembered what Dr. Low told us about spotting a reaction and stopping it before it has a chance to produce a vicious cycle. I then spotted my restlessness, and sat down and kept sitting. The tightness and pain disappeared in no time. In former days, I would have rushed around the hall all afternoon and evening and would have tried to direct everybody and get things done. And I would have believed that all the responsibilities were on me, and I would have gotten nowhere except into more tenseness and more symptoms. In the end, I would have been exhausted and coming home, would have thrown a honey of a tantrum."

What Frances described may be called *restlessness* or *aggres-siveness*, or *a meddlesome disposition*, or *a tendency to be domi-neering*. But what precisely drove Frances to display her rush of energy and her burst of activity? Was it a chaotic volley of impulses? Or was it, rather, a well ordered, though by no means balanced, philosophy? Let me tell you that it was a philosophy, wild, stormy and untamed, but aiming at what philosophies generally aim: to guide conduct and–miscon-duct.

I told you repeatedly about philosophies (of life), and having studied my writings, you ought to be well acquainted with the three philosophies which I distinguish: Realism, Intellectualism, Romanticism. When Frances per-mitted herself to flit through the reception hall, skipping from guest to guest, pestering the one with unsolicited advice, the other with an uncalled-for direction, messing up things and getting nothing done, she answered clearly to my description of the romantic busybody. This type of an eter-nally rushing and pushing personality, the lively and ener-getic and mercurial "go-getter," is the ever-present and unavoidable "live-wire" at gatherings, meetings, club func-tions and receptions, and the power which drives this self-exhausting volcano is called *ambition*. Why was Frances ambitious to push people, to advise and direct them, to pester and impose on them?

Ambition, well conceived and sensibly pursued, is the breath and spark of life. Mothers are ambitious to train their children "properly." And businessmen are moved by the ambition to take "adequate" care of sales and purchases, of customers and employees. And physicians ought to be guided by the ambition to render the "right" kind of service to their patients. And a hostess' ambition should be to pro-vide "suitable" entertainment for her guests. You see here that ambition means the determination to do what is "proper" and "adequate" and "right" and "suitable" with reference to the job in hand. The job is the goal which you have set for yourself, and unless you are determined to "go about" it with ambition, you may not employ the proper, adequate, right and suitable means toward achieving it. Which was the goal Frances set for herself? Did she "go about" it with the proper, adequate, right and suitable means? I may here mention, parenthetically, that the word ambition is derived from the Latin verb "ambio" which means to "go about" a job, a task, a plan.

I quoted the ambitions of the mother, the business-man, the doctor and the socially active woman. Ambitions of this kind aim at long-range goals, lasting a lifetime, or a goodly portion of it. While pursuing his long-range endeavor, a person is bound to strike against obstacles, resistance, ill-will, frustration. It takes strength, perseverance and courage to face and fight these difficulties. On many occasions, the individual, faced with a forbidding obstruction to his effort, will become discouraged. Then he needs ambition to bear the strain and continue the march toward his goal. Take the case of the mother. If the children are unruly or ailing or somehow deficient; or, if the mother happens to be self-conscious and timid, doubtful of her capacities or fearful of her responsibilities, then she may develop a sense of frustration, confusion and discouragement. But discouraged or not, the maternal task must go on. No matter how threatening the obstacle or how severe the strain, the mother must continue "going about" her job. For this she needs ambition, the ambition to give the "right," "proper" and "adequate" care to the children and "to do right" by husband and home.

You will now understand that ambition is needed for long-range goals. On the other hand, short-range goals, usually of a simple nature and extending over a brief period of time, can hardly ever strain the energies and persistence of a person because they require very little of them. Moreover, short-range goals, as a rule, are of little importance, and if, in reaching out for them, your perseverance gives out, no great harm is done. Nothing of significance is involved in the goal of taking a swim or going to a show or visiting a friend. And if for some reason you wish to forego or postpone the activity, you may do so without any serious consequence. But mothers cannot forego or postpone the task of caring for the children. Nor can physicians or businessmen afford to drop or neglect their business or profession. And even the hostess is not permitted to deal lightly with her social engagements because her club meetings and dinner parties, although in themselves short-range, are woven into the long-range fabric of sociability, reputation and prestige. Summing up: ambition is indispensable for long-range goals, especially if they are important. For short-range goals, an unambitious, carefree attitude will be sufficient and perfectly "right and proper."

Frances, entrusted with a relatively unimportant, short-range task, went at it with an ambition which would have graced any responsible, long-range endeavor. For some reason, presumably irrelevant, she felt that "things went wrong," that she "had to take a hand," and that "all the responsibilities" were on her. This is exactly the philosophy of petty romanticism. The romantic person is intoxicated with his own importance. His feelings, experiences and observations appear to him to be singular, exquisite, interesting; hence, he feels important. Being important, he knows how to do things. He knows what is "proper," and "right" and "adequate." He knows, but the others do not. These others are not important. They do not know how to do things "right." When they try, things tend to "go wrong." When this happens, the romantic soul feels impelled and obliged to "take matters in hand," to show people how things are done, to direct them, advise them, push them around.

After Frances had done her quota of directing, advising and pushing, her temples tightened, her neck pained, and her muscles tensed. We may be certain that it was not her ambition to accomplish such disastrous results. What kind of results did she expect? What precisely was the object of her ambitious meddling? In order to answer this question intelligently, we shall have to realize that ambitions are of two kinds: the one aims at gratifying *personal inclinations*; the other tends to discharge *social obligations*. We shall call them the *personal* and *social ambitions,* respectively. Either of them carries its own reward.

If you manage to give free rein to your inclinations; if you impose your will on people; if you are successful in pushing them around, directing and advising them; if they meekly submit to your "leadership," you feel vital and dynamic. This gives you a feeling of glamour and grandeur, a sense of power and importance. Nothing more delightful can happen to a romantic soul. Every particle of it craves the thrill of glamour and power. The misfortune is that men and women seldom relish the privilege of being pushed around. They react strongly, resent the intrusion and rebuff the intruder. If this takes place, the illusion of glamour bursts, and the sense of power collapses, and all that remains is weariness, defeat and humiliation; and if the romantic person, thus deflated, chances to be a nervous patient, the final outcome of the romantic adventure is likely to be a storm of symptoms: tightenings and tensings and spasms and pains. This was the reward which came to Frances when she launched out into a reckless spree of what we may now call *romantic ambition.* She exercised glamour and power and reaped humiliation and defeat as reward. The romantic ambition, proceeding from unrestrained personal inclinations, landed her in frustration and agony.

Compare now Frances' romantic ambition with the ambition displayed by the mother anxious to tend her children. This mother feels important because her objective and realistic task is important. She may feel grandeur and glory but only because she conceives of her realistic and objective goal as grand and glorious. You see the difference. In Frances' mind, her own person figured as the center of importance, and her own personal qualities appeared to be reflecting glamour and grandeur. The mother derives whatever reward she expects from a realistic accomplishment in a group, in the group of her family. Hers is a *realistic ambition,* founded on the proper discharge of social obligations. In contrast, Frances' ambition was romantic instead of realistic and was based on personal inclination instead of social obligation.

In point of distorted views, Frances is not alone among my patients. They all are romanticists (or romanto-intellectualists) with romantic ambitions and romantic, unrealistic goals. If there is any realistic pursuit, it is health. It is long-range and calls for the exercise of extreme patience and relentless perseverance. But my patients treat health as a short-range goal, demanding instant relief and quick cures. Their sense of importance impels them to crave a ludicrous amount of attention. Their suffering, instead of being borne silently, is continually broadcast as "exceptional" agony. They do not ask for help as humble persons would but demand it as is the right and privilege of important personages. They feel singular and are convinced that theirs is "the only case" of its kind. They think of their frustrations and conflicts as "interesting" and expect to have a prodigious amount of exploring, probing and analyzing wasted on them. Their impulses impress them as so powerful, that they consider them "uncontrollable." With all of this, they enter a claim of being "different" from the general run of sufferers. If their claim is not acknowledged, they prove the uncontrollability by throwing what Frances calls a "honey of a tantrum." They pamper their feelings, coddle their thoughts, which points to the conviction that their experiences are different, singular, powerful, exceptional, interesting, that is, romantic.

After going through training in Recovery, they gradually learn to do what Frances did. They spot and stop their romantic inclinations and engage in a course of action which has due regard for social obligations. After they have learned the techniques of spotting and stopping, they acquire a philosophy of life which values realistic goals and scorns romantic ambitions. Frances travelled this road from unrestrained romanticism to disciplined realism, with the result that her ambitions are now centered around home and children and husband instead of on chimerical efforts to hunt for glamour, power and self-importance. Her reward is a peaceful life, with health and happiness compensating copiously for the lost illusion of glamour and the self-deception of importance.

CHAPTER FIFTEEN

Intellectual Validity and Romantic Vitality

Mona, on the Saturday panel, reported that some time ago, before she even knew the name of Recovery, she waited her turn to purchase meat. When the butcher called "next," a woman answered who had entered after Mona. "I got red in the face, my heart raced, my throat tightened, and I turned to the woman and told her I was first. She mentioned something about people sleeping, which made me mad, and spoke to the butcher in a foreign language, which made me more mad yet. I got so confused that when the butcher called my name next, I could not think what I had come for and bought a piece of meat that I really didn't want just to get out of the store quickly. All that afternoon, I couldn't forget what nerve that woman had and how yellow I was. . . . I worked myself up and became so tense and irritable that when my little daughter asked a question, I pushed her back in anger. That made me feel more sore at that woman because she had made me abuse my child. For hours I talked about that awful woman and told the story to everybody who would listen. . . ." Mona then added that since she joined Recovery, she has had similar experiences, but she spotted both symptoms and temper imme-diately, and when she felt like telling the story to "everybody who would listen," she commanded her speech muscles not to move.

What Mona described could easily furnish the material for a big volume. The story it would tell is that of temper producing symptoms and disturbing adjustment. This would be nothing new to you. However, two brief chapters of that hypothetical volume would bear quoting. The one might carry the heading, "She was wrong." This would be an intellectual judgment. The other could be fittingly worded, "I was yellow" and would constitute a romantic declamation. Which adds up to the conclusion that Mona, our dear, plain-thinking and soft-speaking Mona, was addicted, in her pre-Recovery days, to the type of thought which we call intellectual and the type of feeling which we call romantic. Like Mona, all our patients have been intellectualist and romanticist prior to their Recovery training and have adopted a realistic philosophy only after they joined our group.

I told you repeatedly that the judgment "He is wrong" cannot be passed except by a duly appointed judge. And in social or domestic "differences of opinion" there is no judge to decide whose opinion is right and whose wrong. But I see already how your eyes flash and your speech muscles twitch to protest emphatically that the woman who edged ahead of Mona was "clearly in the wrong." Does it require a judge to brand that woman's behavior as outrageous and impossible and unquestionably offensive? That woman used unfair means to secure an advantage over a neighbor; she employed aggressive tactics, was pushy, reckless, rudely inconsiderate. How can anybody deny that Mona was right and that woman wrong? Well, I offer the denial and will presently produce the reasons.

At the time of the incident, Mona was in the throes of a depression which had lasted close to five consecutive years. She was self-conscious, preoccupied, hardly able to think of anything but her physical torture and mental anguish. Many of you who have gone through a depression know that in a condition of this kind, everything is done with the utmost effort. The simplest acts of walking, speaking, thinking, are executed with the greatest difficulty. Finally, even listening to plain conversations and trying to understand what people say becomes a fatiguing exertion. At this stage, the patient ceases concentrating on what he hears or sees and is continually preoccupied with his worries and anxieties, his helplessness and seeming hopelessness. With concentration gone, he does not attend to the business in hand. His thoughts wander, his alertness suffers. When his name is called, he may not hear it. His turn for an assigned task is at hand, but he has all but forgotten the purpose of his waiting.

That's what happened to Mona in the butcher shop. Preoccupied and with her attention wandering, she missed her turn and stood wool-gathering. Perhaps "that woman" paused to see whether somebody would step forward and when nobody stirred, concluded that she was next in line and quite properly placed her order with the butcher. The order might have been given in a vigorous, sonorous voice which aroused Mona from her preoccupation. When now Mona contended for her "rightful" turn and insisted that she was "wrongfully" passed by, the remark made by "that woman" about people sleeping was rather discourteous, but was it "wrong?"

Mona knew that she tended to be preoccupied, inattentive, dreaming. In the preceding five years, she had amassed a prodigious record of tasks neglected, things forgotten, remarks not heard. She knew her defect of not hearing, seeing and recalling properly. When at the butcher's she missed her cue, her first thought should have been that something went "wrong" because of her nervous condition; that her attention had wandered again as it had on so many previous occasions. Instead, she jumped to the conclusion it was "that woman" who caused her to lose her "rightful" place. You see, even in this "clear-cut" case, there are two sides to the story, and it would take a very wise judge to decide which was the right and which the wrong side. Mona looked at her own side of the story only. The part of the story which could have been told by "that woman" was thoroughly neglected. It is the distinctive mark of the so-called intellectual to emphasize, or over-emphasize, one side of an issue only, usually his own side, and to look away from the other side. Much of what I have told you in the past ten years about temper can be safely condensed in the one concise formulation: temper is, among other things, the result of an intellectual blindness to the "other side of the story."

When Mona exclaimed, "How yellow I was," she stepped from the sphere of intellectualism into the realm of romanticism. I do not know precisely how the colloquial expression "yellow" came to acquire the meaning of cowardly, low-spirited and faint-hearted behavior. But somehow it must have derived from the idea that a "he-man's" blood must be red and not yellow, or that a man must be able to get "red in the face" or "see red" in order to lick the fellow who dares step on his toes. This romantic view assumes that excitement is the spice of life, that if you want your daily existence to be interesting and stimulating, you will have to assert yourself and draw first and strike fast. You must show red blood and not a green yellowish bile. Be that as it may, you will realize that temper is born from the intellectual theory that you are the judge to decide who is right, and from the romantic conviction that a person is not worth his salt if he shirks a fight. If you object that a woman of Mona's type, endowed with a disarming sweetness of manner, could hardly be charged with intellectual rudeness and romantic combativeness, I shall remind you that temper has precisely this effect, that for the duration of the outburst, it abolishes refinement of culture, putting in its place the coarseness of raw nature.

Why did Mona feel the urge to rant about her experience for hours and tell her story "to everybody who would listen?" A story endlessly repeated becomes stale and hackneyed and monotonous. The listener is bound to respond with weariness, boredom and disgust. If Mona's objective was to convince her listeners, to gain their consent and endorsement, a concise recital of the episode would have served the purpose far more effectively than the tiresome rehashing of the story which the countless rehearsals were certain to deprive of its freshness and plausibility. Let me state briefly that this ceaseless recounting of experiences is at the root of what may be called the "complaint hobby." My patients are generally addicted to this hobby, and Mona, in her pre-Recovery days, was one of its devotees.

The main pride of the average person is that his views, opinions, plans and decisions are right, sensible and practical. Essentially, this is a claim that the thought processes are solid, that they can be depended on to prove true, in short, that their premises and conclusions are valid. This may be called the *intellectual claim to validity*. A parallel ambition of the average individual is to prove to himself or to others that his heart is "on the right spot," that he is emotionally responsive, ready to fight for his rights and to defend his convictions. His feelings and sentiments, he insists, are generous, noble, vigorous and vital. This is the *romantic claim to vitality*.

The abiding distress of the nervous patient is precisely his inability to trust the validity of his thoughts or to have pride in the vitality of his feelings and sentiments. He states it as his opinion that his suffering is unbearable and is not even listened to. He repeats untiringly that he is doomed, that he is threatened with collapse, but his predictions, failing to come true, are ultimately laughed at. The fact that he cannot secure a respectful hearing is proof positive that the validity of his statements is doubted or ridiculed or rejected. His feelings and sentiments share the same melancholy fate. He protests that his interests in family, business and social obligations are as vigorous and vital as ever; that he neglects them only because of his handicap, but is told to quit being lazy and to use his will-power. With this, his vitality is indicted. He aches to prove that he is both valid and vital, but his words fall on deaf ears, and his pleas meet with dull responses. Exposed for years to the skepticism and ridicule of those around him, he finally accepts their verdict that he is basically lacking both qualities.

Then comes the temperamental spell. It works a miraculous transformation. All of a sudden he is aroused to a fit of anger. He fumes and raves; he is indignant and fairly panting for a fight. What else can that be but strength, vigor and vitality? And that insult that was hurled at him by "that rascal" was clearly and undoubtedly an injustice, an unprovoked attack. That he is right and the other fellow wrong cannot possibly be questioned. In a "clear-cut case" of this kind, who but a fool or knave could challenge his premises and conclusions? The temperamental spell reestablishes, as with magic, his intellectual claim to validity and his romantic claim to vitality. No wonder he is eager to rehash and rehearse and repeat the story to "everybody who would listen." He has found a convincing story and interested listeners, and he is going to make the utmost of the opportunity.

CHAPTER SIXTEEN

The Vanity of Knowing Better

Lucille, on the Saturday panel, reported that some time ago, she bought an ashtray and "just loved the looks of it." She showed the new acquisition to her sister Martha, expecting to be complimented on her good taste. But the sister, little impressed, burst out laughing. "Why," she exclaimed, "that's no ashtray. It is something to hang on the wall. Don't you see it has a hole in it?" An argument developed, Lucille insisting it was an ashtray "for sure" and the sister claiming, with equal insistence, that it was a wall decoration "at best" and "certainly not an ashtray." Lucille was upset. "I hated to admit that I had made such a silly mistake. But I checked my temper and refused to continue the argument. . . . A few weeks later, I was in the same store where I purchased the dish and saw it was still on sale there. Just for curiosity, I asked the salesman what kind of an article it was. 'Why,' he said, 'these are ashtrays.' I felt the impulse to rush home and tell my sister that she had been wrong, but that would have led to an argument again and might have given me my symptoms. When I arrived home, I said nothing about my conversation with the salesman and felt proud that I could exercise self-control."

What Lucille and Martha fought about was not the ashtray or its possession or its value. The contest was to decide who of the sisters was more competent in discerning the meaning of the otherwise paltry and insignificant object and finding the proper name for it. As such, it was a matching of wits in which the question at issue was: Who knows better? Whose is the superior intelligence? Bursting with contemptuous laughter, Martha indicated that in her mind Lucille figured as a dunce, a person who did not know the difference between an ashtray and a wall plate. Lucille, with the humility born of persistent Recovery training, retired into silence, tacitly admitting that perhaps she did not know, that perchance her intelligence had its limitations. To admit one's limitations is humility, to insist on one's superior knowledge is vanity. Martha was vain, Lucille was humble.

I well remember the time when Lucille used to come to my office complaining about her choking and sweating and palpitating, her air-hunger and pains and numbness. All I had to do was to inquire about her recent experiences at home to find the unfailing source of her symptoms and distress. It was invariably battles with her sister, her son and husband about sheer trivialities in which she was "sure she knew and was right," and the others contested her claim and were equally "sure she did not know and was wrong." From these battles about superior knowledge, Lucille emerged regularly, prostrate with agony and weariness and torturing symptoms. In those days, the vanity of proving her superior knowledge rocked her body with endless turmoil and torment. Today, with a humble awareness of her average limitations, her body is in repose and her mind at peace. Which method effected this transformation of a vain superiority hunter into a humble person, mindful of her average limitations?

You who have gone through the process of training in Recovery techniques know that the method is that of spotting. From what you have been taught in Recovery, you know that everybody, not only my patients, has the natural impulse to prove the superiority of his thinking abilities (intellectual validity) and to demonstrate the exquisite quality of his strength, forcefulness and prowess (romantic vitality). Both impulses result from claims. The intellectual person claims he knows better how to think, the romantic individual has the equivalent claim to know better how to act. Both insist they "know" and know better. This claim to know better, being a claim, is nothing but a pretense, a vanity.

The trouble is that your brothers and sisters and friends have the same variety of claims and vanities, belonging, as they do, to the same universal tribe of romanto-intellectuals who people this globe of ours. All you have to do is to advance your claim of superior knowledge, and they will promptly feel that their identical claim was challenged. Your statement will be hotly contested and stiffly resisted. This merry exchange of claims and counterclaims we call *temper*, and its essence is that vanities clash and pretenses collide. The violence of the clash and the heat of the collision produce anger; the anger gives rise to tenseness which, in nervous patients, precipitates symptoms. If my patients are to be rid of their symptoms, they must learn to dispense with the vanities of claiming superior knowledge and to cultivate the humility of realizing their limited efficiency in thinking and acting. This requires continuous and unrelenting spotting, the pre-eminent method of self-control taught you in Recovery.

In order to spot your temper correctly, you must give up your claim to know, to know more and know better. This ought to be easy. It ought to be easy to drop a claim which is nothing but a pretense, a vanity, an illusion. The tragedy is that the illusion of superior knowledge provides you with stimulation, excitement, thrill. It gives you an opportunity to fight, to score a victory, to prove your shoddy excellence and spurious value. Your symptoms make you feel helpless. They deprive you of your vitality, of zest and self-confidence. Dragging along day after day, tired, weary, listless, despairing of ever again experiencing the thrill and rapture of being alert and dynamic, you crave the exhilarating sense of being vigorous, vital and self-assured. As it is, with your symptoms straining your energies, with your nervous fatigue sapping your efficiency, you miss the spark of life, the stimulation of interest, the throb of spontaneity. You would do anything to recapture that delightful feeling of being alive, active and forceful.

Along comes the occasion for a temper outburst. You feel challenged to maintain your claim to superiority. True, it is nothing but a claim, a pretense and vanity. But if it promises to restore, even for a few minutes, your waning sense of vitality, you will plunge into the fray and again live through the rapture and ecstasy of fighting and proving to yourself that your vitality, far from being exhausted, is again brimming with energy, throbbing with life. If a miracle of this kind can be performed by the sheer claim to know better, well, let it be a pretense, a vanity and illusion. It has the mysterious capacity to restore vitality and spontaneity. And if spotting it correctly is likely to undo its effect, you will strain every nerve to avoid spotting. You will rather retain your symptoms than relinquish the supreme thrill of a rejuvenated vigor.

And memory is fresh yet of the days when I grappled with Lucille, trying to persuade her that the thrill provided by the tantrum is nothing but a momentary exhilaration, certain to be followed by intensified suffering and aggravated symptoms. She listened and seemed convinced, but when the occasion for a temper reaction arose, she craved the thrill and yielded. One day, she came to my office beaming with joy. She told the story of how she felt provoked by a neighbor, how her temper rose, and she controlled it. "After that," she continued, "I was relaxed and comfortable as never before. I really felt proud of myself." She had hardly completed the sentence when a shadow settled on her face. "Doctor," she said, "if I feel proud of myself, doesn't that mean that I am vain instead of humble?" I asked her, "Is a mother vain if she is proud of her child? A wife if she adores her husband? A citizen if he basks in the glory of his country?" And I went on explaining that to be proud of actual and realistic accomplishments is desirable and valuable.

What the mother prides herself on is the effort and labors and deprivations which the raising of the child entailed. She is proud of her self-effacing or self-control. And if a wife is proud of her husband, be certain that what she has in mind is his accomplishments which are the result and product of his self-control, and similarly with the citizen extolling the virtues of his nation. These virtues are an index to the labors, successes and exploits of past generations which were secured at the cost of vigorous group discipline and collective self-control. Lucille understood. As I continued my explanations, she grasped the fact that every act of self-control produces a sense of self-respect. This self-respect is a form of pride. Another form of pride is vanity. The latter does not point to actual and realistic accomplishment, to no effort or self-discipline. It is merely a claim, pretense and illusion. Lucille learned the distinction between the two varieties of pride, the one realistic, the other illusional. Realistic pride leads to self-respect, repose and relaxation; illusional pride or vanity to self-torturing, momentary thrill and enduring tenseness. In nervous patients, it leads, in addition, to perpetuation of symptoms.

Many a patient has told me, "I have learned to control my temper outbursts. I no longer want the victories of vanity and prefer the peacefulness of humility. But my fears are still active." With the one patient, it is the fear of collapse, with the other, the fear of the permanent handicap. These fears do not seem to stem from the vanity of knowing better. To the contrary, a fear appears to be the expression of a shrinking and retreating disposition, hence, to be related to humility rather than vanity. But when I try to explain to a patient that his fears are groundless, that they are due to a thought of insecurity in his brain, that he can dispose of this thought if he accepts my authoritative knowledge, that he can brave his fatigue and step out forcefully without any danger of collapse; when I tell him that his so-called sleeplessness is a myth, that even if he feels he hasn't slept, nevertheless, he did a good deal of sleeping and perhaps of snoring; when I confront him with the store of my knowledge about these subjects and point to my solid experience of half a lifetime, he argues and opposes and clings stubbornly to his notions and engages in insipid verbal fencing and–knows better.

He knows he has not slept a wink last night; he knows the fatigue is "real" and not nervous; he is certain his head pressure is the result of hypertension. And when I take his blood pressure and assure him that it is within normal limits and nothing to worry about, he is likely to counter with the exclamation, "But, Doctor, when I am in your office, I relax, and my blood pressure goes down. I am sure it will go up the moment I step out on the street." You see, whether it is the angry or fearful temper, the situation is the same. The patient "knows better." He is an arch romanto-intellectual who knows and is sure and cannot be convinced without a long, drawn-out struggle. If he is to be cured, he must be trained to assume a humble attitude and to divest himself of the vanity of knowing. The road to humility leads through spotting to the determination to abandon the craving for the divine thrill of knowing better.

CHAPTER SEVENTEEN

Temperament and Temper

Betty, on the Saturday afternoon panel, reported that several weeks ago, she had an appointment to see Dr. Low at his office. "I had to wait from 2:30 to 4:00 P.M. Then I had to go shopping for a belt and a pair of shoes. After that, I had to go to the insurance office and to be there before closing time. At the department store, I had to spend time picking the merchandise I wanted. Then it took more time yet before the saleslady took care of the purchase. I got to the insurance office just five minutes before closing time. By now, I had a severe head pressure, and when I was on the street, it occurred to me that I had to get a few things for supper, and that after supper, I had to attend the monthly Recovery meeting of the panel members in the evening. The head pressure became worse, and I felt exhausted. Finally, I arrived home, trembling and sweating and palpitating. Then I noticed that my husband had not returned from work, although it was past his usual time. My first thought was that something had happened to him. My symptoms became worse. Then I remembered my Recovery training and thought I shouldn't anticipate danger. Instantly, I felt better. . . ."

Betty, in an emotional upheaval, summoned forth a slogan she had learned in Recovery and obtained instant relief. Experiences of this kind are now commonplace among our members. They know that all they have to do to stop emerging symptoms is to spot their emotionalisms and to refuse to accept the suggestions of doom and disaster offered by their temperamental lingo. And if Betty managed to secure instant relief from her spotting, the conclusion seems inevitable that she spotted correctly and applied the appropriate technique taught her in Recovery. But Recovery techniques and Recovery maxims stem from me, your physician, and if it is true that I ever taught Betty, or anyone else, not to anticipate danger, I must have been dreaming or utterly careless in the choice of my words.

How can anybody be alive and avoid anticipating danger? To be heedless of danger is a sure prescription for running straight into it. Just cross streets and turn corners unmindful of the dangers of a busy traffic, and I will not want to be responsible for what might happen to you some day. Clearly, Betty applied a Recovery slogan correctly but in quoting it distorted its phrasing.

No wife worth the name can avoid uneasy thoughts and anxious anticipations if her husband is unduly late in arriving at the customary time. The image of an accident, of collapse and even misgivings about foul play must, of necessity, arise in her brain if she is possessed of affection and imagination. In a situation of this kind, the thought of possible danger is the unavoidable and proper response. No teaching of any kind, Recovery or otherwise, will ever be able to eliminate this response which is necessary for life and desirable for human relations. The question is how a person experiencing the response of apprehension will react to the experience. Will he worry with reflective calm? Or, will he work himself up to a burst of emotional hysteria? If he permits himself to become emotional and hysterical, then, the *original response* of plain worry has been "worked up" or "processed" into a *temper reaction.* What patients are taught in Recovery is to curb their tempers and to leave the original responses to run their course, that is, to let them rise and fall, come and go. Temper keeps them rising and coming and prevents them from falling and going.

What I here call "original responses" are the ordinary run of thoughts, feelings, sensations and impulses which, in the average individual, come and go, rise and fall. They are inherited and constitutional. A dog jumps at you unexpectedly. You are startled, and the startle is an original response which everybody is likely to experience in an event of this kind. It would be absurd to tell you not to get startled. The response is rooted in your racial inheritance, embedded in your constitution. It is original, natural, hardly changeable. Another example: your ear is assailed by a harsh word or your eye by a disdainful gesture. If you are at all responsive, you will feel hurt or insulted or shocked. That is again your original response, just as constitutional and refractory to change as is the startle occasioned by the dog's jump.

Original responses of this kind are without number. The pity aroused by suffering, the joy and warmth produced by a smiling infant, the enthusiasm created by a stirring speech, the delight felt at the sight of a friend, the anger provoked by an affront, the impulse to run in the face of danger–these and a multitude of others are all original responses. The sum total of original responses which a person is possessed or capable of are called his *temperament*. Temperament means that a person is sensitive, receptive, impressionable to events inside and outside him. If your temperament is receptive and impressionable, your original responses will be many and varied; if it is dull, they will be few and static. It is temperament which responds to events with readiness or sluggishness, warmth or coolness, sympathy or aversion, interest or indolence, thrill or chill.

When Betty, arriving home, found her husband missing, the thought struck her that something might have happened to him. Every wife would or should have experienced the same response, provided her temperament was endowed with the average qualities of warmth, affection and tenderness. If Betty's temperament was of this description, she had to feel concern, worry or misgivings. You see here that when temperament stirs, feelings are apt to rise. In the present instance, the feeling was that of worry. Betty might have acted on this natural and original response of worry. She might have telephoned to the husband's place of employment or to any locality at which she could have reasonably expected him to stop on his way home. Had she done that, her original *response* would have guided her to a rational, sane, well adjusted *reaction*. Or, she might have analyzed the situation in the light of previous experience and reflected that her husband's arrival had been delayed frequently in the past by overtime work, by a traffic jam or by a decision to have his hair trimmed before setting out on his homebound trip. This again would have led to a rational and sane reaction. Betty would have simply waited, calmly and patiently. But Betty's temperament was not disposed to release the responses of calm and patience. She is or was a nervous patient, and if the temperament of a nervous patient stirs, it is likely to develop–*temper*. And you know that temper is incompatible with calm and patience.

Temperament raises mild and moderate fears, worries, angers and joys. But temper acts differently. Its responses are always vehement, immoderate, excessive and even explosive. In her pre-Recovery days, Betty responded to disappointments with temper. After she had gone through her Recovery training, her responses became again those of her native temperament–calm, even, sane. In former days, her temperament led her straightway into hysterical emotionalism. Now it produces feelings of average intensity. Formerly, when disappointed, her temper suggested a grave emergency. Now her temperament merely hints at a possible average danger. To think of danger–calmly–is undoubtedly wholesome and necessary in life in general but particularly so in the hustle and bustle of our metropolitan life. Why, then, did Betty think she "shouldn't anticipate danger?" Obviously, she confused two types of anticipation, those generated by a wild temper and those inspired by a mild temperament.

In Recovery, she was taught not to entertain hysterical anticipations in response to average dangers which merely call for gentle and moderate worry. When she met with the average situation mentioned in her panel example, her temperament produced the original response of concern. But unwittingly, and following a year-long tendency, she thought of a dire emergency and developed temper. The result was that her "symptoms became worse." Now she remembered her Recovery training, spotted her temper and felt instant relief. She acted correctly, but when she reported the event, she used a wrong phrasing. She claimed she spotted and stopped her temperament when, in actual fact, she put a stop to her temper. She applied properly the Recovery techniques for curbing temper but misquoted the implied principle when she presumed to have checked her temperament.

My patients will do well to ponder the lesson of this clear-cut distinction between temperament and temper. Afflicted with nervous ailments, they are extremely sensitive, and the original responses of their native temperament are aroused by actions, statements and events which other people, less impressionable, would overlook and ignore. Somebody maintains silence in their presence. Instantly, my patients are likely to construe the reaction as slur or indifference or neglect. Or, they commit a minor blunder or sustain minor losses, failures or defeats. The average person would take these insignificant mishaps in his stride, and not a ripple of excitement might cross his temperament. But my patients are apt to respond with self-blame, embarrassment or a sense of inefficiency. This is in itself no calamity and merely indicates that my patients are unfortunately blessed with temperaments which pour forth endless streams of original responses.

The responses as such are no wise different from those experienced by men and women not the victims of nervous trouble. Everybody may at any time feel slurred or neglected and may on occasion indulge in self-blame and a sense of embarrassment. With the average person, such common inner disturbances are readily forgotten or dismissed. But with my patients, there are no minor or common disturbances. Every disturbance has to them the major aspect of an urgent emergency. And if an emergency is thought of, emotion is mobilized and temper released. Minor apprehensions are then fanned into major explosions, into panics and tantrums. These dramatic or dramatized developments can be checked if the patient is trained to regard his worries, embarrassments, misgivings and forebodings as what they really are: the innocent outpouring of a temperament which has been sensitized by an endless career of suffering and has acquired the habit of producing an unbroken succession of harmless original responses. The nervous patient will have to learn to be tolerant of his responses and to refrain from processing temperament into temper.

CHAPTER EIGHTEEN

Temper Masquerading As "Feeling"

Florence, on the Saturday panel, spoke with surprising candor about her marital life. "I was always jealous of my husband," she said. "All he had to do was to invite some girl to ride home with us from church, and I became jealous and felt very insecure. Before I joined Recovery, I did not know that this was temper. I felt I had a right to ask my husband not to pay attention to any woman but me. But when I got my Recovery training, I learned that I was not the judge to decide who was wrong and who right. Today, I know that when the jealousy gets a hold of me, I feel irritated, but nobody is wrong. I have learned to let the irritation run its course, and it does that in a few minutes. And after my jealousy is gone, I feel good and feel proud that I am able to control it. In this manner, I endorse myself, and that makes me feel better yet. In former days, when the jealousy came over me, it produced a blurring of my eyes and gave me a headache that would last for days, and my married life was a mess all the time. Today, I have very few of the symptoms, and both I and my husband lead a much happier life than we ever did before I joined Recovery."

Florence suffered from jealousy for many years but did not know it was temper. That was before her Recovery training, and at that time she merely "felt" insecure. She also "felt" she had a right to be jealous. I shall ask: Who or what did Florence "feel" for? The answer is: She felt for her own security and for her own rights. She showed little if any feeling for the husband's security, which was gravely threatened by her jealousy, and for his rights, which were ruthlessly ignored when he was forbidden to extend simple courtesies to a fellow church member. And my conclusion is: Florence in her pre-Recovery days had feelings for her own dear Self only whenever the jealousy took hold of her. The feelings for the husband were either absent or feebly operating. Yet the couple had formed a life partnership. They were united in matrimony, and the marital union, assuredly, called for mutual feelings, for sharing, communicating and exchanging. Instead, whenever she was in the throes of jealousy, Florence made her feelings flow out toward her own Self only; the partner's Self was denied its legitimate share of consideration and affection. If the concern about security and rights was at all the outcome of feelings, they were certainly self-centered and not group-centered. And self-centered feelings (self-pity, self-blame, self-disgust, self-importance) are temper, of course. For you, the members of Recovery, this is commonplace and needs no explanation.

Florence aimed her jealousy at her husband. Since he was her partner in their marital group, the feeling was group-oriented, although in a superficial sense only. But it declared the other person as wrong and oneself as right, and that quality stamped it as unquestionably temperamental. Her jealous temper led Florence to be resentful, sullen, suspicious, indignant, perhaps also hostile and vengeful. All these feelings tie in with jealousy, their main characteristic being that they adjudge the other person as wrong and oneself as right. Though they must be classed among the group-directed responses, nevertheless, they are tempers.

Many of you remember the time, some eighteen months ago, when Florence first joined Recovery. None of you realized that she was of a jealous disposition. How could you know? She never showed temper when she was with us. She was unfailingly sweet, considerate, patient, forever willing to be helpful. As a member of our group, she displayed a vast capacity for joy and enthusiasm, affection and forbearance, devotion and selflessness, fellowship and compassion. Needless to say, these were feelings, group-centered with regard to their aim, genuine in intent, sincere in application. As such, they were emphatically not temperamental. Her affection had, of course, no implication of somebody being branded as wrong and herself extolled as right. Feelings of this kind, whose exclusive tendency is to benefit and serve the group, go by the name of sympathetic responses. They may properly be called the *feelings of sympathy*. By their very nature, they cannot be suspected as furnishing the material out of which temper is woven.

You will also remember that at times, Florence appeared in our midst with drawn features and a worn look. Her mood was depressed, and her depression, we know now, was largely the result of her physical ailment. In these periods of depression, her countenance reflected silent grief, a soft resignation, a touching sadness. But there was no wailing and complaining, no self-pity or self-blame. Nobody was assessed as wrong, nobody as right. She just suffered in placid resignation. Feelings of this kind signify a lowering of the feeling tone, from joy to grief, from sympathy to apathy. They are known as the apathetic responses and may be fittingly called the *feelings of apathy*.

My opportunities for observing Florence were limited to office, classes and meetings. I had no occasion to study her behavior in such casual situations as encounters with sales persons and elevator operators, in chats with neighbors and friends, at card games and on visits to theaters. What was the nature of her responses in these contacts? We know that Florence is a warm person, easily stimulated and eagerly responding. So we may take it for granted that in most instances, her reaction was mainly that of sympathy. Occasionally, more particularly when her severe physical ailment dulled and lowered her receptiveness, her attitude might have been that of apathy. But when an idle sales girl, busy with her make-up, kept her waiting impatiently at the counter; when a neighbor was sharp and a friend neglectful; when her bridge partner spoke in a sarcastic vein, or when an unmannered person, with tactless remarks and distasteful noises, prevented her from enjoying a show, we may safely assume that she was a prey to irritation, annoyance or outright anger. Under circumstances of this sort, it was more than likely that she was chilled in her sympathy, roused from her apathy and seized with *antipathy*.

Was this a feeling? Or was it temper? The answer is plain: if she was merely irritated and annoyed, it was a more or less unadulterated feeling; if she proceeded to condemn the offender as wrong and to exalt herself as right, it was temper. You will now understand that feelings are of three kinds: sympathy, apathy, antipathy, either toward oneself or others. Temper is of one kind only: antipathy, against oneself or the other person, plus the judgment of right and wrong. On the basis of these formulations, we may sum up the meanings of the various reactions displayed by Florence. When she was moved by jealousy, she was resentful, sullen, suspicious, indignant, perhaps hostile and vengeful. This was antipathy plus judgment of right and wrong, hence, temper. When she was free from jealousy, she responded with genuine or tolerably genuine feelings of either sympathy, apathy or antipathy, with no judgment of right and wrong marring the relative purity of the responses. This was feeling without admixture of temper. As everybody does, Florence expressed both feeling and temper.

Feelings should be expressed. This does not mean they ought to be acted on or acted out. It merely means they should be communicated to or shared with somebody who can be trusted to understand them. If the feelings are those of sympathy, their expression will create goodwill and, thus, further the interests of the group. If they are those of apathy or antipathy, their expression will give relief to the person oppressed by them. Obtaining relief, the oppressed person will be purged of antisocial trends, and the ends of the group will thereby be promoted. This is different with temper. Feelings can be reported. They lend themselves to matter-of-fact discussion and calm appraisal. But temper, involving a claim to being right, cannot be reported objectively, calmly and matter-of-factly. It invariably leads to arguments,

177

debates and rebuttals. Even close relatives and intimate friends, asked to pass a verdict on the justification of a temper outburst, may, and frequently do, voice disapproval, criticizing the uselessness or harmfulness of the explosion. If the temperamental person resents the rebuff, a new temper reaction is released, this time involving the relatives and friends. The result is that the temperamental hothead obtains no relief from his tension, and group life is disturbed. Temper should be checked and controlled. It should not be given any expression at all. It should merely be avoided or, once it has occurred, it should be prevented from recurring. Feelings call for expression, temper for suppression.

Florence needed training in Recovery to learn that temper is different from feeling. Why did she fail to make the distinction herself? She has a keen intelligence and a refreshing willingness to learn by experience. Her intelligence could have told her that most feelings are noble, that even those that lack the attribute of nobility are not likely to injure the group. By the same token, she could have discovered, by sheer use of her native intellect, that temper, far from being identical with feeling, is its very opposite. It is positively ignoble and disrupting group life. And should she have consulted her past experience, she could have easily learned the fact which I mentioned, that feelings, when communicated, give relief, while temper has no such effect.

How is it her intellect and experience failed her? The answer is that men and women derive their views not merely from their own observations but mainly from public opinion. And contemporary public opinion has fostered a type of thought which glamorizes temper by the clever trick of identifying it with feeling. The trick is of an engaging simplicity. Temper and feeling, in the present-day psychological jargon, are deftly lumped together under the common name of emotion, and emotion is nimbly interpreted as feeling. The next step in the argument, assiduously promoted by modern psychologies, is that emotions, being the driving power in the human economy, are infinitely more important than intellect. And since intellect is generally considered as a valuable function, the conclusion drawn by the average person (and by professionals) is that emotions, being superior to intellect, must also be of superior value.

With this, emotion is not only glamorized but also raised to the rank of dignity and nobility. This view, given wide currency by recognized professions, leading universities and philanthropic foundations, has found its way into the channels of communication with the result that dailies, weeklies and monthlies, radio, film and television fairly vie with one another in the gentle art of catering to unbridled tempers, carefully avoiding the odious word and slyly substituting the terms "emotion" or "emotional experience." Antisocial impulses, born from dark temperamental dispositions, are then portrayed as "just emotions," as "plainly human," indeed, as of valuable "human interest." True, these emotions (read: tempers) may also be troublesome; they may cause tenseness, maladjustment and symptoms. But the newer psychologies have wisely anticipated this unfortunate inconvenience and provided a suitable remedy by spreading the gospel of "free expression" of "emotional" frustrations and aggressions.

That this vicious doctrine of free expression has had a prominent share in the spread of both individual and social tenseness and of all kinds of antisocial trends is plain but will not be elaborated here. What interests me at this point is the deplorable fact that my patients have been exposed to the sinister influence of this modern dogma of the identity of temper and feeling and have been reached by the insidious propaganda, carried on by textbooks, by the stage and the press, to the effect that ungoverned emotions (read: aggressive tempers) can be cured by the expedient of "free expression." Well, Florence, under the influence of an utterly irresponsible public opinion, gave formerly "free expression" to her temper and almost wrecked her marriage. Today, when through old-fashioned Recovery teaching she has recovered her mental balance, she expresses her feelings but suppresses her temper, and with temper curbed, her feelings, properly communicated and shared, spread their warmth and glow over a happy marital scene.

CHAPTER NINETEEN

Tantrums Have Much Force but Little Feeling

Ada thought she was rid of the fear of being alone in her home. For years her sister, who occupies the apartment next door, was not permitted to leave unless she took Ada with her. But "for the past couple of months," Ada related, "my sister left me alone, and I handled myself very well." This splendid record of improvement was suddenly interrupted by that severe reaction which is known to our patients as the well-nigh unavoidable *setback*. On the morning of the panel discussion, Ada's sister announced she was going to a luncheon. Instantly, "a ball of fire shot into my face. I felt dizzy; my heart palpitated, and the room was going around and around. I meant to plead with my sister not to leave. But I had too much Recovery training to do that. I rushed to the phone and called Rosalie. She reassured me. But soon after my sister was gone, I felt tense and fearful. Before long, I had myself worked up into a panic. I dashed at the phone and called my husband. He suggested a walk, but I was so weak I could not drag my body. At that moment, I thought of our Recovery training and became disgusted with myself. I felt ashamed that I had practiced such dreadful sabotage. When this thought struck me, I felt calm all of a sudden, picked up my sewing and kept sewing till after lunch. And now I am here sharing in the panel, and I am all right."

Ada's experience illustrates three points: (1) that patients, after they recover, are apt to have setbacks; (2) that the setback, usually mild, may attain the violence of a panic; (3) that with proper Recovery training, even the wildest panic can be broken in a fraction of a second. I told you frequently that in my very extensive experience, I have met few nervous patients who did not suffer from setbacks after they improved. Therefore, it is of the utmost importance for all of you to know how to deal with setbacks, more particularly, how to deal with them if they threaten to develop into a panic.

A panic must be broken, abruptly and decisively. If it is permitted to go on unchecked, the danger is it will leave the patient discouraged and demoralized. He may then give up the fight for health, reflecting that "What's the use struggling if even Recovery cannot help me." The result will be the defeatist belief that, once a nervous ailment becomes "chronic" it is incurable. You know that our Recovery language calls this the "fear of the permanent handicap."

In the ordinary man's language, as distinguished from Recovery usage, the word *panic* connotes a condition in which a person is gripped by a violent fear that is overwhelming and irresistible. It is a fierce storm that lashes the organs of the body into a frantic burst of palpitations, sweats, dizziness, air-hunger, tremors, tenseness and weakness. If that storm is overwhelming, how are you going to check it? If it is irresistible, how will you resist it?

Common language speaks of "irresistible" impulses, emotions, tantrums and spells. Recovery denies emphatically that any inner experience of the nervous patients is irresistible. It knows of situations only that *were not resisted.* This refers to common everyday experiences, the common tantrum, the common crying spell, the common anger and common fear. All of them can be resisted, none are irresistible.

Diseases cannot be resisted. If a patient is seized with a prolonged depression of his mood, I shall not tell him to resist the depression. He needs expert medical treatment. But a depression of this kind is not a common everyday experience. A few other experiences may fall into the same category. If a mother loses her child, her sadness may have an irresistible quality. This is perhaps true also of the condition of "being in love." Whether human beings, except in certain brain diseases, can develop a truly "irresistible" rage, I do not know, but I have reason to doubt it. You will realize that the grief of the mother, the infatuation of the lover and the blind rage of the person ravaged by brain disease are not common, everyday situations.

The tantrums and panics which our patients experience in the course of a setback are common, everyday occurrences; they are the result of nothing more unusual than–temper. Ada suffered from an ordinary, commonplace temper outburst and "worked herself up" till she drifted into a panic. Soon she felt ashamed and disgusted with herself and dropped the panic as you would a silly thought.

Thoughts can be formed and reformed; they can be accepted and rejected; they can be retained and dismissed. Feelings are of a different make. You cannot change, reject or dismiss them. They descend upon you, and you must wait until they depart. Ada formed a temperamental idea, worked it up to a pitch, then rejected and dismissed it.

Ada was enabled to perform this feat because of her Recovery training. In the language of Recovery, temper is distinct from genuine feeling. The sadness of the bereaved mother is a genuine feeling. That feeling is original, primary and pure. In contrast, temper is derived, secondary and adulterated. I shall try to explain these terms. Every feeling has thoughts attached to it. A sad person is bound to think that the world is flat and stale. In this instance, the feeling of sadness produces the thought of staleness. It is not so that the bereaved mother forms first the thought that the world is stale and, consequently, falls prey to sadness. The reverse is true: she is first sad and then thinks the world stale. The feeling of sadness is original, the thought of staleness is derived from the feeling of sadness. You can express the same relation between feeling and thought if you substitute "primary" for "original," and "secondary" for "derived." You will then understand that, in the instance of the mother, the feeling of sadness is primary, and the thought of staleness secondary.

The terms "purity" and "adulteration" are easily explained. The mother feels sad, pure and simple. She is not angry, fearful, jealous or envious. She has no desire to dominate others, to be consoled by them. She is just sad, and her feeling is not contaminated by an admixture of other feelings. It is original, primary and pure, i.e., genuine.

Contrast now this genuine feeling of sadness with Ada's temper tantrum. In Ada's own words, after the sister left, "before long I had myself worked up into a panic." The feeling did not descend on her; she "worked" on it, produced it and fanned it into a lusty fire by means of inflammatory thoughts. What precisely was the nature of her thoughts? Ada says it was the idea of being left alone, the idea of helplessness, the idea of perhaps needing help and not getting it. If that was true, she could easily remedy the situation; visiting a friend or merely going for a walk, or to a show would have cured the loneliness.

Instead, she "worked herself up." We know what that means. It means that Ada now gave herself up to all kind of sinister thoughts. "The nerve to leave me alone. They know I can't stand it. What do they care how I feel? All my sister thinks of is her own pleasure. My suffering means nothing to her, etc., etc." You see, the train of ideas that set temper afoot and keep it growing are the familiar resentments and indignations that find their simple expression in the temperamental phrase, "They are wrong." Dwell on this thought, expand and deepen it, and the sky is the limit to which you may "work yourself up." Ada had the idea of herself being right and the sister wrong. That thought produced a feeling which, being derived from a thought, was not original, and being adulterated with resentment, indignation and vindictiveness, was not pure. Lacking the qualities of originality and purity, it was not genuine. A thought produced it, and a thought could drop it.

Ada, a loyal member of Recovery and devoted disciple of its teachings, knows the meaning of temper. She knows that the thought, "I am right, and they are wrong," is an utter absurdity. She has undergone thorough Recovery training and undoubtedly has discarded the arrogant attitude of being a judge on the rightness and wrongness of actions. If she has learned anything, she certainly learned the Recovery principle that right and wrong must be no issues in domestic and social contacts. If, in her tantrum, she endeavored to revive a thought that she had discarded, she obviously tried to deceive herself into believing something she no longer believed.

You heard me frequently state that temper is an effort to deceive oneself into the belief that somebody is right and somebody else wrong. Ada tried to practice the temperamental self-deception but did not succeed. All she accomplished was to "work herself up." The emotional flame which she was able to fan into existence had a great deal of sentimental smoke and verbal fury but lacked the genuine fire of feeling. A mere breath of common sense, suddenly remembered from her Recovery training, extinguished the weak conflagration, and when cool reasoning cleared away the smoke of excitement, Ada noticed that not even embers and ashes were left. She was calm, resumed her sewing and "kept sewing till after lunch." The emotional storm was nothing but shallow and empty self-deception. The feeling that steered it was shallow; the thought that directed it was empty.

Whether pure and genuine feelings exist anywhere in this imperfect life of ours is doubtful, the only possible exceptions being the instances cited above. Even a mother's love for her child is ordinarily adulterated with the sense of possessiveness; the lover's affection is frequently contaminated with some stirring of jealousy or vanity. There is perhaps no purity, hence no genuineness, in the sphere of common human feelings. And if I tell my patients that their temperamental feelings of anger, fear, disgust lack genuineness, I merely wish to remind them that their explosions, tantrums, impulses and obsessions share the fate of all human feelings. They are mixed and adulterated with other feelings and overlaid with all manner of thought. Not being genuine, they lack the irresistible force that is credited to genuine feelings. Being largely directed by thought, they can be originated and dropped at will as any thought can. Keep that in mind, and you will have little difficulty disposing of your temperamental upheavals.

CHAPTER TWENTY

Genuine Feeling and Sincere Thinking

Clara, in the course of a panel discussion on "Sabotaging Sleep," commented on her difficulties of sleeping which she experienced prior to her Recovery training. "I would awaken from a nightmare; I was shaking and sweating, and my heart pounded, and I felt as if nothing in the room looked familiar. I was sure I was dying. The first thought I had was to awaken my husband and ask him to hold my hands. . . . There was no rest for me. I felt scared and was waiting for that something awful to happen. . . . Today, when I awaken at night, I instantly know that my sensations are not dangerous. I wait, and though I am not comfortable, I lie still in bed and do not think of waking my husband. In a short time, I fall asleep again."

When Clara was "sure" she was dying, she asked her husband to hold her hands. Then she waited "for that something awful to happen." But it would seem that if death threatens, it would be wiser to summon a physician than engage in the serene practice of holding hands. From this I conclude that Clara was not at all sure she was dying. Indeed, the inference is inescapable that she was "sure" she was not dying. You may question the propriety of casting doubt on Clara's account. Is Clara a liar? Assuredly, she is not. A liar deceives others. What Clara did was to deceive herself. She believed something which, judged by the standards of genuine experience, is impossible. She *thought* "for sure" she was dying, but she did not *experience* the fear of death.

Clara spoke of a nightmare, of shaking and sweating. The look of things had changed, and she was scared. All of this points unmistakably to fear. And if I stated that she did not experience the fear of death, what kind of a feeling was it that produced all these frightening reactions? It certainly was a fear and most intense at that. Why do I refuse to call it the fear of death?

I told you that Clara, with the "certainty" of death in her mind, asked her husband to hold her hands. Suppose a baby is seriously ill, and the mother makes ready to go to a dance. You will conclude that this mother has strong feelings for dancing but none, or very dull ones, for the fate of her child. How did you arrive at your conclusion? You observed an *act* (the mother preparing for a dance) and gathered that a *feeling* (for the baby's fate) was weak or missing. The point I wish to make is that a given act may or may not fit into the pattern of its underlying feelings. Or, acts and feelings may or may not match. Clara's act (of holding hands) was not properly matched with her professed feeling (of fearing death).

An act expresses a feeling and a thought at the same time. The act of tending the baby, for instance, expresses the mother's feeling of love and also her thought of what the baby needs or what is best for it. In this combination, the feelings and thoughts are the *inner experiences* and the acts their *outer expressions*. If an act expresses a feeling in its true and real significance, then the meaning of the act matches the meaning of the feeling. If the matching is thorough, we say that the outer act gave *genuine* expression to the inner feeling. This is different with thoughts. They are not judged from the viewpoint of genuineness. Instead, they are considered as either *sincere* or lacking sincerity. If an act really and truly matches the meaning of the inner thought, the expression is said to be sincere. If act and thought fail to match, the expression is insincere. When Clara, awakening with what she calls the terror of death, roused her husband to hold her hands, did her act of behavior express genuine feeling and sincere thought? Did her outer act match her inner experience?

A mother craving amusement while her baby is sick may feel some sort of affection for her suffering offspring. But her act of going to a dance does not match the feeling of motherly love. It matches another feeling, namely, the feeling of boredom and the love of excitement. If, while preparing for the outside engagement, she explains in so many words that, after all, a competent nurse is in attendance and the physician within easy reach, her act of speech expresses an insincere thought. That thought is not focused on the welfare of the baby; it is merely offered as a face-saving excuse for an inexcusable neglect. The inner experience and outer expression *mismatch.* The feeling lacks genuineness; the thought bears the mark of insincerity.

The real meaning of Clara's behavior ought to be clear by now. The feeling of approaching death, if genuine, can only be matched by a life-saving act, for instance, an emergency call to a physician or the instant rush to a hospital. Holding hands is no such life-saving performance. All it can be reasonably expected to give is comfort. If what Clara craved was to be comforted, her feeling must have been that of discomfort, perhaps a very intense and torturing sort of discomfort. Even if you add that she feared not to be able to stand up under the "terrific" strain, if you add further that the harrowing vision of a night of never-ending torment caused an almost unbearable fear, nevertheless, the feeling was that of discomfort, nothing else. It was not a genuine feeling of threatening death. That Clara was "sure" she was dying contributes nothing to the situation. Feeling and act were decidedly mismatched. Was her thought of death sincere? Well, I have no record of what she expressed in words about the kind of thought which dominated her brain at the time. But it would be easy to reconstruct her thinking processes on the basis of experience with a multitude of patients in similar pseudo-emergencies. Their first thought was that the husband will again refuse to believe their protestations, that the reality of their agony will be doubted, that their anxious outcry will not be taken seriously. But with a sincere thought of impending death, the only consideration that will match the inner experience is the necessity for securing instant help and not the desire to be believed. No doubt, Clara's feeling of death approaching was not genuine, her thought of life ebbing away was not sincere.

Feelings lacking the mark of genuineness and thoughts devoid of the touch of sincerity are the commonest features in the lives of average individuals who, being just plain average, are neither leaders nor saints nor heroes. Lack of genuineness and sincerity are indeed the warp and woof of daily existence. And if Clara is frequently insincere in her chats with neighbors and in her dealings with tradespeople, if following the common pattern she displays little genuineness in her devotion to civic virtues and social obligations, she is just average, with all the failings and deficiencies characteristic of average endeavors. But Clara is a nervous patient endowed with a nervous system that is unduly sensitive to tenseness. And if she practices insincerity and lack of genuineness with regard to her symptoms, she will misinterpret discomfort as meaning danger, and the result will be panics and vicious cycles. With reference to his symptoms, a nervous patient must be genuine in feeling and sincere in thought.

In order to practice a suitable degree of genuineness and sincerity, patients must be made to know that their inner experiences, if applied to symptoms, are woefully lacking these qualities. To know one's inner experiences means to gain insight, and insight requires spotting. The very moment the feeling of fear stirs in his body and the corresponding thought of danger rises in his brain, the patient must instantly spot the condition as one of severe discomfort with no danger attached. Continuous spotting disposes of insincerity and lack of genuineness. What Clara demonstrated and demonstrated with singular force was that after a relatively brief training period in Recovery, she is now able to spot her frightening inner experiences as being nothing but silly emotionalisms or inane rationalizations. Having acquired these insights, she is in a position to redirect her acts and to match them properly with her experiences. When she said, "Today when I awaken at night, I instantly know that my sensations are not dangerous," she merely indicated that she masters the techniques of spotting and that her outer acts are now well matched to the meaning of her inner experiences.

CHAPTER TWENTY-ONE

Group-Mindedness and Self-Mindedness

During a panel discussion on "Temper and Insight," the following example was offered by Bernice: "Several weeks ago, my husband went with his buddy to a nearby tavern to watch the football game on a television set. I asked him when he would be back, and he said, 'About four o'clock.' When four o'clock came, I got dressed, as I expected him to be home any minute. Well, 4:30 came, and no Bill. Five o'clock came, and Bill wasn't home yet. I became temperamental and began to work myself up. I thought, 'He doesn't care how I feel, and he thinks more about that d. . . football game than he does about me.' Before long, I had palpitations, tightness in the stomach and pressure in the head. I thought of calling up the tavern and telling Bill that I wouldn't stand for the way he treats me. By that time, I was very uncomfortable. Suddenly it came to me that this was sabotage. I said to myself, 'You think he is wrong and you are right.' But in Recovery we learn there is no right or wrong in domestic life. There are only irritations and discomfort, and we must not judge who is right and who wrong. So I said, 'These things will happen in married life,' and it wasn't worth working myself up over it. Pretty soon I calmed down. About six o'clock, Bill walked in. I asked, 'Is this four o'clock?' He looked at me and said, 'When I say four, you should know I mean six.' I was irritated, but I didn't make an issue of it. Before I had my Recovery training, I would have told him exactly how I felt, how wrong he was to do that to me, and I wouldn't have spoken to him for days. But then I would have developed all kinds of symptoms and would have suffered from them for weeks.

When Bill kept Bernice, his wife, waiting for two solid hours without troubling to call her, he was undoubtedly rude. But was rudeness his intention? Did he *mean* to be rude? Most of you know Bill, and none of you will hesitate to credit him with a gentle disposition, with the will to please, to help and to make himself liked. And if his main features are as I said, why does he neglect to practice them in his approach to Bernice? You may be inclined to be charitable and explain Bill's lack of consideration on the basis of his keen interest in football and television. You will then argue that he became wrapped up in the fascinating spectacle on the screen and–naturally–forgot wife and home. Suppose this is true and the whole incident the result of an innocent lapse of memory.

But when, in response to his wife's reproach, he had the incredible impertinence to proclaim, "When I say four, you should know I mean six," no explanation in the world could possibly atone for the crudity of that reply. Then you will no doubt revise your charitable opinion about his being two hours late and will grant that the delay was inexcusable and certainly called for an apology which Bill failed to offer. And taking it all in all, you will agree that Bill, our gentle and likable Bill, was rude in the one instance and savage in the other. And the question arises: Did Bill intend and plan to display rudeness and recklessness? Did he *mean* it? Was it his deliberate will to insult his wife, to crush her feelings?

Putting it into different words, this is what Bill intended to convey to Bernice: "If I say something, I may mean something else. What precisely I mean is my sole con-cern. I am the boss, and I do not have to account for my actions." If you read this meaning into his statement, you will understand why I call it rude and savage. Married life calls for sharing, and Bill denied Bernice her due marital share. With this, he launched a rude and savage attack on the very foundation of the marital structure. Was that his intention? Did he really mean to muzzle Bernice and to deny her the status as a wife? Was it his deliberate will to wreck his marriage?

Marriage is a Will. It is the will to share experiences, to enjoy and suffer together, to plan jointly and to act in concert. All of it is called *companionship*, which is a Will, the will to be and remain companions. Implying jointness and togetherness and sharing, companionship rules out individualism, which implies self-centeredness, inconsiderateness and single-handed action. Nobody can be a companion and an individualist at the same time or in the same situation or relationship. But that's precisely what Bill intended to be. He wanted to be married and single-acting, companion and individualist, all in one piece. His scheme of life was based on two mutually exclusive Wills: the will to companionship and the will to individualism.

I want you to know that everything in life that is of significance and value is a Will. Friendship is the will to have and keep friends. To be and remain on amicable terms with your neighbors calls for the will to cultivate neighborly relations. Citizenship is the will to be a desirable citizen, honesty the will to honest dealing, fairness the will to practice fair procedure. You cannot be understanding unless you free yourself of the will to misinterpret, to find fault, to be captious or literal. In the same sense, thinking is the will to draw correct conclusions from solid premises. There is the will to doubt, to believe, to be well. Even plain possessions constitute wills. Your house expresses the will to ownership, your garden the will to add charm to your life, your automobile the will to enjoy legitimate comforts. Needless to add that religion, education, race and nationality, and countless other trends, strivings and ambitions are all Wills.

You will readily understand the reason why I stress this matter of the Will as a force which permeates all significant phases of our daily lives if you realize that the contemporary and modern tendency is to place the emphasis on emotions, drives and instincts as the main power which governs human action. We in Recovery will have nothing of a theory which relegates life, more particularly life in a group, to blind instincts and capricious drives. We have solidly embraced a viewpoint which considers action as based, or capable of being based, on deliberate plans and settled decisions, on reasoned conclusions and firm determinations. And plans, decisions, conclusions and determinations are guided by the Will; they are not or do not have to be driven by instincts. This is in the nature of an aside remark, but a very vital sort of an aside.

The wills which I mentioned before are centered around the needs and requirements of group life. They are called *group-oriented* or *group-centered*. Opposed to them are the wills which are centered around the individual or personal self. They are individualistic or *self-centered*. The desire to be in a tavern instead of at home, to spend time with a chum rather than with one's wife is a self-centered Will. It may be unobjectionable at times, but it is self-centered, nevertheless. In order to be group-centered, you must control or hold down your self-centered desires and cravings, that is, your individualistic trends and drives. The control is exercised by the Will.

Once you have declared the will to join hands with another person, in marriage or friendship or business, or even in a mere act of casual conversation or some fleeting and transient endeavor, you have tied your hands and have assumed the obligation to act jointly, to share with the partner and to consider his or her needs, tastes and feelings. Henceforth, you are no longer free and independent. You are committed to your obligation and have lost the freedom to enact individualistic behavior. In our democratic order, there is ample room for free action and independent conduct. Nobody is forced to work or marry or practice friendship or worship or vote. And if you avoid obligations, partnerships and group ties, then, you retain a good measure of freedom to indulge your personal tastes and your self-centered inclinations, provided they do not clash with law or morals. But even in our democratic way of life, while you are free to shun certain obligations, once you assume them, you tie yourself and lose your independence. Democracy means freedom of choosing (within certain limits). But after you have chosen, you lose your *freedom of inclination* and are bound by the *restraint of obligation*. Bill assumed the marital obligation to share but retained his individual inclination to lead an independent life. The needs, tastes and feelings of the person he had tied himself to were neglected, ignored or shocked. He insisted on practicing contradictory and incompatible modes of living at one and the same time: self-centeredness and group-centeredness, independence and restraint, refusing and sharing, drive and will, individualism and companionship, inclination and obligation.

You remember I asked whether Bill *meant* to be rude, whether he *meant* to rob Bernice of her due share of matrimonial life. This term "to mean" refers to that singular capacity of the human Will to toy and trifle with some activities and to "mean business" with others. A Will which makes group-centeredness its business means the group and not the self. It is then unqualifiedly *group-minded* and ceases to be *self-minded*. If it oscillates and alternates between self and group, then, it toys and trifles with one or with both tendencies. It does not mean business. Bill was a good provider. At heart, he was deeply concerned about his wife's welfare. When Bernice was ill, he went out of his way to help her. In a sense, he *meant* to be a companion and to maintain the marital group. But he permitted his personal inclinations to interfere with and frustrate his group obligations. His Will was divided, serving partly the group, partly the self. He was both group-minded and self-minded. Meaning both members of a team of opposites, he did not "mean business" with either. Perhaps he did not mean to be rude. Perhaps he meant to share. But whether meaning or not meaning, at all events, he did not "mean business."

Now a word about Bernice. When she felt mortified and decided not to work herself up over it, when she burnt with indignation and concluded that "there is no right or

wrong in domestic life," when she was crushed by humiliation and refused "to make an issue of it," when she did all of
this, she exhibited a degree of self-control that is truly touching in its gentleness and nobility. In a savage assault on her
feelings, she used her Will and conquered emotion. She was
thoroughly group-minded and self-oblivious, devoted to
obligation and forgetful of inclination, in short, the flower
and consummation of Recovery's self-help spirit. She had
the Will to companionship and the Will to health and *meant*
both.

CHAPTER TWENTY-TWO

Subjective Wants and Objective Needs

Annette, on the Saturday panel, recalled an episode from the days when she was ill already but had not yet joined Recovery. The incident referred to an experience in her premarital life when, expecting a Valentine gift from her present husband, Clem, her expectations were disappointed. "Valentine's day came," she said, "but there was no gift or card or any sort of a token of attention. I got angry and tense, and had a pain in my side and had no appetite for supper. When I made an effort to push down the food, forcing myself to eat, there was a tight feeling in my abdomen. I went to bed, and cried and felt I had been let down. In the middle of the night, I awoke and had a strange sensation in the abdomen. I felt nauseated, went to the bathroom but couldn't vomit. Then I began to tremble all over. I felt wretched all the time, I boiled inside, and was furious at Clem and worked myself up into a panic. . . About two years after this miserable night, Valentine's Day came around again. By that time, I had my Recovery training and knew the difference between important things and matters that are trivial. And after dinner, I asked Clem calmly, 'Did you forget today is Valentine's Day?' He said, 'No,' and went to his coat and pulled out a box of candy. At that moment, I realized how I had changed. . . ."

Annette failed to receive a box of candy (Valentine gift), and, as a consequence, worked herself up to such a degree of excitement that she developed an agonizing night of pain, tightness in the abdomen, nausea, tremors and a "boiling fury" at her boyfriend and later husband, Clem. In other words, she disturbed the peace of her inner organs and the harmony of her marital life because of–a box of candy. At the time of the incident, Annette assures us, she had not yet gone through the process of Recovery training and did not know the "difference between important things and matters that are trivial." Some years later, she had a similar experience but behaved in accord with Recovery principles, controlling temper and refusing to sacrifice inner and outer peace to–a box of candy. "At that moment," Annette commented, "I realized how I had changed." But does it take the cumbrous machinery of Recovery training to make a person recognize the difference between trivial matters and important values, between the relative insignificance of a Valentine gift and the supreme relevance of individual well-being and marital happiness?

To make this distinction requires nothing more than a modicum of intelligence. From what we know about Annette today, she must have had a generous amount of that commodity even before she joined Recovery. And if she insists that she has changed, the change cannot refer to her intellectual powers but rather to her sense of values. What Annette learned in Recovery, and what all my patients are expected to learn there, is to approach things with a proper set of valuations. It is your table of valuations which tells you what is important or trivial, what is essential and what insignificant. In her pre-Recovery days, Annette's table of valuations was in a muddle, contradictory, jumbled, confused. Today, it is solid, stable, balanced. And if this is so, Annette must have changed, indeed.

You may object to my manner of simplifying and distorting the story of the Valentine gift. The meaning of that gift is by no means exhausted by calling it a box of candy. As a Valentine gift, it was meant to be a token of affection and attention. As such, it represented a value, and if Annette felt hurt and provoked because that valuable object was denied her, is it fair to charge her with a poor sense of values? Another question may be properly asked: two years after the first incident, another Valentine came around, and Annette's husband, Clem, arrived home without offering a gift. On that occasion, Annette raised no fuss about Clem's seeming lack of attention and affection. Due to her Recovery training, she claims, she now realized that a box of candy was a triviality. But attention and affection can hardly be called trivialities. Was Annette's sense of values now blunted? Was it blunted precisely by that much vaunted thing we call Recovery training? You see here that it is by no means easy to manipulate the sense of values.

Briefly, a thing is valuable if it promotes inner peace leading to contentment, well-being and self-respect; or, if it advances the cause of outer peace, resulting in adjustment to family, friends, neighbors, co-workers. If your main aim is to secure peace, you are a realist. Then, the attainment of inner and outer peace is your supreme value. Unfortunately, if life is nothing but peaceful, it is apt to acquire a note of drabness and monotony, a quality of dull routine with a conspicuous lack of variety and novelty. People are likely to be bored by an existence that is gently flowing along in its unruffled course with little change and newness. Many people crave activities which are flavored and spiced. They want a measure of excitement, stimulation, adventure. They prefer the thrill of "dangerous living" to a peaceful, well settled and thoroughly ordered daily round. To them, mere peace is deadening, flat, colorless and lifeless while excitement, thrill and adventure are vitalizing, sparkling and energizing.

To many men and women, the supreme value is that which is interesting, agitating, stirring. If they are romantic, they want to be stirred by emotion; if they are intellectualists, they prefer the thrill of bold views and daring thoughts. Summing up: The realist strives for peace, the romanto-intellectualist for thrill and excitement. Peace, order and balance are the supreme values of the one; thrilling excitement, variety and adventure, those of the other. Unfortunately, many persons prefer romanto-intellectualist excitement to realistic peace.

I shall admit that excitement, producing thrills, is the spice of life. But it is not life. It is merely its spice. If spices are added to food, they contribute nothing to its value as nourishment. They merely make the food more tasty and palatable, more appetizing and desirable. But mark here that taste and palatability, appetite and desirability are highly personal and subjective. What is tasty to me may not at all suit your taste; what whets my appetite may blunt yours. My palate may be tempted by what yours is repelled; my desires may run to things which yours shun. Food is in a different class. You may dispense with spices altogether, but you cannot eliminate food from your life any more than I can. In other words: food is an *objective need*, spices are *subjective wants*. Returning to our original subject, we may conclude that peace is the food of life, a value and objective need, while excitement is merely the spice and thrill of life, a desirability (not a value) and nothing but a subjective want.

I said that peace is a supreme value. This implies the existence of lesser and lower values. Such lower values are affection and attention; conversation and conviviality; joy and entertainment. They go by the name of *mental comforts*. Another series of lower values is concerned with the various desires for physical recreation, with the stimulation of food and drinks, with the effort to ease the exactions of the daily routine, and with the craving for attractiveness in point of personal appearance and personal property. These go by the name of *physical comforts*. Both the thrills of excitement and comforts of the lower values are legitimate pursuits if cultivated in moderation. However, if they clash with the aims and needs of the supreme value of peace, they must be suppressed or checked or controlled. To know which thrills to tolerate and which comforts to admit within one's scheme of life requires a delicately balanced sense of values. The sense of values is not born with you; it must be acquired through training. The one to train you is your leader. It may be parents, teachers, ministers or anyone who knows the distinction between values, on the one hand, and thrills and comforts on the other. For the nervous patient, the proper source for leadership is his physician.

My role as a leader of nervous patients is difficult and, in a sense, embarrassing. My patients suffer agonies of discomfort and torture. Hence, they desire quick or immediate relief. This is their subjective want. It is legitimate and should be granted if possible. Unfortunately, a *quick relief,* even if it could be secured, is not a *lasting cure.* As your physician, I must insist on the final cure because it alone will restore your health. Relief is mere comfort while health is a value. Health returns you to a useful and valuable life in family and community. Relief does nothing of the kind. I should like to relieve your discomfort, but my main endeavor is to regain for you the value of sustained mental health.

There is another disturbing element in my function as a leader to my patients. Handicapped by the torments of suffering, they are barred from an active social and occupational life. Their existence is, therefore, deprived of the excitements and thrills of stimulating experience, of accomplishment and self-respect. Their daily round is carried on in an emotional void, in an atmosphere of drabness and boredom. In order to fill the void and to escape the boredom, they want excitement. And if they cannot secure it in routine channels, they hunt for it in devious paths, in endless complaints, in all kinds of devices for attention-getting, in tantrums and tempers. That these excitements are wants and not needs is obvious. Even these excitements might sometimes have a proper claim to toleration. But as your leader, I have the embarrassing obligation to emphasize needs in preference to wants.

We shall now be in a better position to understand the meaning of the incident in which Annette disturbed her inner peace through symptoms and her outer peace through a clash with her fiance. The missing Valentine gift meant to her a token of affection (mental comfort) and the anticipation of a surprise (thrill). When the expected comfort and thrill were denied her, Annette threw a tantrum and jeopardized the values of health and marriage. With this, she displayed a tendency to favor subjective wants in preference to objective needs. But endowed with a good native intellect, it should have been easy for Annette to reason that needs are more important than wants, and that peace is more essential than thrills and comforts. Why did her intellect fail her?

The answer is that a person's reasoning is powerfully influenced by the values cultivated in his group. And our contemporary group has placed a preposterous valuation on romanto-intellectual wants to the detriment of realistic needs. This statement does not require detailed exposition. All you have to do is to inspect the system of education as practiced in our schools and colleges and you will realize that present-day teaching has the almost exclusive ambition to cater to the student's want of mental and physical comfort, and to pay far less attention to his need for training and discipline. That the modern home has abandoned the effort to train and discipline children is too well known to call for special mention. The average parent of today, encouraged by popular philosophies and psychologies, gives his youngsters ample freedom to express their individualistic wants and to ignore the needs for group control and group discipline. If I add that the newspaper headlines, comic strips, radio, movies and television fairly vie with one another in their sordid occupations to cater to the comforts and thrills of their readers, listeners and viewers, I have about completed the circle of the sinister influences which today pervert the tastes and corrupt the valuations of children and adults alike. Our modern media of "education" extol, knowingly or unwittingly, the superiority of wants over needs and the priority of thrills and comforts over discipline and values.

Annette, in her pre-Recovery days, could not possibly escape the overpowering pressure of these organs of public opinion and, from them, imbibed the pernicious contemporary philosophy which favors subjective wants and scorns the value of objective needs. This modern philosophy was largely responsible for her ailment and her torturing symptoms and might have wrecked her marriage had not Recovery intervened and made her revise her faulty sense of values.

CHAPTER TWENTY-THREE

The Unconvincing
Complaint

The panel discussed the subject of "Helplessness Is Not Hopelessness," taken from the October 1946 issue of the *Recovery Journal*.* Caroline mentioned a recent experience in a department store. Approaching the elevator, she was preoccupied with her inner difficulties, and instead of pressing the elevator button, she pulled a light switch. The store section went dark. "I immediately realized my mistake, felt tense and trembled. But then I applied the spotting technique and knew that average people make mistakes of this kind. And if I didn't have the courage to make mistakes in trivial matters, I did not consider myself a person of average, but as one of exceptional, inefficiency. After the spotting, I was calm. . . . In former days, I would have become hysterical, would have thought that surely something was wrong with my mind. I would have suffered awful sensations and would have rushed to the phone, telling my husband that was again proof I couldn't get well and trying to convince him that I was hopeless."

---

*The *Recovery Journal*, edited by Abraham A. Low, M.D., was published from June 1946 to June 1947.

Caroline described in graphic detail the striking contrast between her present and her past behavior. In the past, prior to receiving her Recovery training, she felt helpless and hopeless when a minor mishap occurred. Now she feels helpless for a moment; the idea of hopelessness presents itself in a flash, but she spots it instantly and commands her muscles not to respond to her silly feelings. This is all in accord with the basic principles of Recovery's self-help system and requires little comment. By now it ought to be a commonplace that our patients are trained in Recovery to deny muscular expression to their feelings of fear and anger and to control their temper through the process of spotting.

There was one phrase in Caroline's account that arrested my attention. In the past, she said, she would have rushed to the phone, trying to convince her husband that she was hopeless. A statement of this sort has a weird and uncanny note. It seems to me that were I faced with a hopeless situation, I might either resign myself to my fate or I might make a desperate effort to force the issue or I may pray for deliverance or I might yell for help. But the last thought that could conceivably enter my mind would be to want to convince somebody that, really and truly, I am actually helpless and hopeless. Yet, Caroline, in a condition of seeming despondency, had no other thought but–to be convincing.

If Caroline's ambition was to convince her husband, she must have assumed that he needed convincing, that he doubted her stories of suffering and agony, at the very least, that he thought them exaggerated or colored or twisted. Her stories were what we call "complaints." And if Caroline's case is somehow representative of nervous patients in general, we must conclude that the leading fear in the minds of our patients is that their complaints are doubted, that their sincerity is questioned, in short, that they are not convincing. No wonder they make heroic efforts to compel conviction.

What the patient wants his listener to be convinced of is that he is a helpless victim of his symptoms, that he tries everything within his power to be calm but does not succeed, that he is trapped by his handicap and cannot escape its grip. His tantrums, his bursts of dizziness, his weakness and fatigue, his tremors and palpitations, he thinks, are all of one cast: they are beyond endurance and beyond control. These complaints lack conviction because they are grossly contradicted by the facts of daily observation.

The tantrums have a peculiar quality of being enacted at home only, perhaps also in the physician's office, but never at a concert or at a social gathering. The fatigue, unendurable in the forenoon, disappears miraculously in the late afternoon and in the evening. The headache, "splitting" or "killing," follows immediately upon a domestic squabble and vanishes conveniently when a welcome guest arrives on the scene. Several of my patients were unable to stop a jerk in the arm whenever they were at home but kept it under perfect control when they went shopping in the morning or visiting in the evening. Some had vomiting spells in restaurants but never at home or vice versa. I have seen patients whose throat "locked" exactly at 1:00 P.M. every day. I have seen others who scratched away furiously at an "uncontrollable" itch at home but controlled it perfectly in the presence of friends and strangers. There is the patient who experiences his "unbearable" fatigue on Sundays and holidays only. On weekdays, in the office or factory, he is alert and chipper; or, the girl who vomits in the morning only and at home only, never after 9 A.M. and never outside the home; or, the woman who is nauseated in the afternoon only after the husband returns from work. On Sundays, the nausea persists all day, the husband being home all day.

Most suspect of insincerity and most damaging to the patient's reputation is his incurable fondness for monstrously exaggerating the intenseness of his symptoms. If month after month and year after year he clamors that he "simply can't stand it," that "if something isn't done immediately" he is "surely going to end it all," that he "can't take it any longer," and that today he is "positively at the end of his rope"; if these hackneyed phrases are repeated monotonously, spell after spell and tantrum after tantrum, the relatives cannot fail to realize how well the patient "can stand it," how little he is inclined to "end it all" and how the rope has a mysterious way of lengthening without reaching its end. The threats are then ignored and the alarms treated with contemptuous indifference. There is no point multiplying these examples, although it would be easy for me to cull additional hundreds or thousands from my records. They all tell the same story: the nervous symptom is not convincing, and if the nervous patient wants to be believed, he must make it his supreme goal to compel conviction. That's what Caroline did. In a panic which seemed to shake her with elemental force, she did not cry for help but thought of one thing only: to convince her husband that her plight was beyond remedy.

That the patient's complaint sounds unconvincing to the relatives is a calamity. But that calamity turns into outright tragedy if the patient is unable to convince himself. And conviction is denied him irrevocably. The complaint may be a frequency of urination which "forces" him to run to the bathroom every five minutes. "That surely is something I cannot stop," he exclaims or thinks. Then he sits through a show or card game for solid three or four hours without even a passing thought to his otherwise "uncontrollable" bladder trouble. How can he possibly believe his own doctrine of helplessness if a mere card game helps him check his trouble? Another complaint may be that of "unbearable" pressure in the head. "Clearly, that is out of my control," the patient insists. When questioned, he admits that the pressure is absent when he is in his office, "but once I step out, I have it."

Or take the case of the mother who yells at her own children incessantly because they are "intolerably" noisy. With the neighbor's children, she is a paragon of charm and sweetness in spite of their equally "intolerable" loud and boisterous behavior. That mother cannot, by any twist of logic, make herself believe that her temper is out of control. The ease with which she controls it with the neighbor's children stamps her complaint as insincere and renders it unconvincing. Experiences of this kind admit of one conclusion only: the patient has good control but fails to practice it under certain conditions. Fully aware of his ability to help himself, he is unable to believe his own protestations of helplessness. And trying to convince his relatives, his efforts are stymied by his own lack of conviction.

If a person is unable to believe himself, he loses or weakens his *self-respect*. If he is unable to make others believe him, he loses or weakens their respect for him, that is, he ruins or impairs his *reputation*. It is difficult to live without proper self-respect. But life becomes an almost unbearable affliction if both self-respect and reputation are wanting or markedly defective. From this vantage point, it is easy to understand the tragic plight of the long-term nervous patient. After years of futile and ludicrous complaining, his self-respect is in tatters and his reputation torn to shreds. He could restore both should he decide resolutely to give up his plaints and lamentations. If he fails to do that, he is doomed to lead a life of indignity and self-contempt, a life of stigmatization and social isolation.

An existence of this kind is possible only if somehow, by hook or by crook, the illusion of uncontrollability is maintained and fortified against all evidence to the contrary. The doctrine of helplessness and hopelessness must then be hammered unceasingly and unrelentingly into the patient's own head (to save his self-respect) and into the heads of the relatives (to save his reputation). Hence, the imperative urge to carry on a veritable crusade of convincing, that is, complaining. The proudest achievement which Recovery can claim is the thoroughness with which it has purged its members of their pernicious habits of wailing and lamenting. Trained in the techniques of spotting and commanding their muscles, our patients have ceased complaining and are now convincing.

CHAPTER TWENTY-FOUR

Partial Views and Total Viewpoint

Loraine reported her recent setback. She had been well for the past several months but suddenly got back her fears of riding alone on elevated trains and subways. She suffered the "most awful" palpitations, sweats and panics when she took rides. Before long, she employed the Recovery techniques of spotting fears and using muscles and controlled her symptoms, manipulating rides without difficulty. But in spite of all her pluck and determination, she was unable to relax. She was tense and restless and thoroughly disgusted with herself. She then decided that what was really wrong with her was that she was not sufficiently busy. So she increased her average quota of shows, bowling, swimming and sundry other recreational activities. "I needed something stimulating," she said, "so I wouldn't think of myself all the time. . . ."

Loraine wanted stimulation, which indicates that she was bored. Being bored, she was disgusted with her Self. And in order to escape boredom and Self-disgust, she decided she had to avoid thinking of her Self "all the time." But it seems to me that to think of one's Self ought to be a most stimulating occupation. Why was it irritating and disgusting to Loraine?

To be bored means to be disinterested. You cannot experience boredom while you read an interesting story or attend an interesting show or take part in an interesting conversation. In all these instances, your interest is held, engaged, attracted. If the interest deepens, you are absorbed, engrossed, fascinated, perhaps enraptured. In a situation of this kind, most or all of your attention is directed toward the object which interests or fascinates you. But once the interest wanes or the fascination lifts, your attention reverts to your Self and is no longer diverted from it. Now you are alone with your Self, not distracted from it but attracted to it. And whether your Self bores or interests you depends on the view you take of it. Clearly, Loraine viewed her Self as something that could not engross her interest, as something that bored her, as something devoid of fascination and stimulation, perhaps as something odious, repelling and loathsome. Beholding that Self which she thought of as detestable and hateful, she became "tense and restless and thoroughly disgusted." No wonder she "needed something stimulating." Her own Self was "disgusting" and irritating.

I know Loraine; I know her husband, mother and sister; I know her home life and her social activities, her character and tastes. With all this intimate knowledge of her conduct, history and circumstances, I cannot share even a fraction of the disastrous view she takes of her Self. To my view, her Self is of good or fair average; to her own view, it is of the poorest quality, not fit to be looked at, not suitable to be left alone with. What precisely makes our views clash so radically?

If you look at an object, let me say a table, you place yourself at a certain point and take your view from there. This is *your point of view* or your *viewpoint*. If the point from which you observe the table is too distant, you will miss many details. Your viewpoint will then furnish you with a *general view* only. If the point on which you take your stand is too close, you will miss the general features of outline, shape and style. Your viewpoint will then provide you with a *particular view* only. The correct view is the one which combines both the particular and general views. This is the *total view*. Whether your view of an object is more particular or more general, in either case, it is a *partial view* only. The total view must combine both particular and general views.

The object which Loraine viewed was her Self. She noticed her tenseness and restlessness and concluded that her Self was "disgusting." She knew what was "really wrong" with it; it "needed stimulation." With this, she diagnosed the condition and prescribed the cure. If so, her viewpoint was that she (her Self) was a competent diagnostician and efficient healer. She claimed expert knowledge and made a show of authority, that is, she paraded her Self as important, highly informed and superior. You, my patients, know that this is what I call the *romanto-intellectualist attitude.*

If Loraine held the view that her Self had the qualities of excellence and superiority, how could she, at the same time, subscribe to the very opposite view that it was disgusting? This is clearly a contradiction which you will not understand unless you consider what I told you about the difference between particular and general viewpoints. If you look into yourself, you will discover within you many features which are excellent, superior and exceptional. At times, you displayed unusual courage, at other times there was an act of singular loyalty or a performance of superior skill or an exhibit of extraordinary wisdom. If you merely view these isolated instances of your behavior (particular viewpoint), you can easily form the opinion that yours is an exceptional Self.

But if you review the broad lines of your past development, you are likely to find a great deal of misdirected effort, of goals missed and purposes frustrated. Judged in the light of this general viewpoint, your record may appear as one of mediocrity and incapacity in which the instances of failure crowd out those of accomplishment. Your particular viewpoint, focusing the gaze on scattered triumphs, gives you the impression of an exalted and superior Self; but the general viewpoint, surveying the larger field of your past endeavor, offers you the picture of failure and futility and may make you feel "disgusted."

I told you that my view of Loraine's life was decidedly more favorable than was her own. I knew many details of her life. I knew particular occasions when her conduct had been anything but a credit to her. I was acquainted with her tantrums, her temperamental explosions, her craving for attention, her stubbornness and vanity. This was the particular view I had taken of her behavior. Aside from this, I had studied the various aspects of her past history, and my verdict was that it represented a crazy-quilt of good intentions and poor execution, of lofty aspirations and petty performance. This was the general viewpoint I had of her. But in reviewing her record, I judged her neither by the particular nor by the general viewpoint. Instead, I applied the total view. And surveying the totality of her experience, I reached the conclusion that it had the average quality of a fumbling, erring and straying existence. But no matter how deplorable was her fumbling, how distressing her erring and how disconcerting her straying, it was all average. Having drawn this conclusion, I formed the *average viewpoint* which is based on common sense and ought to be the *common viewpoint* held by everybody.

In order to gain a full understanding of this average viewpoint, you will have to realize that the life of the average person is punctuated by precisely the features which were characteristic of Loraine's Self: temper, attention-hunting, stubbornness and vanity. Being average, these features cannot, by the wildest stretch of the imagination, be called degrading or disgraceful or "disgusting." If Loraine applied precisely these terms to her Self, I conclude that her philosophy was that of exceptionality. She had not yet absorbed the Recovery philosophy of averageness and condemned when she could have condoned, accused when she might have excused.

You see here that the total view is closely associated with the *average view*. With the average view to guide you,

you will be able to behold the deficiencies of your Self and will judge them as average failings. They will not strike you with terror; hence, you will not be tense. Being reconciled to them, you will not try frantically to run away from your Self; hence, you will not be restless. And losing your tenseness and restlessness, you will be relaxed and will enjoy your Self instead of being "disgusted" with it and bored by it. The average view will teach you to tolerate your Self. Moreover, viewing your own Self as average and acceptable, you will give the same rating to the Selves of others; hence, you will practice tolerance toward them. And being tolerant of the actions of others, you will not become angry at or provoked by them, hence, you will have little or no temper.

No doubt, the average viewpoint, which is essentially the total view of life, has much to recommend it. If my patients could be induced to adopt it energetically and wholeheartedly, temper, restlessness, tenseness and Self-disgust would be reduced to average levels, and symptoms would not develop into panics and vicious cycles. You will now understand why I stress so persistently the importance of thinking and feeling in terms of averageness. What I have in mind is not a high-sounding philosophy but such down-to-earth matters as symptoms, afflictions and torture.

My patients have the exasperating habit of looking at their symptoms with the partial viewpoint mainly or exclusively. They notice a fatigue sensation and rush to the particular view that their body is exhausted and ready to collapse. They notice that their attention wanders, that their concentration lags, or that on a particular occasion their memory fails them, and infer that their mind is unhinged. In all these instances, they observe particulars and base on them a particular viewpoint of doom and disaster. At times, they resort to a generalizing viewpoint. They survey the general features of their painful existence, roam across the years of suffering, across their record of frustration and disappointment and exclaim, "What's the use? After these many years, how can I get well?" They shy away, persistently and doggedly, from the total view that their symptoms are of the average variety although more persistent in duration and more resistant to management.

True enough, the resistance and intensity of the symptoms are such that the patient can no longer control them with his own meager resources. But a total view of life could easily tell them that, generally speaking, certain performances of the daily round can be conveniently mastered by the average person while others, more complicated, more intractable, require the services of an expert. If my patients could be made to accept the total viewpoint, moreover, if they were ready to cultivate the common sense of the average viewpoint, suffering and discomfort would be held to a minimum.

Unfortunately, the general trend of modern development has been to disregard, systematically and dogmatically, the total viewpoint. If you listen to our modern forums, you will find there groups of persons discussing issues, presumably in order to settle them. However, what they discussed are their particular views, their own pet notions, their own "true" opinions. The theme moves from one particular argument to another or loses itself in a sea of wild generalizations. This has perhaps always been the case and may not be peculiar to our age.

But what is decidedly peculiar to our age is the advent of popular psychologies. The exponents of these psychological doctrines seldom if ever touch on the total experience of the average individual. Instead, they prefer to give absurd prominence to particular stirrings and strivings, trying to convince you that this particular trend of yours or that isolated disposition is solely and unqualifiedly at the roots of all your ills. With some of these clever coiners of striking and appealing phrases, it is the sex instinct which causes your maladjustment. With others, it is a mysterious thing which they call "collective consciousness." With still others, it is a shallow conception termed "inferiority complex." With all of them, it is invariably *one thing, one trend, one particular item* of your total experience which is supposed to disturb or wreck your total existence.

Loraine, noticing her tenseness and restlessness, jumped to the conclusion that these distressing but innocent items of her experience needed instant and thorough treatment. Had she taken a total view of her past life, she would have realized that tenseness and restlessness had been frequent occurrences in the scheme of her existence and were nothing but average psychological events. But exposed to the defeatist influence of popular philosophies presented to her on screen and stage, in newspaper columns and magazine articles, in lectures and books on popular psychology, she conceived the vague idea that an instinct was running wild or that a "complex" went berserk or that a "conflict" ran amuck, having broken through the barriers of a so-called repression. All these pretentious and bloated terms are the confused stock in trade preached by modern psychologies. They are based on particular, narrow and one-sided views of life and should have no place in the lives of my patients who, in Recovery, are trained to view events and experiences from the total viewpoint of average experience.

CHAPTER TWENTY-FIVE

Business and Games; Effort and Comfort

Lela, on the Saturday panel, spoke of her habit, noticed since early childhood, of correcting mistakes made by people. "We lived in the country, and salesmen came by and stopped at our house. One of them spoke of a certain town and said it was in Wisconsin. I knew this was wrong and ran for the map and showed the man it was Minnesota and not Wisconsin. My father laughed and thought it was cute and did not say a word of disapproval to me. This habit of correcting people gave me plenty of trouble. It made me unpopular. Worse yet, it made me feel irritated if I could not correct people when they made remarks which I thought were wrong. Today I know, of course, that this desire to prove that people are wrong is temper. It means I am right. In Recovery I have learned to spot the habit, and I think I have it under pretty good control. The other day, I stood with a neighbor in front of a yard, and we saw a weed. I asked, 'What is it?' She said, 'Why, it is a ragweed.' I grew up in the country and know ragweeds, and this did not look like any I know. I was about to say, 'It is not a ragweed' but stopped and said, 'Is it?' I was proud of having controlled my impulse and was grateful to Recovery for having trained me to check my temper."

Lela had the habit of correcting people. She loved to show them up as ignorant and to present herself as possessing superior intelligence. This is what you know as the intellectualist variety of temper. You, to whom Lela is no stranger, will not hesitate to call her a kindly person, gentle in disposition, eager to be helpful and anxious to give no offense. If she was endowed with an amiable disposition, why did she, at the same time, display a tendency to be aggressive, to trip up people, to expose them as stupid, uninformed, intellectually inferior? Clearly, the two trends are mutually exclusive, the one cancelling the other, both working at cross-purpose. Lela's friendly disposition created goodwill, but the goodwill thus produced was weakened or dissipated by her disposition to be critical, fault-finding and antagonistic. Which was the "real" Lela? Which was her "real" purpose in life? Was it to win people over with courtesy? Or, was it to repel them with an uncouth manner? The answer is: ordinarily, and as a rule, Lela made it her *business* to make friends. But sometimes, and as an exception, she practiced the *game* of shocking and antagonizing people, thus making enemies. Lela claims that the game of shocking people caused her "plenty of trouble," making her unpopular and giving her a lot of irritation. If so, why did she continue the game? Why did she insist on toying with life instead of strictly tending to its (and her) business?

Life is a business. There is or ought to be time in everybody's routine to play and toy, to amuse himself with games and to divert his attention from the serious aspects of the business of living. Nevertheless, life is not a game; it is a business which must be toiled at and attended to. Its business is to create and maintain values (family, community, education, religion, sociability). The trouble is that values are tender and delicate and easily disturbed. They are likely to be disturbed through destructive forces arising in inner environment (symptoms and temper) or from commotions and convulsions affecting outer environment (strife and dissension between persons and groups). Since strife and dissension usually are the result of temper, we may safely assume that the peace of persons, families or communities is threatened by two elements mainly: symptoms which interfere with inner peace, and temper which obstructs both inner and outer peace. To sum up: life needs inner and outer peace for producing and maintaining values. The factors which endanger peace are symptoms and temper. Life's principal business is, therefore, to reduce both symptoms and temper to a minimum.

If anyone deserves the title of a conscientious, serious-minded person, it is Lela. She is dependable and generous, has firm convictions and a sturdy quality of character. From what I know of her background, there can be no doubt that even in early childhood, she was thoughtful and considerate, courteous and tactful, treating people with respect and careful not to hurt their feelings. With all these features to her credit, she must have taken seriously the business of her life. Why did she, at the same time, trifle and gamble with that same business? The answer is that even people as lovely and desirable as Lela have a tendency, at times, to be serious about games and playful about business. They are particularly apt to be so if the game they are engaged in is that of romanto-intellectualist temper. Ordinarily, Lela is a realist, taking the business of her life seriously. But at times she feels (or used to feel) the itch of romanto-intellectualism, indulging the game of playing with the business of life. And to play with the business of life means to gamble.

If you start a game, you are not obliged to continue it. You may drop it because you don't like it or because it bores you or because luck is against you or because you have as trivial a thing as a headache. Conversely, if you engage in business (job, marriage, the rearing of children, helping a friend, civic activities, club work), you are under obligation to continue it, to see it through, to finish what you have started. Headaches, boredom, dislike, strain are no justification for shirking the duty you have assumed or the commission you have accepted. Games are *personal inclinations;* business is *group obligation.* Games are *pleasures,* business is a *task.* A task may be pleasing, which means that pleasure and task can be combined. But if a game, no matter how pleasurable, interferes with the serious task of a business, the thing to do is to stop the game and to continue the business. Tasks must have unquestioned priority over games. Lela, going through months of Recovery training, imbided this supreme principle of Recovery philosophy that in the business of life, tasks must invariably take precedence over pleasures. In life, even a plain conversation with a neighbor acquires the character of a task. It imposes the obligation to be courteous, to be friendly, to show humility, to create good will, to avoid criticism and intellectual snobbishness (the desire to show superiority).

In commercial business, there is one goal only: to produce income. But businessmen are human, endowed with human desires, whims and inclinations. There is the inclination to take it easy, to go off on a trip, to over-expand, to run up debts because of hastily conceived plans. These inclinations are human stirrings and human strivings and, as such, the direct offsprings of "human nature." It is human and natural to crave an easy life or to long for the amenities of a trip or to take chances with indebtedness. But no matter how human and natural these desires are, they turn into a wild gamble if they clash with the one and only business aim: to produce income.

Getting well is a business. It is emphatically not a game, certainly not a wild gamble. Unfortunately, my patients have the tendency to play and gamble with their health. They give unthinking and wanton precedence to the stirrings of their "human nature" to the detriment of their only legitimate goal: to get well. It is human and natural to want quick relief, to be impatient with the irksome obligation to wait for the final cure; it is understandable and natural to hate the discomfort of laborious and untiring practice, to want to give way to temper, to play for attention, to crave sympathy and to indulge in self-pity, to complain and to work oneself up. But all of this is gambling with the business of getting well. It is the game of giving in to human nature, not the business of health. The one and only goal of the patient must be to regain his mental health. In order to achieve it, the goals and whims and wishes of "human nature" must be held down with ruthless determination.

Games provide relief from strain; they provide diversion, entertainment and relaxation. All of this means comfort. Business is in a different category. At times, it may be conducive to relaxation, diversion and entertainment. But ordinarily it requires toil and strain, patient application and ceaseless exertion. All of this means effort. Games are conducted with the *Will to Comfort;* business is executed with the *Will to Effort.*

Time was when the Will to Effort was systematically cultivated in homes and schools, on farms, in stores and factories. Men and women were trained routinely to expect of life a great deal of effort and a small fraction only of comfort. In the process, they developed a rugged disposition which means: the Will to Bear Discomfort. Unfortunately, the accent is today on comfort, on fun and entertainment, on making things easy and pleasant. With the Will to Comfort scoring heavily over the Will to Effort, people are no longer prepared to endure strain and anxieties and suffering. And when suffering strikes, especially the excruciating suffering of nervous ailments, they expect the cure to be effected with the proverbial ease of a child's play and perhaps in as brief a space of time as the average game may last. This means playing with the illness and converting the business of getting well into a game of trying to secure effortless comfort.

In Recovery, you are taught to approach the business of getting well in the spirit of performing a task and meaning business. The business calls, first and foremost, for labor and exertion and self-control, in other words, for the Will to Effort. A good portion of the effort must be directed toward the business of curbing the romanto-intellectual temper. As you know, it is temper primarily which creates and maintains tenseness, and it is tenseness which creates and maintains nervous symptoms. Lela, having learned in Recovery that temper interferes with the business of getting well, decided to take seriously the principles of Recovery training, to keep a vigilant eye on her temper and to consider health as the supreme task to be accomplished by a patient. She is not well yet but is certain to obtain her final cure if she continues as doggedly as she has done to pursue the serious business of realistic health and to avoid the frisky game of romanto-intellectualist comfort. With the Will to Effort effectively curbing her Will to Comfort, she is bound to attain her ultimate goal: to get well.

CHAPTER TWENTY-SIX

Interpretations and Conclusions

Ada recalled the agonies she suffered for many years when at times her throat suddenly "locked." "The locking happened," she said, "when I became irritated, when my feelings were hurt, or when I became temperamental. I was sure I had a growth in the throat because how could an irritation or upset produce that awful pressure I felt in that spot? When the locking took place, I would jump from my seat, my heart would pound, and I broke into a cold sweat, and I shook with tremors, and I was sure I was choking to death. My brother lives with us, and when he was present, he would grab me and pound me and hit me on the back as one would revive somebody who is choking. If that didn't help, as it usually didn't, he would drag me on the back porch and continued the pounding there, and I made a terrible noise, and the neighbors would rush out of their apartments to help. Because of these panics, I developed all kind of fears. For instance, I was afraid to take orange juice because the pulp might stick in my throat. I was of course afraid of being alone at home because I might get a spell and nobody around to help me. I was also afraid to go out on the street or visit people because I might be seen in a spell.

"After I joined Recovery, the spells got less and less, but sometimes I have them yet. Not so long ago, I was sitting at the table reading a newspaper when I picked up an apple and took a bite. Suddenly, the throat locked. I got scared and felt like smothering. My brother ran over to pound me, but I motioned him not to. I spotted the spell as a sensation and knew it was distress but no danger. So I got up and walked to the kitchen, and when my brother reached me and saw that I had gotten my breath, he said, 'Why, I can't believe it. How did you manage to stop the choking? I swear it did not last more than thirty seconds.' I tried to explain and said something about spotting, but he did not seem to understand. Finally he said, 'I don't understand what you folks talk about in Recovery. But it certainly works.'"

Ada stated explicitly that her throat "locked" when she was irritated or when her feelings were hurt or when she was in temper. This can have one meaning only, namely, that the locking was caused by emotions, frustrations and mental upsets. Receiving this information, I was certain that Ada considered her trouble as nervous and psychological and not as organic and physical. If this is so, you will realize how amazed I was to hear Ada continue: "I was sure I had a growth in the throat because how could an irritation or upset produce that awful pressure I felt in that spot?" In the first pronouncement, the condition was declared to be psychological and nothing else; in the second, it was said to be physical and nothing else. How is it that Ada, usually possessed of clear thinking and precise expression, launched out today into such a flagrant contradiction? Did her customary logic fail her? Did her mind "lock?"

What Ada actually did was this: She noticed or *thought* that her throat tightened. The tightening was experienced or *felt* by her as a choking which stifled speech and impaired breathing. What she thus thought and felt produced a panic which gave rise to distressing *sensations* (palpitations, tremors, sweats) and produced the *impulse* to run for life ("I jumped from my seat"). All of this means that when the locking happened, Ada made, in a flash, sundry *observations* about her inner experiences, cataloguing them in her mind as a varied assortment of thoughts, feelings, sensations and impulses. She noticed further that whenever the locking occurred, it was preceded by irritations, frustrations and temper. From this series of observations, she drew two *conclusions:* (1) the cause was psychological, (2) the cause was physical. This process of drawing two contradictory conclusions from one and the same set of observations we call *confusion.*

When Ada, with her throat "locked," made observations and drew conclusions, she practiced what is called the *process of thinking.* This process is an art based on a technique and governed by rules. The technique is that of dependable observation; the rules are those of valid conclusion. When my patients get ready to employ their thinking process for reporting or studying their symptoms, they almost invariably bungle the observations and jumble the conclusions. That happened in Ada's case when she observed a tightening and concluded that it was a "locking." The throat is a tube which serves the purpose of letting the food pass through the esophagus and the air through the larynx. Nervous patients experience frequently a tightening in this locality. But it is merely a tightening, perhaps not even a narrowing of the passageway, certainly not a complete closing or "locking."

Had Ada, in her pre-Recovery days, been trained in the technique of making pertinent observations, she could have noticed that air circulated freely and food traveled unhampered through the tube even if the throat was "locked." She never had an opportunity to observe an actual stoppage or occlusion or obstruction. What she reported on the panel demonstrates conclusively that she suffered no such thing as a "locked" throat. On her own accounting, when her brother dragged her out on the porch, she "made a terrible noise, and the neighbors rushed out of their apartments to help." That "terrible noise" assuredly required a great deal of air. How did Ada manage to push through her "locked" throat a quantity of air sufficient to produce a "terrible noise?" Clearly, her thinking process had acquired the habit of rushing into hasty observations and jumping to shaky conclusions.

If observations are made and conclusions drawn with regard to symptoms, the process is called the *art of making a diagnosis.* That this art is difficult, utterly complex and reserved for thoroughly trained persons only is generally accepted. But my patients ignore what everybody knows, and when they observe a symptom, they promptly rush to supply a diagnosis of their own. They notice a pain in the chest and conclude it means a weak heart. They feel a pressure in the head and "know" it is a tumor. A nervous bladder drives them into endless journeys to the bathroom, and "what else can that be but a kidney disease?" Some of my patients discovered that on some days, they had two evacuations instead of one, soft but not at all "running," and on the basis of that flimsy observation, they concluded it was a "running bowel" or a "diarrhea" or a "colitis." Experiencing a pulling sensation in the neck, my patients are apt to conclude that the pulling "must be done" by a growth, at the very least by a swollen gland. Many of them delight in the practice of "observing" themselves in an obliging mirror. The mirror invariably tells them that their features are drawn and haggard, that the eyes have no luster, that the tongue is coated. The diagnostic inference is that "there must be something wrong somewhere. Don't you think so?" They paw over the entire expanse of their bodies, find a swelling in the leg, flabbiness in the arms, glands in the neck, a quickened pulse in the wrist and, forthwith, indulge in a riot of grisly diagnoses.

Their theory is that anybody who is not an outright moron knows how to use the thinking process, and that for a person of "normal" intelligence it is "no trick" to make reliable observations and draw valid conclusions. In this, they display an enormous contempt for the complexity of the techniques and rules of solid thinking. Putting it differently, my patients approach their symptoms with the philosophy of shallow intellectualism, rushing headlong into uncritical observations and jumping recklessly to immature conclusions. It is the particular mark of the petty intellectual that he has a boundless disrespect for the pitfalls which beset the utterly complicated process of correct thinking. He is smart, and his intellect, he is convinced, has a native sharpness and quickness. So why bother about clumsy techniques and cumbersome rules?

Observations are of two kinds. You observe either the world outside you (with your senses) or the world within you (through introspection). The one furnishes outer experience, the other inner experience. Suppose you meet a man on the street and observe, through your senses, that he is walking at a leisurely pace, carrying a briefcase and looking straight in front of him. You advance toward him, offer a friendly greeting, and he responds with a smile and the assurance that he is glad to see you. There is hardly any possibility of bungling this series of outer observations. Everybody whose eyes and ears are not damaged by disease or injury is qualified to make them without previous training in technique and rules.

The difficulty begins, however, the moment you go beyond the domain of *observation* and pass into the area of *interpretation.* After observing the smile on the man's face, you may ask yourself, for instance, what precisely that smile means. It may mean warmth of feeling and joy of seeing you. The proper interpretation, then, would be fellowship, friendship, good will. Or, it may mean nothing more than conventional politeness; that would be indifference. If the smile is associated with strained features, the proper interpretation might be annoyance or resentment of your intruding. And finally, the smile may have an expression of irony or sarcasm. In that case, the proper label would be haughtiness, disrespect and perhaps hostility.

This simple example indicates that the pitfalls of thinking reside in interpretation rather than observation. The trouble is that once you have made an observation, you feel an imperative urge to interpret it. And if interpretation is difficult even in outer observations, the attempt to apply it to inner experiences increases the obstacles to such an extent that only a mind trained in the techniques and rules of the thinking process can be expected to conquer them. When Ada experienced the tightening in her throat, her observation played on an inner experience. Had she merely stated that she felt a tightness, hers would have been a plain observation, secured through introspection. Like everybody, Ada was in a position to make such introspective observations. But when she interpreted the sensation as one which "locked" her throat and stopped the free flow of air, she lacked the qualification to employ this very difficult part of the thinking process. After reaching her dismal interpretation, she had no choice but to conclude that something terrible had happened and that a grave emergency was set going. The result was a panic, with the attendant vicious cycle and the unavoidable commotion and confusion.

While doing her disastrous piece of interpreting and concluding, Ada was not aware of the fact that in doing so, she had the temerity to engage in the subtle art of diagnosis. To her untutored perception, this was merely the innocent act of "thinking about" her symptoms. And Ada, being a child of this most modern of all ages, had, on many occasions, been exposed to the contemporary slogan that a grownup person has not only the right but the solemn duty to "do her own thinking." But I am not at all interested in the philosophical profundities of this so horribly advanced age of ours, and whether my patients have the right or duty to "think for themselves" is a question which concerns me not in the least. My supreme and only duty is to relieve my patients of their agonies. And if their panics and vicious cycles result from their faulty use of the thinking process, I shall advise them to throw overboard the rubbish of modern slogans and let me do their thinking in the matter of interpreting and concluding with regard to symptoms.

My thinking process has had the benefit of many years of thorough training and disciplining, and my thinking about symptoms is not likely to rush into interpretations and jump to conclusions. What you, my patients, have to do is to let me, your physician, teach you how to exercise your thinking process when you attempt to apply it to your symptoms. This is what I have described as "spotting." Spotting means for you to be perpetually on guard against your inveterate tendency to "do your own thinking" when observing a symptom and its accompanying temperamental reaction. It means a ruthless determination to eliminate self-diagnosing and thus to do away with panics, vicious cycles and endless horrors of agony. Ada reported an instance in which the resort to spotting was almost inhumanly difficult. It was of such stupendous difficulty, that her brother refused to believe that it could be done. But even that skeptical brother had to admit that "it certainly works."

CHAPTER TWENTY-SEVEN

Symptoms, Fellowship and Leadership

In a recent panel discussion on Imagination, Temper and Symptoms, taken from the December 1946 issue of the *Recovery Journal*,* Kenneth made the significant statement: "I was always troubled with self-consciousness, and down at work about four months ago, some of the girls at the office were laughing and joking, and for some reason I decided they were laughing at me. I got very tense about it, and my eyes got blurred, and my throat got choked, and the first thing I decided was that Recovery was no good, and it did not help me, and I was going to drop it. . . . I was so disturbed, that I decided it would be better to join the army again. I had no symptoms there. . . ."

Listening to the panel discussion, I was struck by Kenneth's remark, and attempting a hurried analysis, I noticed three main points in his utterance: (1) Kenneth traced his self-consciousness, and I may add, his symptoms, back to early childhood; (2) his self-consciousness has made him so sensitive that the innocent giggling of bantering girls was likely to exasperate him; (3) while he was in the army, he lost his self-

---

*The *Recovery Journal*, edited by Abraham A. Low, M.D., was published from June 1946 to June 1947.

consciousness and, with it, his morbid sensitiveness and his symptoms.

Let me first tell you that many of my patients, concealing their past record of a nervous or mental ailment, enlisted in the armed services. They all seem ready to subscribe to Kenneth's thesis that life in the army provided a mysterious tonic for jaded nerves and that the supposedly peaceful routine of civilian existence meant constant grating and grinding for the same nerves that relaxed so beautifully in barracks, dugouts, under air bombardments and artillery barrages. While in the army, close to four years in the Pacific theatre, Kenneth had his due share of privation: jungle, insects, heat, humidity, monotony, worry about an uncertain future, threat to life aplenty and menace of dreadful disease galore. But he felt relaxed and secure all the time. There was incessant danger to his *physical person*. But his *social personality* was protected and sheltered. What was it that secured this protection for the personality of the soldier while he was in the army? Which was that factor in military life that made the nervous patient feel that he was basically sheltered?

The answer is this: in the army, there is *fellowship* and *leadership*. The fellows make for contentment and relaxation; the leaders supply certainty and assurance. A person who is accepted as a fellow in his group and enjoys the leadership of men endowed with stability of character and steadfastness of purpose, feels secure and loses his sensitiveness. If he is a nervous patient, he also loses his symptoms.

If this is true, it will be important to know why the singular benefits of fellowship and leadership are so stubbornly denied our group of nervous patients. What is a fellow? What is a leader?

A fellow is a person who shares your activities, habits, tastes. He may also share your views and beliefs. If he does not, he respects them. A leader does not have to share your life. His part is to tell you what to do and how to do it. He gives you plans, instructions and directions. They are based on principles, standards and values. Suppose the set of habits and tastes which you shared with your fellow comprised in the main such joint activities as visiting one another, going to shows together, bowling and swimming. All of a sudden, the fellow conceives a dislike for sports and shows, preferring races, card games and taverns. Unless you follow suit and adopt the same interests and tastes, fellowship will be disrupted. We conclude that *fellowship rests on stability of habits.*

Consider now the matter of leadership. A leader guides your conduct by means of the principles, standards and values which he imparts to you. He gives you the policies and patterns for your daily activities and sets the goals for you to aim at. Suppose now that the men to whom you look for leadership change their principles, standards and values as it may suit them, a few or many times in succession; the policies which guided you and the goals you aimed at will become shifting, capricious and whimsical. And without stable principles, firm policies and steady goals, there is no leadership. We conclude that *leadership rests on stability of principle and policy.*

Let me be brief now. In the army, habits and tastes hardly change, and principle and policy remain almost unvarying. Fellowship and leadership are there founded on the rock of stability. Caprice, whim, passion for frequent changes have little or no place in its rules and patterns. The physical person of the soldier is perpetually confronted with novel and perilous situations, with incessant shifts and changes. But his personality is thoroughly stabilized by the twin influences of the fellow's adherence to stable habits and the leader's commitment to firm policies. In such a moral climate, the nervous patient finds security and relaxation. His person is in continuous danger, but his personality is solidly sheltered.

It is the curse of our modern life that stability of habits has become impossible. Everything around us is in constant flux. We have drifted into a mode of life in which change, under the guise of "progress," has been turned into an ideal. Home life is continually changing. Moving from one district to the other has become a mania. Furniture that served its purpose last year is no longer wanted the coming year.

Automobiles are traded in, although they may be in working condition, just because a "new" model is wanted. We have adopted the pernicious philosophy that the "new" is desirable and the "old" obnoxious. Stable tastes and habits are impossible under a system of this kind, which glorifies everything that has no other distinction than its novelty and scorns the value of things for no other reason than that they are no longer modern. Fellowship is dying or withering under the impact of a system which idolizes novelty and modernity.

If we "moderns" contented ourselves with merely changing furniture, homes and automobiles, the threat to our personalities would be serious enough because novelty hunting interferes with fellowship. Far more fatal, however, is our modern craving for scrapping time-honored principles and exchanging them for recent "advanced" and "progressive" patterns of life. What I refer to here is our tendency to discard, with a callous ruthlessness, well established systems of education, to rush at "reforms" with unholy haste, to display a contemptuous attitude and outright ridicule for ancestral standards, to condemn the past as "Victorian" and to extol present-day endeavors as the inspiration of "advanced thought." All of this digs the grave for principle and values and standards. It casts stability of policy into discard and establishes the prerogative of caprice, whim and erratic impulsiveness. And with caprice, whim and impulsiveness to guide our action, there can be no firm policy. And without settled policy, there can be no leadership. And without leadership, the nervous patient is bound to be victimized by the sense of insecurity, tenseness, self-consciousness and symptoms.

No wonder Kenneth felt at home in the army and helpless and lonesome after he returned to his home community. In the army, he had fellows and leaders. At home, he was thrust into a stream of life whose stabilizing influence had yielded to the disintegrating effect of novelty and modernity.

Kenneth, noticing the reappearance of symptoms, felt desperate and despaired even of Recovery. But he is here among us today, and his mere presence, apart from his participation in the panel, testifies to his abiding faith in the Recovery system. He knows that in Recovery there is stability of habits, hence, fellowship, and stability of principle, hence, leadership.

Chapter Twenty-eight

Leadership Versus Information

Gertrude, during a Saturday panel, spoke of her condition prior to joining Recovery. "My main symptom," she said, "was the fear of death. I had palpitations, and felt weak, and could hardly eat and lost weight, and I was sure I was just dying away. Dr. Low asked me whether I was afraid of riding in an automobile, and I told him it didn't mean anything to me to race 60 or 70 miles an hour. And he said, 'Well, one thing is sure, you are not afraid of death in an automobile accident.' That reminded me that I did other things which were dangerous, but I didn't fear them. I wasn't scared at all when I went on high rides in Riverview Park. And where I live, I have to pass three cemeteries every day to get to where I work. And in the evenings, coming back from work, I pass the three cemeteries again, frequently late at night. That doesn't frighten me a bit.

"When I told Dr. Low all of these things, he said, 'What you are afraid of are your own thoughts and impulses and sensations. You don't fear physical death.' That was hard for me to understand, and I don't know whether I understand it much better today. But one thing is sure: I have learned to spot my fear as distressing but not dangerous. And since

I don't attach the idea of danger to my palpitations, they bother me only once in a while. And when I have them, they go as fast as they come."

Gertrude was given an explanation about the nature of her fear and did not understand. Then she was given instructions about spotting her inner experiences, and she promptly learned to practice a rule and to dispose of symptoms. My theoretical explanations failed, but my practical directions succeeded. When I offered explanations, I was a teacher; when I gave directions, I functioned as a leader. Gertrude reacted poorly to my teaching but responded magnificently to my leadership.

What I tried to teach Gertrude was the simple fact that what appears to be an outer danger may be an inner threat. There is nothing mysterious or obscure about a statement of this kind. It is plain and simple and ought to be grasped without difficulty. Why was Gertrude unable to understand this obvious and not at all complex explanation? As I see it, the substance of my teaching was clear in language and transparent in meaning. It certainly had greater clarity than the rather complex directions I gave her when I acted as leader. As such, I told her to employ our spotting techniques. Assuredly, the principles of spotting are far more difficult to manipulate than a simple sentence about inner and outer dangers. And if Gertrude is still unable, even today, to understand my teaching but ready to accept my leadership, I suspect that it is not so much a matter of understanding but rather one of preference. Whether she knows it or not, the fact is she prefers dynamic leadership to pale and dry teaching.

I wish that all my patients shared Gertrude's preference for leadership. Then, I could tell them what to do in order to control their temperamental leanings, how to curb their romanticisms and intellectualisms, how to check their sabotaging trends and how to eliminate their fondness for self-diagnosing. If that came to pass, suffering would be reduced to a minimum, and improvements might rise to an optimum. But unlike Gertrude, the general run of my patients have an absurd hankering for explanations and probings, for discussions and arguments. At the time they consult me, they are in a state of confusion.

For Gertrude, this confusion was a source of untold agonies. In the morning, she felt exhausted, and "beaten up" and had the desire to stay in bed but knew that it was her duty to prepare breakfast for her husband. Duty conflicted with desire. Should she tend to what she conceived as her health? Or should she discharge what was clearly her marital duty? The dilemma confused her. To the physical torture of the symptoms was added the mental torture of not knowing what was right and what wrong. Life appeared to her as an unbroken series of confusions. When she was petrified by the fear of death and dreaded being alone, she rushed out of the house, hurrying in a senseless haste to her mother or sister, seeking comfort and assistance. But, on arriving, the panic was gone and what was left was a crushing sense of shame for acting like a baby and causing distress to those she loved. Was that proper? Was this not evidence of inconsiderateness, even of cruelty?

It was all so puzzling, so perplexing. At times, her husband reprimanded her in harsh terms, insisting on her using her willpower. To her this appeared to be a lack of understanding. She was resentful and felt ugly impulses rising within her. Was she getting irresponsible? Could she no longer trust her impulses? How confusing! Then the racing of thoughts, the inability to concentrate, the difficulty of following her own trend of thought or of "taking in" what others told her. Did that perchance mean that her mind was slipping? Confusion was with her all the time, in every place, on all occasions. If she only knew what it all meant. If she could only understand.

This was her state of mind when I first saw her. Every fiber in her ached to get understanding, to be shown what was right and what wrong, to escape her doubts, to relieve her ignorance. And doubts can be cured, she thought, by explanations, ignorance through knowledge. That called, obviously, for teaching, discussion, exploration and talk. In this, Gertrude acted the part of the intellectual. It is the intellectual's way of thinking that problems, issues and perplexities are the result of ignorance, and the proper remedy is education which he calls *enlightenment*. Confusion, reasons the intellectual, is created by darkness, and darkness is dispelled by light, and once the individual "sees the light," impulses become docile and sensations turn reasonable. The scheme, I admit, is easy to understand; it represents the purest logic and the most attractive reasoning. But does it work? Is it successful?

It is possible that I lack the astuteness and logical skill of an intellectual. Perhaps I am deficient in the art of devising snappy formulas and trim slogans. And so it happened that when I offered Gertrude what I considered solid explanations about sensations and impulses, she was not at all relieved, and her confusion was not lifted. "That was hard for me to understand" was her way of indicating that my attempt at re-educating her had miscarried. Plainly, she was not impressed with the quality of my teaching. This is the verdict of the majority of my patients. Few of them take kindly to my explanations. Most of them "find it hard to understand" what I tell them. Yet, I am certain that what I tell them is about as substantial and lucid as explanations can reasonably be expected to be. It is not true that my teaching is "hard to understand." The truth is that patients cannot be taught by teaching alone. What they need is teaching supplemented by leading. Gertrude failed to understand what I taught her, but when I added leadership to instructorship, her confusion gave way to clear vision and her puzzlement to firm grasp.

Nervous patients suffer from fears and must learn how to conquer them. Learning suggests education, but education is by no means identical with teaching. What teaching does is to give you information. Many things can be adequately acquired through information. If you wish to gain knowledge in history and geography or in languages and literature, mere information will or may fill the need.

The teacher in geography or literature need not be a leader. This is different if you want to learn a trade. The foreman who teaches you must supply leadership besides technical information. He will have to make you translate into practice what he taught you through information. To make a person practice what he is learning is the essence of leadership. In making you practice, the leader will insist on patience, perseverance, self-discipline. While you practice, your attention will frequently wander, your effort will lag, your courage will ebb. The leader will then, through precept and example, revive attention, redirect effort and restore courage. He will watch your performance and correct mistakes. He will demand numerous repetitions of part acts until the total act will be mastered. You will understand now why I say that to lead means to make one practice.

In Recovery, my patients receive a prodigious amount of information, in meetings and home gatherings and in the profuse literature which I have provided for them. In this, I am their teacher who dispenses information. But when I make them practice, unremittingly and untiringly, the information which I gave them, I am their leader who supervises the practical training. Like all my patients, Gertrude secured for herself the benefit of both information and leadership. And since she succeeded in conquering her symptoms, leadership must have been effective and information helpful. Why, then, did she conclude that what I told her was hard to understand? Why was she doubtful whether she even understood it "much better today?" Apparently, my brand of information, although thoroughly effective, did not appeal to her and does not appeal "much better today."

I know that what I teach my patients lacks appeal. They do not relish the thought that they suffer "just" from inner threats. They insist that what they fear are outer dangers, "nothing less." They do not take kindly to the dictum that their symptoms are "merely" distressing but not dangerous. They resent emphatically my instructions to step out boldly when their muscles feel exhausted or to lie quietly in bed when they cannot sleep because their body is rocked by tenseness and shaken with agony. These items of information and principles of leadership do not suit their fancies. They sound too simple, even childish. They lack the glamour of sophistication, subtlety and complexity. In their unadorned and naive phrasing, my instructions are a positive insult to the intellect. And when my patients come for their first interview, they are intellectualists, and judged by the standard of intellectualism, my information and leadership must be found wanting. What Gertrude found difficult to understand was my temerity to offer simple information for a suffering so singularly deep and so exquisitely complex. She had not yet gone through her training in Recovery, and steeped in the philosophy of intellectualism, was shocked by this rude insult to her intelligence.

I told you repeatedly that the romanto-intellectualist tendencies of my patients are fostered by contemporary thought. And our age is hopelessly addicted to the worship of sheer information. Present-day men and women receive the bulk of their education through the channels of information, especially after they have reached adolescence or adulthood and are eligible for what is called "adult education." Then they are given the doubtful benefit of lectures and forums, book reviews, popular expositions on science and psychology, advice in child rearing and family management, instruction on how to make friends and influence people. The implication is that correct information is the surest way to correct action, and that all a person needs for improving his habits is to be told how to do it. Training, practice, leadership have been radically, and perhaps joyfully, discarded in this weird scheme of life in which grownup persons are expected to repose childlike faith in the magical power of theoretical knowledge. The scheme has produced such absurdities as the quixotic plan to reform criminals through psychology, to prevent delinquency by spreading the information that "crime does not pay," to convert races and nations to democracy by teaching them the advantages of the democratic way. The notion that, by some trick, information can change action and direct impulses has gripped the imagination of the age.

We in Recovery refuse to believe in magic, and if we want to change our action, we devise proper counteraction. And if our impulses need controlling, we provide for adequate means of checking them. Our method is that of patient practice supervised by a leader. In our old-fashioned scheme, information is merely the preliminary to training and practice, not a substitute for leadership. Gertrude demonstrated the effectiveness of the system. As long as her mind was focused on the questionable blessings of information, she paid dearly in terms of tenseness and symptoms. After she decided to accept leadership, she was rewarded with relaxation and freedom from suffering.

CHAPTER TWENTY-NINE

The Passion for Self-Distrust

Margaret, taking part in the Saturday panel, reported an experience which she had while attending an auction in one of the Loop galleries. "I was tense," she said. "The auctioneer was handling things too fast for me. There was noise; the people were talking and laughing. I intended to bid but was afraid I might do it at the wrong time. But I made myself sit it out, and when some cocktail forks were offered, I put in my bid. A girl came to collect the deposit for a three-dollar bid. I was confused and felt a tightening in my chest. Finally, I got up the courage to ask the girl how much of a deposit was required, but she did not answer. Maybe I didn't hear her. I became more confused, and the tightening in the chest got worse. I fumbled in my pocketbook and took out a five-dollar bill. The girl said she did not have the change. I looked for a dollar bill but, in my confusion, pulled out a ten-dollar bill. Realizing what I had done, I put it back only to pull out another ten. By this time, the confusion got worse, and I could hardly see.

"I was doing what Dr. Low calls processing and realized that I was busy working myself up to panics and vicious cycles. So I collected my wits, so to speak, and made up my mind to look calmly for a one-dollar bill, and if it wasn't enough, the girl would tell me. Several months ago, before I had my Recovery training, I would have been sure I was losing my mind. My confusion would have grown worse and that would have made it surer that my mind was going."

Margaret, fumbling in her pocketbook for a one-dollar bill, pulled out five- and ten-dollar notes in three successive attempts. Noting the three times repeated error, she drifted into a confusion which was so intense, that it made her head swim with dizziness, threw her muscles into tremors and created a vicious cycle which threatened to precipitate a panic. In former days, she said, "Before I had my Recovery training, I would have been sure I was losing my mind." But errors are the most common occurrence in everybody's experience. Indeed, there would be no sound and tested experience unless errors were made, and made repeatedly, and then corrected. It is precisely the correction of errors which gives correct experience. If this is so, then, errors are a necessary and desirable and wholesome part of life even if they are repeated three times and dozens of times and hundreds of times. What made Margaret think that the commission of errors is an indication of a mind crumbling?

Margaret has the record of many years of faithful and efficient service in a government office. She is married, has friends, belongs to a church and holds membership in various civic groups. In all these spheres, she has witnessed numbers of mistakes made by multitudes of people. Yet, it never occurred to her to suspect this blundering humanity to suffer from mental deterioration because of the innumerable errors chargeable to it. Whenever she was faced with an "erring soul," she knew that "to err is human" and viewed errors, failures, neglects and oversights as what they are: an acceptable and unavoidable "part of life." Why did she assume that erring must not be permitted to be part of her own life? Why did she practice gentle tolerance with others and was preposterously intolerant with herself? To put it differently: when Margaret observed occasional slips in other peoples' mental activities, she did not conclude that their minds were slipping beyond repair. But when she noticed a similar temporary weakness in her own mental function, she instantly jumped to the conclusion that her mind was going or gone. She has an abiding trust in the mental constitution of others but an abysmal distrust in her own mental capacity. This attitude of wholesale self-distrust is a common feature among nervous patients who, as a group, are afflicted with the PASSION FOR SELF-DISTRUST.

My daily life is crowded with occasions in which I fumble and falter. While walking on the street, I sometimes stumble or bump into another person. Occasionally, I slip or fall on the wet or icy sidewalk. At times, I actually hurt myself. Nevertheless, I do not conceive a violent distrust of my Self but consider the misstep or mishap as part of my life. The same holds true for numerous other experiences of my daily round. It happens frequently that I talk to people and fear I said too much. Or, I feel I did not say enough or said the wrong thing. Or, I fall into the trap of a slick salesman who, taking advantage of my preoccupation, tricks me into an ill-considered purchase. In all these instances, my Self, physical or social, fails me, but I do not lose trust in it.

My patients are of a different cast. They spill water and conclude their coordination is badly damaged. If, misplacing an object, they have difficulty retrieving it, they are "certain" their memory is gone. While reading a magazine, their attention may wander, and they are "sure" they lost the power of concentration. They may make a wrong decision in some paltry endeavor, and it is "clear" to them that their judgment is unreliable. There is the matter of forgetting a name, the inability to recall an event, the difficulty of collecting their thoughts for the purpose of writing a letter or the sudden "freezing up" when called upon to voice an opinion at a club meeting. In all these situations, and in a thousand others, they are "certain" and "sure" and "positive" that their functions, physical and mental, are disintegrating and cannot be trusted.

If I try to persuade them that their errors and failures are sheer trivialities, trite and meaningless, they launch into a fierce argument, laboring heavily to convince me that it is "clear" and "plain" and "obvious" (and "how can anyone doubt it?") that their mental and physical capacities are utterly beyond redemption and that their Selves cannot be trusted. It is this insistence on the "clear evidence" and "certain indication" and "positive proof" that stamps their attitude as the "PASSION FOR SELF-DISTRUST."

To have trust in one's organs and functions is to be spontaneous. Spontaneity means many things. It means, for instance, that you have an intention, and your muscles carry it out, promptly, without hesitation, with precision and determination. This happens in the ordinary performances of your daily routine. You decide to go shopping. This involves a running series of part acts: dressing, walking to the next streetcar stop, boarding the coach, paying the fare, entering a store, giving orders to the salesperson, riding back home. Take the item of the streetcar ride. You enter, pay the fare, take your seat, chat with the neighbor until you finally arrive at your destination.

During this time, you performed hundreds of movements and spoke thousands of words. Your muscles acted and spoke without your active intervention. No coaxing, prodding or urging was needed. You passed your intention on to the muscles, and they went ahead and implemented it. This gave you the feeling of *vitality and accomplishment;* it gave you the *sense of "I can."* There was no doubt in your mind that the muscles were competent to perform the task. The absence of doubt made for *self-confidence.* Since no watching or checking was required, you drifted into a state of *relaxation.* The relaxation caused an *absence of tenseness.* With no tenseness to irritate your nerves, the activity gave you *enjoyment.* You felt like an active, living, dynamic personality. Life was pleasure, perhaps bliss and abandonment.

My patients have gone through months or years of torture and, in the process, developed sustained tenseness and symptoms attending it. Their weariness, their pains, fatigues, pressures and spasms have made them self-conscious in the extreme. Hence, they lack the feeling of vitality and accomplishment; they have lost their self-confidence, are unable to relax or enjoy things. Required to formulate plans and intentions, they are instantly gripped with the fear that their muscles will fail them, that they will not be ready to carry out what they are asked to do. Being the victims of an unrelenting self-consciousness, they question their capacities, watch and check every one of their moves and perform with hesitation and anxiety. Their attitude is that of an abiding pessimism; they feel whipped and defeated; their guiding philosophy of defeatism has hardened into a settled conviction. They are "sure" and "certain" and "positive" that acting is impossible, that their muscles will defy orders, that their power to get things done is lost, that their personality functions are doomed. Their philosophy of "I can't" has assumed the status of a dogma; it is implicitly believed, hotly defended and fondly sheltered.

The calamity is that the relatives and friends do not share the patient's defeatism and refuse to subscribe to the cult of "I can't." They look at the sufferer and notice a blooming complexion, a strong voice, a lively facial expression. They observe the patient in a fit of his frequent tantrums and witness a display of force and energy which belies the claim to invalidism. Their conclusion is that the patien*t could* but *would not* do the things which are to be done. The idea is forced on them that he is *unwilling* instead of *unable* to perform his function. They upbraid him, urge him to make an honest effort and, with this, they accuse him of shamming disease, of playing a game, of practicing deception. They indict his character, his honesty; they charge him with deliberate neglect of duties and obligations and fasten the label of irresponsibility on him. This strikes at the root of his self-respect, of his personal value and social position. This savage assault must be repelled. The patient feels he must bend every ounce of his energy to the vital task of convincing the others that he "really" can't, that he is "truly" incapable of acting, that he is "positively" helpless.

The patient is now a crusader for the philosophy of "I can't." He concentrates on the effort to win over the others to his dogma of defeatism, to make converts, to spread the gospel of his incurability. In order to convince those about him, including the physician, he must engage in a veritable campaign of complaining, wailing, lamenting. In his interminable moaning and groaning, he is compelled to overemphasize the utter unreliability of his organs and functions. His body is forever about to crumble, his mind is constantly ready to disintegrate. As he continues on this career of self-denunciation, he fairly gorges himself with the idea of distrust and, in the end, develops the PASSION FOR SELF-DISTRUST. His untiring crusading for the philosophy of "I can't" has netted him one faithful and unswerving convert: himself.

CHAPTER THIRTY

The Courage to Make Mistakes

Mildred reported on the Saturday panel that all her life she had a perfectionist attitude. "I set a standard for myself that an Olympic champion could not approach. I work at top speed, and try to do everything at once and drive myself to finish my job in half the time it would take an expert to accomplish it. But then I get tremors, pressure in the head, a feeling of falling apart as though my arms and legs don't belong to me, and some sort of sensation in which space has become a solid wall, and I must push my way through it every time I move. When this happens, I become panicky and feel sure I am losing my mind.

"The other day, I was in the basement washing clothes. I had meat cooking upstairs on the first floor, the vacuum connected on the second floor ready to use and the washing machine in the basement. As if this were not enough, I went out into the yard, starting to untangle a hopelessly gnarled clothesline, blaming myself all the time for messing up my work and accomplishing nothing. I had hardly untangled the clothesline when it began to rain. I became confused and frightened and felt I couldn't move across the yard because the solid wall was there instead of space.

"Suddenly, I remembered my Recovery training

and spotted my frustration as an attitude of perfectionism. I realized that my rushing from one job to another was the desire to do more than an average person can do, and that my confusion was the sense of disappointment at not being able to do the exceptional job. So I stopped the rush, calmed down deliberately and made up my mind to do one job after the other. In an instant, the confusion went, and the fear of losing my mind stopped.

"Before my Recovery training, I would have kept on working fast and would have gotten into the vicious cycle of fear, self-blame and the depression that went with it. The vicious cycle used to last for months, and at one time lasted three years."

Mildred, in a confusion which threatened to unhinge her mind, "calmed down deliberately" and decided to give up her ambition to do the perfect job. "In an instant," she says, "the confusion went, and the fear of losing my mind stopped." But if a mere decision is sufficient to put an abrupt end to a long-standing confusion, my patients ought to have no difficulty getting rid of their perplexities, vicious cycles and tortures. What Mildred did, all of them ought to be able to do.

What was it that troubled and confused Mildred? There was cooking to be done on one floor, cleaning on another floor and washing in the basement. A fourth job was waiting to be finished in the yard: tending to the "hopelessly gnarled clothesline." The issue was: should all four jobs be carried out at once or one after another? If the tasks were done coincidently, Mildred would have the sense of pride, of outstanding accomplishment, of perfection and excellence. If they were done singly and successively, the job would be of average quality, lacking the glamour of top performance and peak achievement. Reduced to these simple terms, the choice and decision which Mildred was to make was between two discrete philosophies: to be average or exceptional.

I spoke to you about philosophies on several occasions. It is precisely your philosophy (of life) which tells you which decisions are correct and which acts are acceptable. You will remember I mentioned three main philosophies which are current among human beings: realism, intellectualism and romanticism. The intellectualist claims superior powers of reasoning while the romanticist boasts of his exquisite capacity for vigorous feelings, interesting sensations and strong impulses. The one strives to be recognized as being distinct from the "ignorant mob," the other as being apart from the "vulgar crowd." Their philosophy is decidedly that of exceptionality. They fear or hate to be rated as "just average." The realist, on the other hand, does not view the members of his group as mob or crowd. To him, they are average persons, not perfect by any means, not exceptional on any count, but worthy people of average efficiency and average solidity. Their averageness may be of good, plain or poor quality, but essentially, they are average in the entire sweep of their daily existence. And so is he, the realist. He is average in thought, feeling and action. He claims no glory or glamour, no excellence or exceptionality.

Mildred subscribed to the philosophy of exceptionality. This is nothing uncommon. There are very few people who do not think of themselves as being of a superior breed, as ranking above the "common herd," that is, as being exceptional. With most of them, it is merely a dream, an ambition and aspiration. They hope to be exceptional but know they are "nothing but average." In their dreams and fancies, they are romanto-intellectuals, but in actual practice, they behave as realists. Their sense of exceptionality is properly controlled by their knowledge of being average. If you keep this in mind, you will realize that most, if not all, people embrace both the philosophy of exceptionality and that of averageness. The average person adjusts and balances the two philosophies in such a manner that the one (averageness) is leading and controlling, the other (exceptionality) is led and controlled. If this is done, then, decisions and actions are balanced and adjusted on a practical level, while dreams and fancies are given free play on an imaginative level.

Mildred had no leading philosophy of realistic averageness to tell her which of her decisions were correct, which of her actions were feasible. In her mind, the two philosophies were not held apart, they were not properly distinguished, the one from the other; they were permitted to merge and fuse. The free fusion of the two philosophies produced a confusion of the mind. What directed her behavior were her dreams and hopes, her wild aspirations and vague ambitions. With these unrealistic leads to guide her reactions, her decisions became fantastic (to act, at one and the same time, on four separate jobs in four separate places). As a result, her actions became tangled, involved and as "hopelessly gnarled" as was her clothesline. In the end, she despaired of ever reaching the correct decision and became lost in a sea of confusion.

The daily round of the average individual consists, in the main, of such trivial performances as reading, conversing, working on a job, cooking, washing, cleaning, telephoning, shopping. The person with a settled sense of averageness does these routine chores with hardly any thought wasted on them, without hurry, without anxiety, without the harrowing fear of possible failure. Considering them as routine, he knows they involve no danger and is happily at ease, poised and spontaneous while engaged in his work. It is only on those relatively rare occasions when highly important or emergency reactions must be faced that the person, possessed of a sense of averageness, may become tense and may suffer a decrease in his spontaneity. Spontaneity means that you are not self-conscious, that you are not on your guard for fear of making mistakes. Spontaneity means the COURAGE TO MAKE MISTAKES.

In trivial or routine activities, no calamity arises if perchance a mistake occurs. This is the reason why realists, that is, men and women of average aspirations, go about their daily tasks with due caution and circumspection, it is true, but without any marked fear of making a mistake. Mistakes made in trivial performances are trivial themselves, and their possible consequences are just as trivial and not to be feared. With the fear of mistakes largely removed from the mind of the realist, his decisions are reached with ease and his actions initiated without undue hesitation. All of this is the result of spontaneity and, in turn, favors its development.

This is altogether different in the instance of the perfectionist or the person consumed with the desire to achieve exceptionality. To him, every puny endeavor, each trivial enterprise is a challenge to prove and to maintain his exceptional stature. His life is a perennial test of his singularity and distinction. For him, there are no trivialities, no routine performances. He is forever on trial, before his own inner seat of judgment, for his excellence and exceptional ability. He cannot achieve poise, relaxation, spontaneity. He cannot afford to have the COURAGE TO MAKE MISTAKES. A mistake might wipe out his pretense of being superior, important, exceptional. With no margin left for mistakes, he is perpetually haunted by the fear of making them. The fear paralyzes decision, hampers actions and confounds plans. Striving for indiscriminate peak performance and confronted with his pitiful record of jobs undone, unfinished and hopelessly bungled, he is horrified by his cumulative inefficiency and becomes confused.

Mildred, a confirmed exceptionalist, turned realist, embracing averageness as her leading philosophy. She did that after she joined Recovery. There she learned that romanto-intellectualist dreams and fancies must not be permitted to express themselves recklessly but must be led and controlled by an average and humble attitude. She also learned that this must be done through a system of persistent spotting, thorough self-control and relentless self-discipline. It was not easy for Mildred to accept and absorb the idea of control and discipline. She is a product of our modern age and, as such, was subjected all her life to the contemporary doctrine of unrestrained expression of feelings and impulses.

Impulses and feelings are precisely those elements in our experience which balk at being rated as average. They are singularly private and intimate and personal, and give you the impression that, through them, you are set off and distinguished from the others. And if you think of yourself as different from others, you are inclined to consider the others as common and ordinary and average, and yourself as distinct and exceptional. With nervous patients, this tendency to set themselves off from the others is apt to assume ridiculous proportions. If you emphasize your feelings, their importance and intensity, if you are forever suspicious that they are not properly understood, if you constantly fear and complain that they are deliberately ignored and cruelly hurt, if you pamper and coddle them and, thereby, work yourself up to a hysterical pitch, then your emotionalism and impulsiveness may easily reach such a fury that they impress you as exceptional, indeed. You will now understand that our modern tendency to favor unrestrained expression of feelings and impulses overemphasizes individual differences and personal distinctions and thus promotes the sense of exceptionality.

Modern education is only one of the factors which promote the philosophy of exceptionality. Another factor is modern machine technique. A machine leaves little or no room for average performance. A machine loses its usefulness if it fails to work at top speed and record efficiency. It must be perfect within the sphere of its application. The numerous gadgets introduced these days in kitchen, shop and office are worthless unless they conform to the "highest standard" of performance. Their work must be faultlessly smooth, perfectly safe and of top flight productivity. In our mechanized existence, the machine has become the symbol of perfection. Mistakes are no longer tolerated in this modern scheme of mechanical excellence. If mistakes happen, as, for instance, in an airplane or railroad accident, the engineering tribe loses no time shifting the blame from the "flawless" machine and placing it where it "properly" belongs: the "human element." The machine can do no wrong. It is always "perfect." It is man, that miserable, as yet unmechanized, backward and bungling creature who is at fault. Man and human nature have become an anachronism, a relic of that unspeakably imperfect "horse and buggy age" which to the modern mind is the epitome of clumsiness and ineptitude. In spite of the "marvelous" advance of technique, man is still in a deplorable state of imperfection. It is he who has failed to measure up to the matchless efficiency of the machine.

We of Recovery have no use for a system which preaches perfection as an ideal to be achieved through the blessings of a machine-regulated existence. If our mortal state of imperfection can only be redeemed through the "faultless operation" of lifeless machines, well, we are old-fashioned enough to renounce the machine and enjoy our averageness and spontaneity. Mildred, trained in the philosophy of Recovery, learned to scorn faultless operations and perfect performances. In the process, she acquired poise and relaxation and is now in the happy position of doing jobs efficiently (not perfectly, not faultlessly) by the simple procedure of practicing the COURAGE TO MAKE MISTAKES in the trivial affairs of her daily round.

Chapter Thirty-one

Predisposition, Partnership and Partisanship

In a panel discussion on "The Illusion of Superiority," Alice made the following comment: "Some day last week, I was waxing the kitchen floor, and my husband sat by the phone watching me. Suddenly, he said, 'Honey, that chair I painted in the basement must be dry. Will you bring it upstairs and then get Charlie on the phone for me?' Automatically I started for the basement and then stopped. 'He is bossing me,' I thought, 'and then he is almost twice my size and can get that heavy chair himself. Besides, he is right by the phone and can get Charlie himself, and anyway, I am busy.' I felt hurt and was good and angry, and in former days, I would have given him a piece of my mind. But this time, I spotted my resentment as temper and said to myself that my feelings are not so important, and I laughed and said, 'I'll help you carry the chair, and you can make the phone call yourself.' I expected an outburst on his part and was already prepared to hold down my temper if that should happen, but he merely said, 'O.K., it's a deal.' After that, I felt proud of myself. And there was no temper, and so I had no tremors and pressures or nausea. And on top of it, I felt fine because I had asserted myself without temper."

What Alice reported was an incident in which Edward, her husband, took the position that he was the boss, and the wife took the contrary position that she was not going to be ordered about. But if two partners to a joint enterprise take opposite positions, the result will be that temper will thwart action. In the present instance, Alice turned her Recovery training to good account, taking the final position that temper is something ridiculous and a healthy compromise the only way to establish peace and cooperation in married life. You see here that whether a partnership is marred by temper or aided by a workable compromise depends on the nature of the positions habitually taken by the partners.

It will be important for you to know that every act of yours, no matter how trivial, is preceded by a *position.* Before you take a swallow of your soup, you have already decided, that is, taken the position, that the food is not poisoned, that it will cause no indigestion, that it is the proper kind of nourishment to take. You may not be, and usually are not, aware of having taken that position, but you took it nevertheless; you took it intuitively and unreflectively. Positions of this kind are taken in advance of every move you make and every sentence you speak. No person in his right mind makes a motion or voices a phrase unless he has first determined or taken the position that the coming action is devoid of danger and the planned statement free from risk. You will understand now that every act of behavior is preceded by a position. What kind of positions you will cultivate depends on whether you are sentimental or realistic. If you are sentimental, your positions will prepare you for emotional excitements; if you are realistic, they will favor peace and compromise.

Another thing you will have to learn: a position is invariably preceded by a *disposition.* If your present disposition is belligerent, it will give rise to a series of fighting positions, and your subsequent behavior will be aggressive, threatening, provocative. If it is peaceful, your positions will be favorable to a courteous, conciliatory and compromising attitude. Alice and Edward were belligerent in disposition, and when issues arose in their marital relations, their positions were likely to be those of the angry temper: sharp, antagonistic, unyielding. After months of Recovery training, Alice changed her dispositions, shelved her temper and tended to take realistic and compromising positions. Her action was calm and peaceful, and the change in her behavior laid the groundwork for a workable and satisfactory marital union.

How did Alice manage to alter her dispositions? Which method did she use to bring about the change? Is such a method available? On first thought, it would seem hardly thinkable that a method of this kind could exist. Just reflect for a moment what the word "disposition" implies. You enjoy a thing because you are inclined or disposed to like it. You hate a person because you are inclined or disposed to hate him. If you swim, eat, walk, speak, rest, work—all of this is done only if you happen to be moved by a corresponding inclination or disposition. Leaving aside purely automatic behavior, there is no act that could conceivably be released without proceeding from an appropriate disposition. And if every act of yours requires its proper dispositional preparation, it must be clear that disposition is the very breath of your life. It is the basis of your existence, your fate and destiny, indeed, your nature. Can nature be changed?

I do not presume to know whether physical nature can be changed. I hope it cannot because I love nature just as it is. I shudder to think that the modern magicians of atomic energy may yet succeed in their ruthless attempt to tamper with the grandeur and majesty of physical nature. I fervently hope that even the frightful inventions of modern technology will find physical nature unchangeable. But what I know for certain is that human nature, that is, human dispositions, can be changed at will and with ease whenever it is convenient, desirable or mandatory. When you are at home, alone with your family and no outsiders present, your nature may be that of an ugly disposition, cantankerous, quarrelsome, demanding and domineering.

Suddenly, you decide to go to the corner drugstore to buy the evening paper. No sooner have you reached the street than your nature undergoes a miraculous transformation. Your disposition is now that of affability, good will, grace and courtesy. You meet the policeman on his beat or the delivery clerk from the nearest grocery store, and the grouch with which you left your home is gone; your disposition is fairly oozing sympathy and geniality; your nature has changed from domination to service. It did that in a fraction of a second, prompted by no more dramatic an event than the decision to step outside the house. You can observe the ready changeability of human dispositions in your daily experience, where you will notice that abrupt transitions from one natural trend to another are carried out with ease, moreover, without reflection or formal decision. The subject has been treated in great detail in the various chapters of volume 3 of *The Self-Help System** dealing with the temperamental disposition.

Out on the street, or at a social function, or in the company of your co-workers, you are well-behaved all the time, and your temper is under rigid control under all circumstances, provided you are a person of manners and not a boor. The man near you disturbs you with unnecessary questions or unwelcome interruptions. You are irritated but retain your courteous disposition. Another man slams the door, and you feel provoked by the lack of consideration, but your disposition remains calm. You see, outside the home, your dispositions are even, always controlled, unconditionally checked. Conversely, at home, your dispositions may be at any time uneven, temperamental, ill-controlled.

This is due to the fact that dispositions are governed by *predispositions*. Arriving at home, you are likely to assume the predisposition to domination, with the result that, henceforth, all or most of your dispositions will be of a domineer-

---

*Editors' Note: This title is also known as *The Techniques of Self-Help in Psychiatric After-Care*. Please see "Other Books by Abraham A. Low, M.D., on pages 417—418.

ing nature. On the other hand, once you step out into the street or join a group anywhere, you will instantly summon your predisposition to service and will be disposed forthwith to mold your behavior in the spirit of accommodation. The change from one predisposition to the other takes place in a fraction of a second, which means that human nature can be changed with lightning-like rapidity, without conscious effort, without deliberate decision, "quite naturally."

Alice shifted her predispositions by means of conscious resolution. In Recovery she had learned to spot the nature and quality of her reactions. Spotting the meaning of her positions, she always knew which set of dispositions were about to take command of her muscles. If they pointed to a temperamental predisposition, she knew that a shift to a realistic predisposition was in order. She effected the *predispositional shift,* and her "nature" changed instantly from temper to controlled behavior. As I mentioned, the ordinary person produces similar shifts routinely without benefit of special training. But what he does is done spontaneously, hence, fumblingly and unsystematically. What Alice did was done with a systematic effort of will, hence, consistently and methodically. What the man in the street does with the aid of vague intuition, Alice was trained to accomplish with conscious determination. Learning to spot her positions and to stop her dispositions, her Recovery-trained Will scored over her "natural" impulses.

What precisely Alice learned in Recovery is this: Human beings are always members of a group. They are wives, husbands, friends, neighbors, citizens, co-workers, schoolmates, executives, employees. If the members of a group are predisposed to realistic cooperation, they act as partners. The spirit is then that of *partnership.* If they are predisposed to temperamental explosions, they act as partisans, and the resulting spirit is that of *partisanship.* Partnership promotes the purpose of the group, partisanship disrupts it. When Alice and Edward joined hands for the purpose of a marital union, their aim was a close partnership. But temper intervened and turned marital life into a sharp partisanship.

Their marriage was clearly headed for the rocks but was saved from disintegration when Alice, racked by nervous strain and tortured by symptoms, joined Recovery. There she was made to realize that temperamental positions can be tracked down by spotting, and that the predisposition to partisanship can be checkmated at will, with ease and with the promise of unqualified success. Recovery had cured a patient and saved a marriage.

PART III

THE PRINCIPAL METHODS OF SABOTAGE

CHAPTER THIRTY-TWO

Sabotage Method No.1
Literalness

The concept of sabotage is basic to the philosophy of Recovery. The nervous patient sabotages his own health, his social adjustment, his efficiency and equilibrium and–most pernicious form of sabotage–the physician's authority. The trouble is that the patient, engaged in a systematic effort of obstruction, plies his trade in such a subtle and almost underhanded manner, that he is not aware of his own plottings and machinations. In former days, the author believed that the patient weaves his obstructionist plots from the depths of subconscious motivations. This absolved him of all suspicion of deliberate conspiracy. Gradually, however, it became increasingly obvious that a good deal of conscious contrivance was at work.

The patient asks the innocent-sounding question, "Don't you think my condition could be the result of a glandular trouble?" That this is a diagnostic statement and therefore an attempt at sabotage is clear to the physician. But is it equally clear to the patient? Is he conscious of the fact that his question challenged the physician's diagnosis? It is safe to say that at the precise moment when the inquiry is made, the thought of antagonism or obstruction may be absent from the questioner's mind. But if we survey the patient's mental activities beyond the immediate scene and trace his meditations no farther back than to the bus trip which he made to the doctor's office, the picture changes radically.

While on the bus, he was preoccupied with the diagnosis given him on the occasion of his previous visit. He was told then that his condition was of a nervous nature, that it implied no danger, that the combination of office treatment and group management would eliminate his complaints. Now, on the bus, he reviews the physician's pronouncements with a critical eye. It seems preposterous to him that his "unbearable" fatigue should be labelled "just nervous," i.e., innocent and harmless.

Why then was he asked by other physicians to take a rest, to stop working? True enough, his present physician is competent, highly recommended and undoubtedly successful. But Drs. J. and F. were no numbskulls, either, and the one diagnosed a mild anemic condition, and the other blamed the fatigue on a low blood pressure. And the doctor who writes the health column in the morning paper suggested yesterday that fatigue states are frequently caused by a lowered metabolism which, in many instances, can be traced to a glandular deficiency. Why should all these possibilities be ignored? The ruminations continue in this vein until the train of thought is interrupted by some incident that diverts the patient's attention. The sabotaging activity is no longer pursued. Leaving the bus, the patient enters a restaurant to take his lunch. He reads the paper, gives some fleeting thought to all kinds of topics and observations, and the subjects of complaints and diagnosis sink to a lower level of consciousness.

When he faces the physician, his diagnostic doubts may still be removed from the upper strata of his conscious awareness. But are they buried in the subconscious? They were mulled over and rehearsed just half an hour ago and are quite active and fresh in memory although not in the forefront of conscious meditation. They wait merely for the proper occasion to be revived. When the physician opens up with the introductory question, "How are you today?" the patient's slumbering antagonism is quickly aroused, and the thoughts, recently rehearsed during the bus ride, are promptly sprung on the physician. That antagonism may not at the present moment be glaringly conscious. But it was in the limelight of awareness a short while ago. It did not have the time to sink down to the subconscious level. We may safely call it half-conscious or quasi-conscious.

Clearly, if sabotage is to be controlled and eliminated, it must be stopped at its source and origin. It originates at times and in places outside the physician's office, in the bus, at home, on the street, in the workshop. In the presence of the physician, the sabotaging thoughts burst forth spontaneously with little reflection and hardly any deliberation. But in the absence of the physician, the sabotaging is done reflectively and deliberately. If a person is spontaneous, his utterances are blurted out and poured forth impulsively. Usually, there is neither time nor incentive to revise the spontaneous performance. On the other hand, when the patient sabotages in clear reflection, he has the time and occasion for correction, provided he has also the incentive to correct. Recovery, with its untiring insistence on a total effort, supplies the patient with the needed incentive. But the patient's endeavor is bound to be vague, groping and ineffectual unless he is supplied with adequate insight into the devious ways in which his own sabotaging tricks operate. Armed with both incentive and insight, he will be properly equipped for the long, drawn-out and gruelling battle against his sabotaging propensities, the ENEMY NUMBER ONE of mental health. Of the many disguises behind which sabotage hides, the most important ones will be mentioned in the present volume. As may be expected, the most common form is one which is frequently encountered in ordinary conversation: Literalness. Essentially, this device makes use of the technique of rejecting a statement made by the speaker without opposing it openly.

Example 1. The patient reported that at a card game, his mother corrected him every few minutes. He was provoked, threw the cards on the table and precipitated a violent argument. He slept poorly that night and awoke in the morning all exhausted. He was told to avoid drawing the temperamental conclusion that he is right and mother wrong. His reply was, "I think that mother is wrong but not that I am right." It was not easy to make the patient see the obvious truth that the question raised in an argument is who is right and who is wrong; that if the one party to the controversy is declared to be in the wrong, it follows inevitably that the other party must be right; that if he thought the mother was wrong, it was obvious that he felt he was right. "Can't I think the one thought and not the other?" the disputant continued. "Not any more," he was told, "than you can think of light without darkness, good without bad, love without hate. Once the one pair of the team of opposites is thought of, the other pair is called up automatically." The patient was then shown that he could have used his own common sense to realize that he was literal and listened to the letter instead of the meaning of the physician's statements. If he had done that, he would have demonstrated a will to conquer his temper. Instead, he distorted common sense, and debauched logic and sabotaged the will to get well.

Example 2. A lady exclaimed in utter frustration, "I can't plan. I get flustered when I begin, and then I do not know what to do next." The physician remarked, "Of course, if you say you cannot plan. . ." but was unable to continue because the lady interrupted him sharply, "I don't mean to say that I cannot plan. It is merely difficult for me to make a decision because I have no determination." She was told bluntly that her manner of reasoning was devoid of logic; that the sharp distinction which she chose to make between planning, making decisions, and having determination was superficial sophistry, a literal differentiation meant to confuse the issue instead of clarifying it. Being a college graduate and possessed of such keen logic as to be an artist at word juggling, she ought to employ her logical capacities to analyze her own statements in terms of sabotage. Her aim ought to be to get well, not to stage a senseless and futile debate with her physician. The result was that she produced a new literalistic perversion of logic. She shouted, "I do not mean to debate with you; I merely wish to make you understand my point of view." Whereupon she was told, politely but firmly, "Whether I understand or misunderstand you is of no significance. The thing that counts is that you make every effort to understand me."

Example 3. A patient turned in an urgent message of distress over the telephone. He complained, in a voice quivering with excitement, that his tenseness was "simply unbearable." "What can you suggest for my relief?" he inquired. He was asked to come to the office that same evening. "But I don't see how I can stand it that long," he replied. He was assured that there was not the slightest danger in a tenseness of this kind and there was no reason for being alarmed. "I am not alarmed, Doctor," he shouted, "but I feel something is going to happen if I don't get help. Can't you let me come to the office right now?" The man is a government official of considerable rank and could easily see the identity of meaning between "alarm" and "feeling that something is going to happen." He had been given a number of private interviews but resented being considered a psychoneurotic person. He protested forever that his distress was physical in origin and was annoyed by the physician's insistence that it was emotional in nature. The words "fear" and "alarm" were tabu to him. Taking them in their literal sense, he wiped them out of existence by using a phrase with a slightly different connotation.

Example 4. A patient suffered from an itch on the scalp for over five years. In the course of time, he developed a marked self-consciousness and tenseness which interfered with his general well-being and his occupation as a drummer in an orchestra. For the past two years, drumming had become an obsession with him. He was compelled to drum incessantly on the table at which he sat, on the outer aspect of his legs when he stood and on the walls of houses when he passed them. The members of his family claimed they "went almost crazy" because of the perpetual drumming. After several months of private and class treatment, the itch was under good control, and the tenseness and self-consciousness had given way to a satisfactory measure of relaxation.

But the drumming persisted. The patient was asked, "Why don't you stop that drumming? You got rid of the itch by learning to ignore the discomfort and by controlling the muscles of the hands when they 'itched' to scratch. You can control the drumming by exactly the same procedure. Whenever you feel the 'overwhelming' impulse to drum, you can check the impulse and can command your muscles not to carry out the drumming movements." The patient replied, "Drumming is music to me, and I like music." He was promptly reprimanded for daring to offer a nonsensical explanation of this sort. "You know as well as I do," the physician said, "that you do not maintain the drumming for its musical value. You know it is nothing but noise." "It is rhythm, though," the patient replied. After some sparring, he finally admitted that his attempt to identify compulsory finger movements with music and rhythm was nothing more than sabotage made possible by a literal misinterpretation of the physician's words.

Example 5. A patient who had lost many of her symptoms continued to complain of blurred vision, which had been declared frequently by the physician to be of nervous origin. "The blur still bothers me," the patient said. "I don't see things clearly." The physician renewed his assurance that the symptom was of a nervous nature and nothing to worry about. "I don't worry," insisted the patient. "I merely thought you might want to examine me again." The eyes were re-examined and the patient told that there was no evidence of any defect. The patient persisted, "Don't you think an oculist ought to look at them?" "I do not object to examinations," the physician replied, "but your solicitude indicates that you worry about your vision." The patient then exclaimed, with obvious irritation, "But, doctor, I assure you I don't worry about my eyes. But, of course, I wouldn't like them to get worse. After all, a person may go blind." The literalistic quality and sabotaging character of this kind of word juggling requires no comment.

Brief examples: A woman patient reported in astonishing frankness about her wild temper outbursts. She related a series of uncalled-for acts of spite and vengefulness, interlarding the recital with comments as, "Of course, I know it's my fault. I am just a nag. What I need is a good licking, I guess." When the examiner warned her not to indulge in an orgy of self-blame, she burst forth, "I don't blame myself; I am just telling my story."

A patient was told not to get sore at herself because that was her main form of temper. She replied, "Doctor, I don't get sore at myself. I am just disgusted with myself." Another patient was warned not to be irritable, whereupon she rejoined, "I am not irritable. I am just upset by what my daughter says."

A patient remarked, "I have been coming here several weeks, and I don't see any results."

EXAMINER: You must not be discouraged.

PATIENT: I am not discouraged. But of course, if one does not see progress. . . .

This patient could have easily told himself that "not seeing results" and "not seeing progress" is identical or synonymous with "being discouraged."

PATIENT: When I go shopping, I wait and wait and have trouble making the purchase.

EXAMINER: So, you are still having difficulty making a decision?

PATIENT: No, I merely cannot get myself to pick the merchandise I want to buy.

The identical meaning of the phrases "having trouble making the purchase," "having difficulty making a decision" and inability "to pick the merchandise I want" ought to be obvious, but nothing is obvious to a person bent on perverting meanings through literal distortion.

EXAMINER: I hope I did not hurt your feelings when I said that.

PATIENT: No, I just don't agree with you, and, frankly, I don't think you have a right to tell me that. It just makes me mad if everybody jumps at me.

The patient developed a mild depression consequent on the mother's death.

EXAMINER: You must avoid guilt feelings.

PATIENT: I don't feel guilty. I didn't do anything wrong.

EXAMINER: You blame yourself for not having done enough for your mother.

PATIENT: This I do.

EXAMINER: Doesn't this mean feeling guilty?

PATIENT: I thought guilt is crime.

This literalism is rather naive, but variations of the theme are frequently encountered with patients steeped in the practice of sabotage.

PATIENT: Yesterday, I had something like a daze.

EXAMINER: You don't have to be afraid of that.

PATIENT: I am not afraid. The only thing, I wouldn't like to have to go to the hospital again.

She feared "to have to go to the hospital again" but was not "afraid"!

In all the situations quoted in the examples, the patients display a tendency to block the physician's effort, to combat his views, to reject his suggestions by means of a literal misinterpretation of the words he uses. Once the patient's attention has been called to his favorite methods of sabotaging, he is in a position to correct his habits. In Recovery, corrections of this kind are made frequently and effectively.

CHAPTER THIRTY-THREE

Sabotage Method No. 2
Ignoring or Discrediting the Initial Improvement

Sabotage is the attempt of an individual to thwart the purpose of a group, usually that of his own group. In this sense, the child sabotages the educational purpose of the parental group when he opposes the effort to make him eat, wash or go to bed. Sabotage is also practiced by the soldier who reports for sick call when, in fact, he is merely lonesome, or discouraged or disgruntled. That soldier sabotages the national purpose. There is no end to the multitude of occasions which lend themselves to sabotaging practices. The member of a parliament who offers needless amendments to legislative proposals, the employee who absents himself without good cause, the member of a club who stalls on an assignment, they all sabotage the purpose of the group to which they belong and to which they owe allegiance. The purpose that is most commonly and most consistently sabotaged is that of the family. This type of sabotage takes the form of domestic temper and was amply discussed in *The Techniques of Self-Help*, volume 3.*

The child is, as a rule, a frank and forthright saboteur. There is little or no equivocation, duplicity or deceit to his sabotaging performance. In most instances, he opposes an order and rejects the parental purpose in candid rebellion. Children, provided they are not sophisticated, do not affect

---

*Editors' Note: The full title is *The Techniques of Self-Help in Psychiatric After-Care*. Please see "Other Books by Abraham A. Low, M.D." on pages 417—418.

loyalty to the group purpose of good manners and self-discipline. They simply refuse to accept the educational purpose. If they sabotage it, they do not thwart their own purpose. They do not practice self-sabotage.

In all other instances which were cited, the sabotage is directed against a group purpose which is solemnly accepted and perhaps cherished and worshipped by the sabotaging person. The soldier, the parliamentarian, the employee, the club member and the quarrelling relative level their sabotaging activities against purposes with which they identify themselves. They sabotage endeavors which they endorse and approve. The purpose which they obstruct is their own, accepted and valued by them. Theirs is self-sabotage.

That the patient who opposes the freely selected physician sabotages a self-chosen purpose needs no explanation. He has adopted and accepted the purpose of health and has appointed his physician to help him realize the purpose. If he obstructs the physician's efforts, he frustrates his own purpose and, by this token, is a self-saboteur.

The situation is clear and transparent in the instance of infantile sabotage. For some reason, the child has no inclination to adopt the group purpose of self-discipline. Carrying out rules and obeying standards is obnoxious to him. It gives him discomfort to have to wash; going to bed in due time is reacted to as an odious imposition; eating spinach may be unmitigated torture. If the group purpose makes the child perform these offensive practices, he logically tries to foil that purpose. What prompts him to resort to his sabotaging behavior is his desire to preserve his personal and individualistic comfort. His own purpose of individualism revolts against the foreign purpose of group standards. The individualistic craving for comfort locks horns with the group purpose of self-control. As a general rule, the child's struggle against "the tyranny" of group standards is plain, transparent, straightforward and aboveboard.

The adult saboteur proceeds differently. Take the case of the disgruntled soldier reporting for sick call. He complains of dizziness or "sick headache." The army physician, as the representative of the national group purpose, examines him and declares him well. But the soldier feels keenly his distress. His individualistic purpose is directed toward relieving the personal discomfort. Hence, he pleads for a day of rest and exemption from fighting or drilling. The group purpose, on the other hand, insists on continued discharge of duty. If the soldier now engages in arguments, contending against the physician's opinion that he is sick and disabled, he fights against the group purpose which he himself has adopted and accepted. This he can do only if he fortifies himself with "good reasons." He must justify the inroads into the approved group purpose in a manner that will satisfy his own conscience. Since there are no such "good reasons," he is compelled to manufacture them. The manufactured reasons are rationalizations. They are a weird compound of half-lies, truth-twistings, forced excuses and tortured evasions. The struggle of the adult saboteur against group standards is anything but plain, transparent, straightforward and above-board. It is a mixture of self-trickery and self-degradation.

The case of the nervous and former mental patient is similar to that of the complaining soldier. He has "enlisted" in the physician's group of patients and has, by implication, obligated himself to pursue the health aim of this group with the vigor of a total effort. The patient accepts at first this group obligation and incorporates the purpose into his own set of values. Then he pleads the case of his own personal comfort and claims exemption from health exercises and health drills. He argues and quibbles with the physician, opposes his individualistic purpose of physical comfort to the physician's insistence on self-discipline. His procedure is characterized by the same disreputable resort to twists, distortions and evasions as practiced by the battle-weary soldier.

The reasons why the patient sabotages his physician are many. Some of them will be mentioned in due course. Surpassing all in importance is the sense of being stigmatized. The patient resents having his complaint considered "nervous" or "emotional." He feels his character is indicted as weak by the diagnosis. If all he needs is insight or assurance, then he is declared to be lacking qualities which everybody else possesses. He resents the implications of intellectual and moral inadequacy and embarks on a process of sabotage. His aim is to convince the physician and others that his trouble is of a physical nature.

In order to get well, it is imperative that a patient upholds his courage or morale. The prospect of getting and keeping well is directly proportional to the vigor with which morale is maintained. But the sabotaging patient is not at all interested in getting well if the only way to health is that of psychological explanations and moral education. Since his main concern is to convince his physician and others that, in fact, he is suffering from a physical ailment, the self-help system of regaining his health is not at all pleasing to him. Should he recover through the methods of will-training and self-discipline, the charge that for years he neglected his will-power and practiced self-indulgence would be unanswerable. To get well would be an admission that his relatives and friends were correct when they attributed his complaints to a weak will and lack of self-control. He senses keenly the danger to his self-respect should he get cured through will-training and morale-building. The topic of morale is repulsive to him. What he wants is vitamin-medication, administration of hormones, perhaps a minor operation, but no morale-lifting.

In Recovery he is, nevertheless, caught up in an atmosphere of high morale, reassurance and encouragement and responds instinctively to the new influence. He improves; the symptoms get milder; the prospect of getting well increases. This gives him a subtle scare. He has visions of accusing fingers pointed at him, of a sneering voice bellowing self-righteously, "I told you it was all up to you." Morale is now his enemy. He will have none of it. And if the present state of improvement is an index to a final cure, well, he is going to see to it that the process of improving does not proceed too fast nor too far. Perhaps he cannot stop the process, but at the very least he can ignore or deny it. The saboteur is now thoroughly committed to a well-conceived plan of ignoring or discrediting the initial improvement. Examples of this type of sabotaging activities will now be cited.

Example 1. A lady's main complaint was a marked anxiety which at times assumed the proportions of a terrifying panic. She slept poorly, had no desire for food and was troubled with a severe headache. The condition had persisted for several years, but in the past six months, it had become "almost unbearable." She was unable to attend concerts and shows because of an "irresistible" impulse to stampede out of the theatre the moment the lights were turned off. She was also afraid to be alone and to drive her car. After four weeks of private and class interviews, her panics and headaches were gone, sleep and appetite were satisfactory, and the fear of automobiling and attending shows had all but disappeared. When at this point she was asked about her condition, she disclaimed any noticeable improvement. "I am tense all the time," she said, "I can't stand the slightest irritation, and sleep hasn't been at all good for the past three nights." On inquiry, she admitted that even on these three occasions, sleep "wasn't as bad as it used to be." She also agreed that she no longer suffered from panics and that the fear of driving the car and sitting through a show were under control. "But, doctor," she hastened to add, "that tenseness and irritability just drive me mad. There must be something radically wrong with me."

She was told, "When you first consulted me, you were just as tense and irritable as now, perhaps more so. But the main source of your agony at that time were your panics and fears. Since they are gone, you ought to be happy beyond description. You ought to derive a new courage from the realization that most of your symptoms cause you no more trouble. Instead, you are despondent because of some remaining minor afflictions. Suppose you had suffered from a gastric ulcer for several years. Therapy was ineffective until a new treatment was instituted. After a few weeks, you notice that the pain decreases considerably, the bleeding stops entirely, the anemia is checked, weight increases. But some gastric distress is still present, and the tenseness and irritability that were caused during years of suffering are still producing difficulty of sleeping and poor relaxation. You would, then, in spite of the remaining tenseness and irritability, take courage in the thought that your vital wish to get well is on its way toward fulfillment. Your morale would improve and would leave no room for despondency. A patient who shows no appreciation for the quick relief from year-long suffering indicates plainly that the relief was not the object of dreams, hopes and desires. A patient of this kind has no genuine will to regain health and is what I call a saboteur."

Example 2. A woman patient had suffered for the past nine years from "intolerable" tenseness, restlessness and irritability, pressure in the head, difficulty of falling asleep, extreme fatigue and gagging when eating. She had consulted numerous physicians and cultists and was emphatic that no treatment ever helped her. She had spent several periods of weeks and months in hospitals, rest homes and sanitariums without obtaining anything but fleeting relief. When a course of electroshock treatment was instituted, she lost practically all her symptoms in a surprisingly short time. The formerly extensive list of her complaints was now reduced to an insignificant headache which she considered quite tolerable. When the question was asked, "Are you not glad you came to the hospital and received the treatment?" she replied, "But, Doctor, that head pressure is still there and as bad as ever. I wonder whether I'll ever feel just myself." When reprimanded, the patient promptly realized the unreasonableness of the complaint and admitted freely that she did not quite relish the thought of improving. "If I were sure I am going to be cured, it would be glorious," she remarked, "but a mere improvement frightens me. I always remember how I got worse after improvements." This explanation is frequently given by patients who realize that their reaction to the initial improvement is the outcome of sabotage. They have gone through the ordeal of the "setback" and dread it. To avoid the thought of the setback, they try to ignore the early signs of the beginning cure.

Example 3. A former college student, who contracted a mental ailment in his sophomore year, was seen two years after leaving the hospital. He presented an inexhaustible list of residual symptoms. The most outstanding complaint was fatigue, procrastination, tendency to remain in bed till afternoon, lack of spontaneity which made him carry out with extreme effort even trifling performances; a constant feeling of hopelessness, tenseness and irritability; difficulty of sleeping; dizziness; annoying habits of twitching and grimacing; forgetfulness; self-consciousness, etc. After obtaining a well nigh startling improvement in the course of a few months of private and Recovery training, he stated, "I have a vague fear that I am doomed. Recovery cannot help me. I may be carrying on for six months, but I'll never get well." After he recognized the sabotaging character of his statements, he volunteered a plausible explanation. He said, "Should I get well this year or in five years, I'll have the thought before me that all these years were wasted." Translated into the language of the stigma, this means he feared improvement because it would make him feel stigmatized before his own conscience.

Example 4. A woman patient had the common garden variety of neurotic complaints: poor appetite, difficulty of sleeping, palpitations, crying spells and air-hunger. Crawling sensations, numbness, contractions of the throat, nausea were less regular but equally distressing when present. The complaints dated back some fifteen years when a high school boyfriend had taken indecent liberties with her. Although she knew nothing had happened, nevertheless, she could not shake off the thought of having been "contaminated." In the past year, she had been tortured by the fear she might do harm to the baby. Coupled with the other complaints, this made her suffering "unbearable." After about six weeks of combined office and class treatment, she reported that the thought of "contamination" had practically disappeared, that the fear of harming the baby was no longer of any consequence, and that the sensations were "much milder." The physician remarked at this point, "So, you made a nice improvement." "Do you really think I have?" she replied, "I am still tense and have quite a bit of trouble in concentrating, and I want you to know, Doctor, that I still have the sensations."

It was explained to her that her refusal to admit improvement in the face of positive evidence of good progress meant that she discouraged herself and lowered her morale. She then conceded that the amelioration of most of her symptoms was a sign of good improvement but continued, "Why can't I get rid of the sensations? I can't help thinking that is more than just nerves." She was one of those patients who resented being stigmatized as "just a nervous case." She was unhappy over the initial improvement because it seemed to clinch the diagnosis of a psychoneurotic condition. And that diagnosis she considered a blot on her character.

Brief examples: A lady suffered from a depression of mood. She did everything with great effort. Sleep and appetite were poor; interests were at a low ebb. A good improvement took place after three weeks. When seen at the office, she denied feeling better. The following conversation developed:

PATIENT: I don't feel a bit better.

EXAMINER: How is your sleep?

PATIENT: I must admit sleep has been better.

EXAMINER: Do you still do everything with effort?

PATIENT: I have to drive myself quite frequently. But yesterday, I felt the desire to go to the movie for the first time in six months.

CHAPTER THIRTY-THREE

EXAMINER: Do you do your cooking and shopping with more zest?

PATIENT: Yes, but I can't get myself to take care of the baby.

She knew she had improved but brazenly denied the fact of improvement, ignoring and discrediting the evidence.

A patient exclaimed, "I had a bad week again." He was asked, "How is your fatigue?" The reply was: "I walked close to twenty blocks today. It really was a surprise to me. But last Sunday, I was awfully tired all day." When questioned about his fullness in the head, he said, "It does not start right in the morning any more as it used to, *but* I am always afraid it will be worse in the afternoon." And this record of good initial improvement was summed up in the phrase, "I had a bad week again." In Recovery, patients of this description go by the name of "but-knockers." Their stock phrases of self-knocking choose the verbal pattern of "My headache is better, *but*. . . ." The improvement is affirmed in the first statement but speedily denied in the second.

Another "but-knocker" stated, "I had a couple of good days last week, *but* this morning I felt nauseated again. . . . I had a good day, *but*, of course, I kept busy, and that helped me. . . . My palpitations are better, *but* I don't understand why my appetite is still so poor."

CHAPTER THIRTY-FOUR

Sabotage Method No. 3
Disparaging the Competence or Method of the Physician

If sabotage is directed against a purpose, it will be useful to the sabotaging patient to know something about the manner in which purposes operate.

In common language, the purpose of a house is to give shelter, comfort and privacy; the purpose of a garden is to supply vegetables or flowers; the purpose of an automobile, to provide transportation. In this loose sense, the house, garden and automobile are conceived as having or being endowed with purposes of their own. This is not correct. The house, garden and automobile merely serve the purpose of their owners. The owner has or is endowed with the capacity for craving, wanting, needing shelter, comfort, privacy, vegetables, flowers, transportation. These various purposes are served by house, garden and automobile. An object that serves a purpose is a means toward achieving it. Objects, having neither needs nor wants, cannot have purposes of their own; they are means through which purposes are realized or accomplished.

A workman, wanting or needing wages for subsistence, works for the purpose of sustaining himself and his family. The maintenance of a family is his purpose, the particular kind of work he performs is the means serving the purpose. The purpose is set; the means may be subject to change. For some reason, the workman may decide that cessation of work (strike) may serve his purpose better than continuation of his activities. Means may change according to circumstances, expediency or policy. Purposes are set, either for a limited time or for life.

The industrialist, for whom the worker toils, has essentially the same purpose as his employee. He maintains his establishment primarily for the purpose of providing for his own needs and those of his family. For both, the purposes are set and stabilized by the needs and wants of their families. This the reason why the institution of the family is credited with exercising a stabilizing influence. It sets the purpose for the individual, makes for constancy of purpose and counteracts flightiness of endeavor.

Unlike the worker, the owner of the factory cannot change at will the means that serve his purpose. Closing the plant may at times be necessary due to circumstances, but it will hardly ever be beneficial to the family purpose. If the manufacturer wishes to maintain his family, he will not be permitted to shut down his establishment for a long period of time. For him, both purpose and means are set and stabilized.

There is also a marked difference between worker and owner with regard to the work done in the factory. The worker may tend to the commodity to be manufactured. But the stock room and heating plant are not his concern. To the manufacturer, on the other hand, every part of the factory is important and essential. His concern extends over all buildings, all departments, all activities. If the owner is to accomplish his purpose, he must exert a *total effort;* the worker may attain his purpose (weekly paycheck) by engaging in a *part-effort* only.

Another significant feature of a purpose must be mentioned. The owner of the factory may be sincerely devoted to his family. But suppose he is addicted to gambling and fritters away his fortune. He is then *divided* between two purposes and not *unified.* The division is between an individualistic purpose (gambling) and a group purpose (family). Everybody is the seat and repository of individualistic and group purposes. In the adult person who has achieved maturity, one group purpose, usually that of the family, is expected to *take the lead* over all other purposes and to guide action towards unified behavior. The dominant group purpose supplies *leadership.* Every purpose which conflicts with the leading group purpose must be checked and prevented from exerting itself. In this manner, the natural conflict of purposes is controlled. If leadership is not established, two antagonistic purposes act against one another, producing the condition known as *cross-purpose or dual purpose.* An individual possessed of a unified purpose is said to represent an *integrated* personality. He is endowed with the qualities of leadership.

The patient suffering from a nervous ailment may be and frequently is an integrated personality with regard to the purposes of family, citizenship and vocation. But with regard to his own body, he has lost leadership. His impulses, sensations, feelings and thoughts embark on action independent of his dominant purpose. The purpose of fellowship may suggest a visit of condolence or his presence at a wedding, but his heart sets up palpitations, suggesting to him the fear of impending collapse. The group impulse to exercise the obligations and sentiments of friendship or neighborliness is thwarted by the individualistic impulse to cater to sensations and fears. The inner functions of the body are no longer under control. They are discharged suddenly and unpredictably, without relation to the dominant purpose of the personality.

Leadership is utterly lost because no leadership is possible under conditions of fears, panics and vicious cycles. The patient may make a half-hearted attempt to help himself. But that attempt is in the nature of a muddled and confused part-effort, guided by the dual purpose of endorsing the group impulse toward self-discipline and catering to his symptoms at the same time. Rocked by a conflict of purposes, he is no longer wholly unified and lacks the qualities of a fully integrated personality.

Having lost control over the functions of the nervous system, the patient consults the physician, asking him to supply the leadership that he himself can no longer provide.

Physician and patient are now forming a partnership in which a unified purpose is set and defined by the physician and accepted by the patient. In this partnership, the physician represents the group purpose of mental health and self-discipline. The patient accepts it and pledges himself to employ all the necessary means to attain the end. But before long, a setback is experienced. The rebellious sensations, impulses and fears reappear, making their individualistic demands and insisting on compliance. The resulting panics induce the patient to ignore and neglect the physician's instructions. The patient demands instant relief, and the physician points to the necessity of self-discipline.

The unified purpose of the partnership is now disrupted. Should the partnership be dissolved? Or should it be continued? The decision is not easy. Changing physicians would not be difficult. However, if, for some reason, the patient continues his visits to the office, he demonstrates clearly that he considers the physician competent, that he thinks his knowledge expert and his instructions pertinent. But if the one partner is well qualified, the failure of the common endeavor disqualifies the other partner. If the patient is to retain his self-respect, he must find a way to disqualify his physician. How can he do that if he continues his visits? The fact of the continued visits emphasizes the physician's qualification. How then can he be disqualified?

The task is not easy. The patient must prove to himself that his physician is qualified and unqualified, expert and inept, proficient and unskilled at the same time. This requires subtle twists, half-truths, shams and sophistry. The dilemma is solved by a simple trick: the physician's competence is asserted explicitly but solidly denied by implication. The patient's conscience is now saved. Continuing his visits, he demonstrates explicitly that he trusts his physician. But using phrases with disparaging implications, he denies the physician's ability to cure him. Tactics of this kind permit the patient to maintain the illusion of accepting the physician's leadership while, at the same time, disputing and opposing it. The partnership is then officially maintained but rendered ineffective by crafty maneuvering. The precise manner in which this sabotaging technique operates will now be described.

Example 1. A woman patient had been in and out of hospitals for the past thirteen years. Her case was diagnosed as dementia praecox. She was dreaming, untidy, given to explosive outbursts of violence. The mental contents showed numerous delusions and hallucinations. On the occasion of her fifth period of hospitalization, she was given a combined course of insulin and electroshock treatment which resulted in a fair degree of improvement with satisfactory insight. She admitted feeling better but added, "Of course, when the weather is more friendly, I always feel better." She then continued, "What I really need is to go to work. I should take up my painting. A trip to the country would do me good, too." These statements were too obviously calculated to disparage the physician's method to require comment. The patient refrained from asserting bluntly that the treatment was ineffective. Instead, she pointed out, by implication, that other methods were superior to those employed by the physician.

Example 2. The patient was in the grip of a deep depression for close to two years. She complained of lack of interest, deficient sleep and inability to do things except with the utmost effort. She thought her inner organs were rotting. She disclaimed experiencing any feelings. The brain was a blank, the abdomen felt like an empty container. Eating was done mechanically and the bowels "would not move." She accused herself of having "committed the unpardonable sin." A course of electroshock treatment produced prompt improvement. At this stage she was asked, "Don't you think it was a good idea to bring you to the hospital?" The patient replied, "Of course, the rest and being away from home and child. . . ." The physician's efforts were disparaged, and credit was given to events and circumstances uncorrelated with technical treatment.

Example 3. The patient, ill for six years, had consulted numbers of physicians without obtaining sustained relief.

When first seen, she suffered from various phobias and compulsions. She was afraid of fainting in the street and had to be accompanied by her husband whenever she ventured out of the house. When performing a task, she was unable to stop and had to repeat the manipulation endless times. Making beds thus consumed hours because the tucking and straightening seemed never done to satisfaction. Thoughts "repeated themselves" interminably in the brain. If she asked a question, it had to be repeated over and again till finally she felt she had found the correct formulation. There were other disturbances: procrastination before retiring and after arising, fatigue, twitches, poor appetite.

After several months of combined private and class treatment, the major symptoms were gone. She was now able to do things with hardly any repetition, took care of her home work without much waste of time and manipulated long walks without fear. Finally, she even mustered the courage to move to a large home, confident that she would be equal to the task of tending to a considerably increased schedule of work. She was sufficiently improved to do all the cooking and cleaning without undue repetition. When she was then asked, "Don't you think that is a good improvement?" she countered with the remark, "Of course, I improved because the new house keeps me busy." The physician's effort was disparaged.

Example 4. A patient, suffering from a depression of mood for upward of three years, had been the beneficiary of all manner of treatment with no success. She received three electroshock treatments and attended classes thereafter. Before long, she regained her spontaneity and was able to do her work without having to drive herself. Sleep and appetite improved, and the mood became balanced. The improvement had set in during the first month and had continued progressively during the subsequent four months. She had a vacation coming but hesitated to make use of it because in the past three years, she had suffered agonies whenever she spent time in resort places. When she finally went to the country, it was done mainly at the physician's insistence.

After she returned, she was asked how she felt and said, "I feel so much better. Of course, the vacation picked me up." The physician's part in her improvement was flatly denied, Recovery's share was ignored, and the influence of class instruction was "forgotten."

At times, a patient will employ less subtle means of expressing his disapproval of the physician's competence. He will then indicate, plainly and directly, that a different therapeutic approach is better suited to the exigencies of his case. The instance of the patient was mentioned who inquired whether glandular treatment was not preferable to attendance of classes and Recovery meetings. The same patient suggested on different occasions that what he needed was psychoanalysis, shock treatment, change of occupation and scenery. He once exclaimed, "I think I ought to get married. Nothing else will help me." When he was told there was no objection to his choosing a mate, he remarked, "How can I get married if I am not cured?" The thought of marriage was obviously meant to sabotage the physician. It was no settled plan, it was no thought at all; it was merely a fling at the physician, intended to disparage his method.

Another patient, who had been experiencing night terrors for many years, said, "My trouble goes back to childhood. Don't we have to dig in my past?" She was told that her past had been dug up so thoroughly, both by her present and former physicians, that few patches of ground were left untilled. She snapped back, "You ask us to get well through self-help. But it seems that a patient should be helped by the physician." Subtlety was here thoroughly discarded in favor of a bouncing slam at the physician's system in its entirety.

One patient, assiduously active in Recovery and indisputably loyal to the physician, was asked what she thought most instrumental in bringing about her recovery. She remarked, "I spoke to Annette and Rosalie. Of course, the classes helped me a lot. But Annette and Rosalie more. They have experience because they went through the same trouble." The physician inquired, "Does that mean that I have no experience?" The patient, noticing her blunder, corrected with more fumbling, "Oh, no, but they are sincere." The physician pressed the argument, "Do you think I am not sincere?" The patient explained, "Well, one never knows whether the doctor is going to tell the truth. He may hesitate to tell me he can't help me."

CHAPTER THIRTY-FIVE

Sabotage Method No. 4
Challenging the Physician's Diagnosis: Outright Insistence on Change of Diagnosis

A student may speak of the examination for which he is preparing himself as being either his present purpose or his goal or his aim. Similarly, a housewife on a shopping tour may claim that the purchase of vegetables is the purpose, goal or aim of her present endeavor. In all of this, the terms *purpose, goal* and *aim* are treated as having identical meanings. Much of the confusion attending plain conversation or important debates can be traced to this careless manner of using the three discrete words and juggling their underlying concepts.

The nervous patient must not permit himself the luxury of employing a confusing terminology. To him, it must be clear that the PURPOSE AIMS AT ITS GOAL. He must then be shown, with unquestioned clarity, which is the purpose that moves him, which the goal he has set for himself and what is the degree of determination with which he must aim at the goal.

The nervous patient here spoken of is an average individual. His purpose is that of the average person, i.e., the establishing and maintaining of a family. There are confirmed bachelors and spinsters, isolated trappers and roaming hoboes whose activities are not centered on the family purpose. There are individuals who devote their lives to religious, scientific or artistic pursuits, escaping or actively avoiding family ties. All these groups, no matter how numerous they may be, do not fall within the scope of average existence. Their lives are fashioned on exceptional patterns, and the purposes which move them are not pertinent to the present discussion. Within the limits of the present discussion, the central purpose of the average person is focused on the family. It is fixed by average constitution, anchored in original predisposition and favored by nature. That purpose is *given*, not *chosen*. It is stable, practically unchanging, and hardly subject to deliberate manipulation, provided it is embraced and not ignored or rejected as in the instances quoted.

The purpose, itself largely unchanging, chooses or sets its goals. They are the means toward accomplishing the purpose. One person may think a profession is the best means of caring for his future or present family, another may choose a business career, a third politics, or agriculture or military service. Once the goal has been set (profession, business, politics, etc.), all significant action must be so contrived that it aims at the chosen goal. The aiming must be effective, i.e., straight, direct, sustained, determined, energetic. It must not be wavering, ambiguous, capricious, hesitating, irresolute.

The student, working for the examination, aims at a degree, let us say the medical diploma. This is an *intermediate goal*. The *final goal* is to attain efficiency or prominence in the field of his chosen medical profession. A great number of intermediate goals must be aimed at after the successful passing of the examination: internship, residency, renting of an office, purchase of equipment, marriage, education of the children. By means of these intermediate goals, the central purpose (of the family) aims at the final and supreme goal.

While aiming, the individual must be able to analyze the nature of his intermediate goals in order to be certain that they really and actually lead toward the final goal. Otherwise, the aim deviates from its target. Campaigning for an electoral contest, for instance, would be good aiming for the final goal of the politician. The conferences with election workers, the addressing of the public, the canvassing of neighbors and friends are intermediate goals that aim straight and undeviatingly at the final goal of victory at the polls. But if the physician should choose electioneering activities as his intermediate goals, he may frustrate his final goal of establishing a solid practice in his community. Aiming must be direct and undeviating, and in order to keep the aim straight, the individual must be in a position to analyze and diagnose the nature of his intermediate goals. Faulty diagnosis of intermediate goals leads to defective aiming at the final goal.

If a physician starting out in medical practice engages in politics, the chances are he is guided by a fondness for the limelight. His action is based on or influenced by personal inclination, emotional craving, ill-controlled impulses, unreasonable desires, in short, by *subjective feelings.* In order to prevent the aim from deviating in improper directions, an individual must train himself to base his action on sane premises, sound conclusions, cool reasoning and good common sense, in short, on *objective thought.* Subjective feelings divert the aim from its proper target; objective thought tends to keep the aim straight in the line of the target.

The nervous patient vitiates his purpose by allowing himself to be deflected in the direction of improper intermediate goals. The physician diagnoses the condition as one of emotional imbalance and prescribes the sustained practice of self-discipline as the final goal to be aimed at. But the subjective feelings of tenseness, distress and panics intervene to suggest that instant relief is needed and that patience and self-discipline are futile remedies in an emergency. If the sufferer yields to the dictates of his feelings, his aim will be deflected from the objective goal of self-restraint to the subjective goal of self-indulgence. The deflection is occasioned by the fact that the patient disregards the physician's diagnosis of an emotional imbalance and substitutes his own diagnosis of a physical emergency situation. An emotional imbalance calls for self-restraint as the goal to be aimed at. An acute emergency may require self-indulgence as the proper aim.

The difficulty would not be serious if the patient limited his faulty aiming to the occasions when he finds himself in a panic. Unfortunately, the regrettable practice tends to persist after the panic has passed. When the patient challenges the diagnostic ability of the physician during the acute distress of the self-diagnosed "emergency," the results carry over into the more quiescent periods when the symptoms cause merely mild discomfort. When, during the panic, he discards the diagnosis of an emotional imbalance, the physician's authority receives, in the patient's mind, a severe blow from which it does not recover easily. His diagnostic ability stands challenged, and the propensity for challenging it gains momentum with each succeeding setback. The final result is a policy of consistent aiming in the direction of self-indulgence by insisting that the condition is one of a physical ailment and not, as the physician puts it, one of an emotional imbalance. The policy sabotages the physician's authority and prevents effective cooperation. In the process of pursuing their sabotage efforts, some patients do not hesitate to voice their challenge with outspoken frankness while others employ more subtle and indirect methods. The precise manner in which these forms of sabotage are practiced will be demonstrated in the following illustrations.

Example 1. A young woman had been suffering from innumerable frightening sensations for over six years. She complained of a crawly feeling over the head, a numbness of the limbs as if they were paralyzed. The eyes felt as if they were being pulled in. She felt a pressure on the nose as if a ton was weighing on it. She had spells of air-hunger in which she felt she was going to suffocate. There were all kinds of pains, pressures, dizziness and dimness of vision, and many bizarre sensations. One day she reported that "out of a clear sky, I felt that something blew up in my head. I thought I was gone." On another day she had a burning in the muscles as if "electric wires passed through them." Her head seemed to be falling forward, the body felt as if it were "floating in space." She knew that the symptoms were precipitated by emotional upsets and disappeared in response to emotional relaxation. One day she volunteered the statement that "of course, it's all nerves. I know that. But that does not help me."

She was a loyal member of Recovery, indicating that she considered her condition subject to treatment through self-help and self-discipline. Nevertheless, she frequently protested that suffering of this severity could "not possibly be of a nervous nature." Once she said, "If I turn my head, it cracks in the neck. Then the pain shoots right up to my hip. How can this be nerves?" On another occasion, she remarked, "I get that pain when I do the simplest thing. All I have to do is to peel an orange, and the pain is there. How can nerves do that? I am so weak, I cannot cut an apple. That weakness must be physical." She craved medication. She was willing to submit to an operation. Her aim was directed toward the intermediate goals of physical therapy and was deflected from those of self-discipline.

Example 2. A woman, whose main symptoms consisted of pressure in the chest with "awful palpitations," was obsessed with the fear of sudden collapse. The condition had been progressing for fully seventeen years before she was seen at the office. After a brief period of combined class and individual treatment, she experienced a considerable improvement and had sequences of good days and even good weeks "the first time in years." She was an untiring Recovery worker and seemed to relish the idea of self-help. But whenever she appeared at the office shortly after going through setbacks, the thought of a physical ailment reasserted itself. One of her numerous symptoms was heaviness of the eyelids. "Couldn't that be astigmatism?" she asked. She also suffered from severe abdominal spasms. "Why couldn't that be an ulcer?" she asked. The aiming was deflected from the intermediate goals of self-discipline toward those of self-indulgence. What she aimed at were prescriptions, diets, operations, bed rest, eyeglasses.

Example 3. A male patient had been maladjusted all his life as far as he could remember. He was always fatigued, pepless and devoid of ambition. At home, he was explosive in temper, on the outside, meek and timid. He suffered from a profound sense of inadequacy, felt flustered in the presence of people and blushed easily. Having attained expertness as a mechanical engineer, he was unable to capitalize on his professional competence because of his abiding self-consciousness. In social contacts, he was clumsy and awkward. When addressed, he had difficulty formulating a proper sentence and felt choked when he made an effort to speak. In the presence of girls, he was particularly bashful. He had been engaged for over three years to a young lady whom he loved dearly but could not muster the courage to get married. After several months of treatment, his self-consciousness improved considerably, but his explosiveness persisted. Finally, he decided to go through with his marriage plans.

He established a home and felt happy. Unfortunately, his periodic temperamental bursts marred an otherwise compatible marital life. He realized that his temper could only be cured by self-discipline. He had studied the volumes of *Recovery's Self-Help System** and attended classes regularly. He knew the distinction between subjective feelings and objective thought, was well aware of his tendency to sabotage the physician's authority. Nevertheless, whenever he was seen after a domestic temper outburst, he advanced alternative explanations for his inability to control temper. "If I am argumentative," he said, "I am sure it is because of my high blood pressure." The blood pressure was on the upper level of the norm, not significantly elevated. One day he asked, "Couldn't my excitability be due to a thyroid condition?" He was currently deflected from his final goal of self-discipline in the direction of intermediate goals of self-indulgence.

Example 4. A male patient had gone through alternating spells of depressions and elations of mood for the past thirty years. In the intervals between the attacks, he was well

---

*Editors' Note: This title is also known as *The Techniques of Self-Help in Psychiatric After-Care*. Please see "Other Books by Abraham A. Low, M.D." on pages 417—418.

enough to make a moderate living but was haunted by the sense of being stigmatized. He was unable to throw off the feeling that he was essentially incurable. During the last spell, he was given a course of electroshock therapy, and the hospital treatment was to be followed up with a well pre-pared program of participation in Recovery activities. Like so many manic-depressive patients, he did not relish a sys-tem that places the main emphasis on self-help and self-dis-cipline. He cooperated grudgingly and mainly on the energetic insistence of his wife. For several weeks after leav-ing the hospital, he complained of a number of residual symptoms. He still suspected that people watched him, felt fatigued most of the day and slept poorly.

Before long, he learned to ignore the fatigue sensations and to reject the suspicions about people watching him. Finally, he mastered the difficulty of sleeping by imbibing the principle that the so-called "insomnia" is no danger to health. At this stage, he felt grateful to Recovery and joined the activ-ities with a better spirit of cooperation. Nevertheless, he still resented having his residual symptoms termed "nervous." "My sensations feel real," he insisted, "they are physical, not nervous." Soon thereafter, he decided to quit Recovery for a while. "I think it would do me a world of good to spend sev-eral weeks without talking about my symptoms." The physi-cian's diagnosis was challenged, and his method of treatment disparaged. Aiming was deflected toward intermediate goals that ran counter to the final goal of overcoming the sense of stigmatization.

Brief examples: A woman patient, who had attended classes for many months, had lost most of the sensations she had complained of originally. After a setback, she said, "I went through an awful ordeal. I still have a pain in the right foot. How is it it does not disappear? That has certainly noth-ing to do with nerves."

A lady suffered from all kinds of disturbing sensa-tions, foremost among them a "sick headache." She improved and seemed to appreciate the desirability of prac-ticing the self-help methods she had learned in classes. After a setback, she reverted to her previous practice of suggesting physical methods of therapy as the proper means for relief. "I am still troubled by these sick headaches," she said. "Don't you think I should have my glasses changed?"

Another lady had received a course of insulin treatment for a mental ailment. She recovered and was given after-care in Recovery. She "just loved" classes and meetings and boasted of practicing self-help "just as the doctor wants it." After a setback, she asked, "I still have that headache. Is that nervous, too? And I have pains in the legs. Is that anything to worry about?"

A woman who was being treated for a psychoneurosis of long standing suffered a setback which was characterized by all manner of disturbing sensations. She was in a marked state of anxiety which she insisted on calling "confusion." Because of a difficulty of concentrating, she anticipated a mental collapse. She knew about sabotage and admitted practicing it. "But, Doctor," she exclaimed with a show of emotion, "that panic I had yesterday was just awful. You can't call that nervous. It looked the nearest to a mental collapse."

CHAPTER THIRTY-SIX

Sabotage Method No. 5
Challenging the Physician's Diagnosis: Implied Insistence on Change of Diagnosis

Once the physician has made the diagnosis of a nervous ailment, a goal is set for the patient to aim at. The patient is given detailed instructions how to manipulate the aiming. He is told by word of mouth and through books and pamphlets that the object is to ignore his disturbing inner experiences, his threatening sensations, his overpowering impulses, his obsessing thoughts or deranged feelings. Above all, he is directed to command his muscles not to do the bidding of the temperamental lingo and the symptomatic idiom. The instructions are clear. The patient is perfectly able to understand them. Moreover, they are endlessly repeated and currently illustrated with telling examples in classes and meetings. There can be no doubt that the patient fully grasps the nature of the goal and the proper means of aiming at it. Why, then, does his aim stray so persistently from the goal set by the physician?

The goal is that of self-discipline. What must be disciplined is the patient's behavior, particularly his behavior toward his inner experiences. His heart sets up frightening palpitations, and if they are to be controlled, thought and muscles must be trained not to respond to the threat of the symptom. But in past years, the patient has developed the habits of indulging himself. He has for many years yielded to the impulse to call for instant relief, to summon the physician, insisting that he cannot "stand it one minute longer." He has for years made use of his panics for the purpose of alerting the house, clamoring for emergency measures, making everybody jump and rush, turning the home into a madhouse, keeping all relatives in a frenzy of suspense and excitement.

These reactions have hardened into stubborn habits of self-indulgence. And if the patient is asked to exchange his present set of habits for those prescribed by his physician, if he is told to discard self-indulgence and to replace it with self-discipline, the task seems to be exacting indeed. The goal scares him, and there is no possibility of a steady, energetic, fearless aiming if the very target inspires fear, weakens the energy and shakes steadiness into quivering agitation. If thus affected, the patient will be inclined to cling to his old habits of self-indulgence. The goal set for him by the physician will strike him as unrealistic, impossible of achievement; he will question its value, will view it with skepticism if not with outright ridicule.

If the patient is skeptical, that means he is not disposed to accept the goal. Yet he accepts it in a sense. The fact that he does not change physicians indicates that he subscribes to the diagnosis of a nervous ailment and pledges himself to practice what he is told to do. But the pledge is given with reservations which find their expression in the statement, "I'll try my best." The "best" to which the patient commits himself is nothing but a weak half-effort, a lukewarm cooperation, a disposition to give up should the first trial prove unsuccessful. Essentially, it means the goal is accepted partially only. It is neither fully rejected nor wholly accepted. But without full acceptance of the goal, there can be no thorough aiming.

In the foregoing chapter, an account was given of defective aiming on the part of the patient who challenges the diagnosis. The examples quoted there referred to outright rejection of the physician's opinion. The patients there described actually substituted a diagnosis of their own. They asked, "How can nerves do that? How can this be nerves? That weakness must be physical." This is about the nearest a patient will come to an outright rejection of the physician's authority if he continues to patronize him at all. This type of sabotage was characterized as "Outright Insistence on Change of Diagnosis" which meant an unqualified challenge of the diagnosis. In the present chapter, the case of the patient will be discussed who, avoiding open defiance, rejects the diagnosis by implication rather than straight denial.

Examples: A woman had been suffering from fatigue, poor sleep, headaches, dizziness, chest pressure and all kinds of other threatening sensations. Most annoying was a sensation felt in the abdomen of a churning and tremulousness which was present all day every day. The churning became almost unbearable immediately after taking a meal. As a result, eating became a continued and dreaded torture. In time, the patient almost loathed food. She was seen by a number of physicians, was hospitalized several times with no effort spared to arrive at a diagnosis. All tests were negative, and the diagnosis was invariably that of a nervous condition. She was seen in the fourth year of her invalidism and made considerable headway in response to private interviews and class treatment. Nevertheless, she insisted that the constant churning must have a "cause." This term "cause" is frequently mentioned by patients who resent having their disturbance classified as nervous. Nervousness, to them, means a condition for which there is no "cause." It means a trouble which has to do with lack of will-power, self-pampering, refusal to get well, in short, poor morale and weak character. The "cause," if found, would instantly redeem the moral status of the patient, and the stigma of low morale would fall to the ground. The patient in question was untiring in her assertion that her symptoms must have a "cause." "I always have diarrhea. There must surely be a cause for that." When questioned about the character of her evacuation, she gave the information that she had two movements, sometimes three, on the days in which the diarrhea was present. When asked whether the stool was solid, soft or liquid, she said, "Today it was solid in the forenoon and soft in the afternoon." And this was called a "diarrhea" which "surely must have a cause." In this instance, the physician's diagnosis was rejected by implication. It was implied, not mentioned explicitly, that in labelling the ailment as nervous, the physician had neglected to look for the "real and true" cause. The diagnosis was challenged by an implied insistence on physical ailment.

Frequently, these patients will quote other physicians whom they consulted in previous years, reciting some diagnostic statement which may be reproduced correctly or incorrectly. "Dr. H.," a patient said, "warned me that vomiting of the kind I have may be due to a beginning cancer." Another patient quoted or misquoted a previous consultant as stating that he found a "thickening of the folds of the sigmoid. He put me on a rigid diet and warned me to keep my bowels regulated. He must have had some reason for doing that."

Another patient exclaimed, "I have an awful pressure in the head. There must be a cause for that." He was told that this was a quest for a change in the diagnosis and meant sabotage. Whereupon he replied, "Dr. C. said, 'You are on the borderline. You go to the hospital and rest your mind.'" This man was one of those patients who insist that theirs is a mental and not a nervous ailment. This insistence on the diagnosis of a mental condition seems to have gained currency since the introduction of shock treatments. To some patients, the prospect of shock treatment is more promising than mere psychotherapy. It holds out the promise of quick relief.

One patient had her hopes pinned on electroshock therapy because she knew it had given quick aid to many sufferers she met in Recovery. She was told that her condition was of such a nature that shock therapy would not be successful. This did not discourage her. She replied, "But I am afraid I am a mental case, and I need shock treatment. Dr. S. told me people develop bad habits, and they stay with them." And this flimsy statement was made the warrant for a change in diagnosis and for the choice of a treatment which entails a great deal of hardship and may even have serious consequences. Some patients, inspired by the desire for quick relief, go even to the length of pleading for the diagnosis of a brain tumor. Any diagnosis seems to them more hopeful than that of a nervous ailment. A brain tumor they view as a possibility for an operation and a rapid deliverance from suffering.

A rather common attempt to reject the diagnosis of a nervous ailment is the recourse to heredity. A nervous ailment, the patient thinks, means lowered morale. This label cannot possibly be attached to a condition which is due to a hereditary predisposition. The patient cannot, on any account, be held responsible for a difficulty inherited from his ancestors. One patient, immediately on being told that her complaint was undoubtedly due to a nervous disturbance, replied, "I hope my son will not get this condition. My mother had exactly the same complaints I have." Another patient said, "My mother was like me. Is that hereditary?" There is certainly no glory in a hereditary ailment. There can be scant consolation in the thought that one's ancestors were "tainted." But anything sounds more hopeful and more comforting than the bleak prospect of having to undergo training in self-discipline. Even brain tumors, mental ailments and hereditary "taints" are preferable to that dreadful indictment as being a weak character and needing training in self-control.

CHAPTER THIRTY-SEVEN

Discourse on Valuation

Goals are of two kinds: short-range and long-range. The process of bringing up and educating children extends over twenty to twenty-five years. It takes the greater part of a man's adult life to establish a reputation, to acquire unquestioned mastery of a profession, to build up a smooth-running business enterprise. Such long-range goals, requiring prodigious amounts of time for their development and ripening, tax the patience, endurance and determination of the individual. Short-range goals are less or not at all exacting. The purchase of a garment, the writing of a letter, the trimming of the lawn or the visit to a friend's home are goals of this description. They call for a minimum of patience, endurance and determination. They are usually accomplished in little time, with scant effort and with negligible risk of failure.

Long-range goals, as a rule, carry considerable responsibilities. If you neglect the cutting of your lawn, you will not be likely to suffer the tortures of self-reproach. But let the thought obsess you that you neglected the education of your children, and your peace of mind will be gravely affected. You will suffer pangs of conscience and bitter despair. Short-range goals permit leisurely, relaxed aiming. But long-range goals demand steady concentration and strained attention. They leave little room for relaxation and diversion.

If your goal is of the short-range variety, you will be able to aim at it correctly if you make use of the proper tool and command the requisite skill and technique for using it. You will do a good job at cutting the grass in front of your home if you employ a suitable lawn mower with moderate skill and a smattering of knowledge about its technical construction. This is entirely different if your aim is directed at a long-range goal. Tools, skills and techniques alone will be of little significance if your ambition is to secure a good education for your children. A goal of this kind demands patient application, sustained effort, unflagging determination, and, above all, an unshakable sense of duty and responsibility. To be brief: short-range goals must be aimed at with *skills and techniques,* long-range goals with *character and will power.*

The fact that you set yourself a given long-range goal indicates that you prefer that goal to another. You might have chosen a business career, but you decided on a medical education in preference to trading or manufacturing. The preference placed a valuation on your choice. You value your activities as a student or practitioner of medicine. Your aim is now directed at a *value.*

A physician may value a multitude of things and activities. Hunting, traveling and golfing may be valuable for his recreation. Card games, radio and movies may be of value to him in point of relaxation and diversion. To be expensively dressed, to own a high-priced automobile and to acquire membership in an exclusive club may be of value to his reputation or to his vanity. He may, of course, value material possessions, and if, in the pursuit of wealth, he engages in stock market or real estate speculation, be certain that the thrill or the mere prospect of amassing a fortune will be valuable to him. But clearly, the faithful devotion to a noble profession and the greedy scramble for money cannot possibly have the same value. Obviously, valuations must be of two kinds. How are they to be differentiated?

An overcoat is of value as protection against rain and cold. If keeping dry and warm is your present goal, the overcoat will be a suitable means with which to aim at the goal. Generally speaking, every means or tool which enables you to aim at your goal is of value for this particular goal. If your goal right now is to escape the summer heat, a swim will be of value. If your goal is to still your hunger, a hamburger or frankfurter will be objects of value. Since everything may at times become the suitable means of aiming at a goal, the possible range of values is limitless. The question is not, however, whether a given means or tool is of value to a given goal. The more important question is whether the goal itself is one of value.

A goal may be of value to the individual or to the group. Whether an overcoat satisfies your desire for protection against the weather and whether a dish of meat relieves your hunger is of no direct interest to the group. These goals serve your personal comfort and are individualistic in nature. They are *individualistic values.* On the other hand, if you bend your energies to educating your children, the group will recognize your endeavor as being valuable to the community and will class it as a group value. Needless to say that when we speak of values, we mean *group values* only.

In order to guide the conduct of the individuals belonging to it, the group has set up a *table of valuations.* All group values, that is, all valued or preferred group goals are there ranged in proportion to the importance they bear to the group purpose. The individualistic goals of personal comfort, vanity, emotional and temperamental dispositions and competitive ambitions are reasonably tolerated within the framework of the table of valuations but are not included in it. To put it otherwise, the group permits a moderate degree of indulgence in gambling, drinking, frolicking. It sanctions certain emotional drives and temperamental leanings. It may even grant a modicum of license to greed, unwise speculation and sharp competition. But all these activities are strictly classed as individualistic and are denied a rating in terms of valuations.

A group strives for stability first and foremost. Short-range goals could never guarantee stability. They are pursued for a short time until mood, caprice, disposition suggest other more convenient goals. If stability is to be maintained, the group must insist on reserving its table of valuations for long-range goals only. As was mentioned, aiming at long-range goals calls for steadfastness, determination, patience and sustained effort. In other words, it calls for character. Character is opposed or indifferent to mood, caprice, disposition. Everything that is purely individualistic and personal is outside the sphere of character.

A person endowed with character aims at his long-range group goals (values) either with rigid, unyielding *principles* or with elastic but firm *policies.* Principles admit of no exception, policies do. It is unprincipled behavior to steal or cheat even once. But it may be good policy to relax discipline frequently in dealing with children or employees. Principles call for relentlessness, severity, perhaps even for fanaticism; policies call for a flexible strategy, for maneuver and careful adjustment to the requirements of the just-prevailing situation. But no matter how fundamentally different they are with regard to rigidity and flexibility, both principle and policy defeat their purpose unless they are acted on with steadfastness, determination, patience and sustained effort.

Health, it would seem, does not figure in the average table of valuations. The group holds its members responsible for their character and, for instance, frowns on dishonesty and lack of responsibility. But it does not set up a code that obliges the individual to tend to his health. There are other important functions which, though they represent undoubtedly long-range group goals, are not included in the table of valuations. Parenthood is one of them, sociability another. The group unquestionably values them but refrains from regulating or supervising them. The reason, presumably, is that the vast majority of people can be depended on to take adequate care of health, children and social contacts without any prompting on the part of the group. Be that as it may, the fact is that health does not seem to be considered a value in its own right. The other fact, however, is that without health, there can be no proper aiming at long-range goals and their corresponding values. The functions of loyal service, religious devotion, patriotic duty, parenthood, friendship, sociability, civic-mindedness cannot be accomplished if the individual is crippled, bedridden or otherwise seriously handicapped. That functions of this order cannot be properly discharged if they are continuously frustrated by frightening sensations, panics and anxieties, needs no comment. Mental health, particularly, is not only a value. It is a necessary prerequisite for the unhampered functioning of all the values represented in the table of valuations.

CHAPTER THIRTY-EIGHT

Sabotage Method No. 6
Failure to Practice
"Spot Diagnosis"

Whether or not health is part of the general table of valuations, to the patient it cannot be anything but a value. As such, it must be aimed at either with rigid principle or with a firm policy. A principle is not permitted ever to deviate from its goal. A policy may at times, but if it is to remain firm, the deviations must be held to an unavoidable minimum.

A physician treating a confirmed drinker will have to insist on principle. He must instruct the patient *never* to imbibe even a single drop of liquor. Should the drinker deviate even once from the goal of total abstinence, the deviations are certain to be continued. For the nervous patient, such a rigid adherence to principle is not necessary. If suffering from "nervous fatigue," he is directed to take brisk walks in defiance of his physical discomfort, he may at times weaken and stray from the goal of self-discipline. In other words, he is permitted to sabotage his goal occasionally. His health practice must be persistent but not continuous. In his case, a performance based on rigid principle can be dispensed with. A firm policy will finally accomplish the end.

In order to hold down the deviations, that is, the acts of sabotage, to a minimum, the patient will have to know the nature of the diagnosis and the acts which constitute sabotage. The diagnosis of a nervous condition establishes that the patient suffers from disturbing sensations, feelings, impulses and thoughts. These symptoms may occur numbers of times every hour of every day. Each time any of the symptoms appear, the patient must have in mind the diagnosis given him after the initial examination. At that time, the physician surveyed the broad field of the patient's reactions. His final diagnosis covered the sum total of the symptoms, the various circumstances in which they may occur, the domestic, social or vocational influences that may precipitate them, the emotional background, the time most favorable for their release. Covering the entire field of their operation, the diagnosis was a *field diagnosis*. This field diagnosis the patient must now apply to every occasion and every spot where the symptoms may be noticed. His part in the diagnostic scheme is to practice *spot diagnosis*.

In order to perform the diagnostic function assigned to him, he will have to acquire skill in *spotting* each symptom as it arises and each sabotaging trend as it emerges. The symptoms will have to be spotted in their initial stage before they reach their peak of intensity. At the moment the "fatigue" begins to stir in the morning, the spot diagnosis of a harmless nervous disturbance must be made instantly. Likewise, if worry or alarm supervene, the spot diagnosis of sabotage must immediately dominate the patient's mind. If the spotting is done promptly, both the symptom and the sabotage will spend themselves without leading to a vicious cycle. In the beginning, the spotting will have to be done consciously and laboriously, but with continued practice and experience, the process will become relatively automatic and spontaneous.

The spotting practice is not easy. The chief difficulty is that symptoms frequently acquire the tendency to shoot forth with the rapidity of a trigger reaction. The palpitation or air-hunger are there before the patient "even had time to think about them." The trigger symptom is not only abrupt in its appearance, it is also extremely intense, overwhelming, threatening, terrifying. Once its terror grips the patient, he will be thrown into a panic and will be caught in a relentless vicious cycle. The terror will instantly suggest that these are "the worst palpitations I ever had," and that "if I don't get my breath quickly, this is sure to be my last gasp." The trigger symptom has now set in motion a whole train of sabotaging thoughts, the thoughts of a heart disease, of a tumor in the chest, the fear of impending collapse. The sabotage sweeps aside the physician's field diagnosis and aborts the patient's spot diagnosis.

Clearly, the trigger symptom must be spotted before it has an opportunity to generate the panic and the vicious cycle. This is possible only if the spot diagnosis is established in the split second when the trigger reaction is born. Stating it otherwise, it means that the spot diagnosis must acquire a trigger quality. The thought, "This is nervous and nothing else," must shoot into the patient's mind precisely at the moment when his body fires off its palpitations. *Trigger spotting must coincide with or follow immediately on the eruption of the trigger symptom.* That spotting of this kind calls for a firm policy needs no emphasis.

Some symptoms have undoubted trigger quality. But most of them are preceded by ordinary tenseness and irritability and gain momentum only because of the temperamental attitude taken by the patient. He becomes provoked at himself or others, indulges in an orgy of self-pity or attention-demanding, and it is this process of "working himself up" that finally leads to panicky reactions. This situation, which is by far more common than the "out-of-a-blue-sky" reaction, demands a firm policy of temper control, that means, *temper spotting.*

Contrary to what might be expected, the average patient encounters greater difficulty spotting his temperamental reaction than he does in the process of spotting the symptom. Even the trigger reaction is more amenable to spot control than is temper. The reason ought to be clear: the symptom scares and creates distress. It is experienced as painful, unendurable. Its capacity for creating severe suffering carries with it the powerful incentive to eliminate it. Temper is neither terrifying nor painful nor unendurable. Instead, it is stimulating, vital, energizing. If it provides any incentive, it is for prolonging the stimulation and pleasure it affords. It is temper, mainly, that resists the diagnostic spotting necessary to avoid panics and vicious cycles. Temper spotting calls for an extremely firm policy. In a sense, it might require rigid principle to curb it successfully.

The suddenness with which nervous symptoms are apt to strike is frightening, of course. Anything that occurs suddenly and unexpectedly has this tendency to scare. You strike against an innocent object in the dark, and you get scared. A dog jumps at you, and instantly your heart palpitates, and your knees shake. Let anybody tap you on the shoulder from behind, and you will start. The scare caused by the suddenly erupting symptom fits into this common pattern. Anyone would be frightened if his eyes suddenly went dim or when his legs were stricken with a sudden limpness. But the patient must learn to deal with the abruptly emerging symptom as he does when a dog jumps at him unexpectedly. In the case of the dog, he gets scared but immediately realizes that, after all, it was nothing but a dog. In this instance, the momentary scare is followed immediately by the correct spot diagnosis. The latter establishes the fact that the scare was produced by an innocent, harmless event. After the spot diagnosis is made, the fright disappears.

Why is correct spot diagnosis done after ordinary scares but not after the scare produced by a symptom? The answer is that correct spotting is easy in the examples quoted but extremely difficult in the instance of nervous symptoms. If a dog is correctly spotted as the cause of an upset, there is nothing to contradict the fact that it was the dog who caused the damage. The thought of another possibility can hardly arise. But after a symptom has made its appearance, the patient's thought processes swing into action. Thinking about a symptom means to appraise it, to assess its significance, its danger, its likelihood to recur, and all of this means making a diagnosis. If at that moment the patient makes the physician's diagnosis, the symptom will be spotted as merely nervous.

Unfortunately, the diagnosis is usually taken from the patient's previous knowledge, and that knowledge was gathered in years past either from his own misconceptions about how symptoms operate, or from misinterpreted statements of other physicians or from popular notions current in the community. No sooner has the symptom struck than the patient recalls in a flash the wild diagnoses that have come to him from sources other than his physician. He now indulges in a veritable orgy of self-diagnosing, preventing the correct spot diagnosis, and precipitating a flood of self-scaring reflections. The diagnosis, gathered from foreign sources, sweeps aside the spot diagnosis recommended by his physician, and the self-scaring ruminations give rise to that variety of temper which, leading to defeatist auto-suggestions, is nothing but plain hysteria.

The patient now finds that the present dizziness is "worse than ever." He has "never before" experienced such a furious bout of dizziness. How can the doctor call a dizziness of this kind nervous if it "just drives me mad?" Or, a patient notices that the room swings around him. "I never had that before. It's something new. And the doctor made his diagnosis without knowing about this symptom." Or, the patient experiences that "awful head pressure," and "this time it is real, it is not merely a sensation." Or, the patient is the victim of palpitations and air-hunger. Suddenly, he recalls a recent newspaper notice that an acquaintance of his collapsed on the street and died from a heart ailment that had not been diagnosed by the physician. And so the hysteria runs on, releasing a veritable hurricane of defeatist thoughts, sabotaging the field diagnosis handed down by the physician and frustrating any attempt at applying the spot diagnosis. The vicious cycle dominates the scene, multiplying symptoms and pyramiding temperamental outbursts.

Examples: A woman patient complained of a soreness in one of her lower teeth. The condition had been in existence for over ten years, alternately affecting different teeth or some part of the gums or cheeks. Most of her teeth had been extracted in deference to her urgent demand to have something done to eliminate "that unbearable pain." She was certain that an abscess or tumor was causing the soreness. She demanded incessantly to be placed in the hospital "for a checkup," insisted on X-ray studies, tooth extractions, surgery. When she described her pain, she hardly ever missed remarking, "This is the worst pain I ever felt. It just drives me crazy. There is a pressure against the root, and I am sure it is a tumor."

Patients of this kind are given the following explanation: "You compare the present pain with a previous pain which you had weeks or months ago. Then you conclude that today's pain is the worst ever. But you must realize that the present pain is actually *experienced* right now while the pain which you had weeks ago is merely *remembered*. Of course, a pain felt right now is always worse than one that is merely remembered. Every experience fades in memory. The pain is remembered, but its intensity is softened and mellowed in recollection as everything softens and mellows if viewed in the perspective of time. As a matter of fact, if your present pain were the 'mildest ever,' it would figure in your mind as the 'worst ever' even if you compared it to the most excruciating experience you had in the past. An experience, no matter how mild, is always more intense than a recollection, no matter how severe."

The "worst ever" theme has its variations. Some patients do not merely refer to one single symptom that is felt as having "now" reached its worst intensity; they experience their total condition as being "most" deteriorated today. A patient who had numerous periods of severe depressions to his record was seen on a day when he suffered from a mild condition that only remotely resembled his previous episodes. He "felt blue," but appetite, sleep and initiative were hardly affected. He admitted that he had no difficulty eating and sleeping. He agreed also that he did not have to drive himself as he knew he had to in his severe spells. Nevertheless, he wound up his account with the statement, "I don't see what sleeping and eating have to do with this. I don't think I've ever been that bad."

Another variation of the "worst ever" complaint was furnished by a lady who had for years experienced a sort of tenseness in the abdomen. She called it, variously, "tremor," "dancing" or "shaking." One day, she declared that the shaking was now "worse than ever. It has never been as continuous as these past weeks." Continuity was substituted for intensity in point of being "the worst ever."

Once a patient confers the epithet "worst ever" to a symptom, it is no longer spotted as nervous. It is conceived of as something new in intensity, as something that the physician has not considered when he arrived at his field diagnosis. One part of the field had not been sufficiently covered. The patient then supplies the deficiency, arriving at the diagnostic conclusion that, "If it is that bad, how can it be nervous?"

Some patients content themselves with pointing to the newness of a symptom without touching on its "worse" or "worst" quality. A male sufferer, who listed a bewildering host of complaints in his repertory, exclaimed, "Yesterday, out of a blue sky, I suddenly felt an electric current through my chest. I never had that before." The patient was an "old-timer" with numerous office visits to his record. The examiner fetched the patient's folder from the files and had no difficulty pointing to several notations concerning electric currents in various parts of the body. The patient was far from convinced. His comment was: "Maybe I had currents before, but that was the most awful experience I ever had."

Patients frequently emphasize the "first" occurrence of a symptom. If it is a complaint which they "never had before," they hasten to add, "Can that be nerves, too?" In many instances, the experience is by no means new and "first," as was easily demonstrated in the case of the patient with the "new" electric current. But new symptoms are, of course, common in psychoneurotic conditions. If they occur, they offer the patient a welcome opportunity to engage in his favorite game of sabotaging the physician's field diagnosis. Whether the symptom is the "worst ever" or the "first ever," it is invariably seized upon for the purpose of avoiding the correct spot diagnosis.

CHAPTER THIRTY-NINE

Sabotage Method No. 7
Failure to Spot
Emotionalism

If the patient is to spot his temperamental reactions, he will have to know those of his acts and statements which give expression to his temper. The coarse varieties of his temperamental expressions ought to be known to him if he took the trouble to read the various chapters of *The Techniques of Self-Help** which deal voluminously with the subdivisions of the fearful and angry temper. The descriptions there given were concerned with the temperamental behavior which precedes and precipitates symptoms. If a patient develops a spell of choking and dizziness immediately following a heated squabble, it is hardly necessary to remind him that his symptoms are the result of his temper. The relation between the two elements is here patent, obvious, self-evident. All that is required to understand occurrences of this kind is plain common sense. The precise meaning of both temper and symptom reveals itself to anybody's native and untutored intelligence and calls for no detailed instruction.

This is different with the temperamental behavior which the patient releases *after* a symptom has set in. The symptom may have appeared spontaneously, out of nowhere, without provocation, perhaps at the very moment the patient awoke in the morning. No commotion of any

---

*Editors' Note: The full title is *The Techniques of Self-Help in Psychiatric After-Care.* Please see "Other Books by Abraham A. Low, M.D." on pages 417—418.

kind preceded it. No sooner were the eyes opened than a heavy pressure settled on the chest, and air-hunger produced gasping and choking. The patient is now scared. The scare is originally nothing but a startle, exactly as in the case of a dog suddenly leaping at a man. The startle would spend itself in a few seconds if the patient had the determination to spot the symptom as what it is: the harmless expression of a nervous imbalance. If the symptom is left unspotted, the scare may persist, and the likelihood is the patient will now drift into a process of "working himself up." Essentially, this is a procedure in which the patient talks or thinks himself into a mixture of fear and anger which may be prolonged indefinitely, just as long as the sufferer cares to maintain his favorite pastime of self-torture. Since the "working-up" process follows the symptom, it properly goes by the name of *post-symptomatic temper*. Its counterpart is the situation in which temperamental behavior precedes and precipitates the symptom. Preceding it, it is called *pre-symptomatic temper*. The latter is patent and obvious and needs no or little spotting. The former is subtle and elusive and calls for a consummate art of spotting skill.

The practice of "working oneself up" follows well defined patterns. The patient may give himself up to a paroxysm of fear or anger. Then he emotionalizes his predicament. He anticipates endless torture; he is certain he is utterly incapable of coping with this "frightful" pressure and visualizes disaster, fatal consequences or outright collapse. After hours of whipping himself up, he may realize that nothing fatal or disastrous has happened or is likely to happen. Then he concentrates on the element of suffering and rages either against himself and his own helplessness or against his relatives and their indifference in the face of his agony. All of it is *emotionalism,* a crazy quilt of senselessly exaggerated fears and angers, either overlapping or following one another.

After a while, the emotional raving may cease, and another reaction may take its place in the form of *sentimentalism.* If this takes the lead, then the patient releases an outburst of self-blame or self-pity, deploring his fate which makes him a coward, a burden to his family, a social outcast and professional incompetent. He laments the fact, tearfully and dramatically, that he is deprived of the privilege of discharging his duties and responsibilities, sets himself down as a pernicious example for the children and a disgrace to himself and his relatives. He indicts his moral weakness which robs him of his will power, and his defective intellect which prevents him from understanding the physician's instructions. Frequently, emotionalism goes hand in hand with sentimentalism, the one providing relief through angry explosions, the other furnishing exoneration by putting the blame on fate and destiny or on one's weak constitution. Both employ subtle and indirect reasoning which requires prompt spotting if symptom and suffering are not to be prolonged indefinitely.*

What is here described represents an extreme expression of the emotional and sentimental character of the "working-oneself-up" process. Even in this extreme development, it is common enough. More common, however, and far more damaging to nervous health are its more moderate versions which, keeping this side of outspoken hysteria, follow the line of specious reasoning and transparent sophistry. The patient tries to convince himself or others that he does his best to get well, but he "simply does not know" why he cannot throw off his obsession. He claims he makes an honest effort to ignore danger, but the sensations persist. What can he do about it? It is his fate to be suffering and to make others suffer. Along with it go pious protestations that it breaks his heart to see the poor wife distressed, the children not properly provided for and the standard of family life declining. The emotionalism is voiced in soft, timid phrases, the sentimentalism couched in suave, tepid language. No excitement, commotion or hysteria, rather calculation, shrewd strategy, and a good measure of cunning. It is these

---

*For a more precise formulation of the concepts of emotionalism and sentimentalism, see the following chapter.

subtle and devious manifestations of combined emotionalism and sentimentalism that call for a maximum of skill in temper spotting.

Examples: A patient gave an account of the ordeal she went through the day preceding the visit to the office. "I was terribly nauseated. Then I felt a heat wave. When these heat waves get me, I feel very, very hot. It gets so bad, I can't stand it any longer and have to call my husband." This is a moderate degree of emotionalism. The language is undoubtedly defeatist, exaggerating the intensity of the experience ("terribly nauseated," "very, very hot") and overstressing its paralyzing effect ("cannot stand it," "have to call").

Another patient delivered herself of a report which, in point of urgency and dramatization, pushed to distinctly dizzier heights on the scale of emotionalism. "This pain," she panted, "just drives me crazy. It's really a pain; it's a sickly feeling; really, it's not my imagination. My hands are so clammy. They feel like ice. The fingers and toes are real cold. I shake like a leaf."

The following description is in a similar vein of forceful dramatization: "I had a chill. My feet got blue. They were almost black. I couldn't even feel them. I had it at least for five hours. And when I got up, I felt so weak, I could not move. I am still awfully weak. I can hardly eat. Even warm milk hurts my stomach. Couldn't that be a tumor?" One patient exclaimed with flashing eyes and tremulous voice, "That pain is just unbearable. I was almost out of my mind. Honestly, I don't see how I can go through this again. I am sure if that happens again, it will be the end. If my husband hadn't come home in time, I don't know whether I wouldn't have done something to myself."

That this emotionalizing language fortifies defeatism, that defeatism intensifies and perpetuates symptoms and that the protracted fury of the "working-oneself-up" process leads to panics and vicious cycles has been explained so frequently in these pages, that a renewed discussion of the topic would be tedious. What must be emphasized, however, is that patients of this kind are in the habit of supplementing their verbal emotionalism by equally emotional muscular behavior. They "notice" the "gas pushing against the heart" and clutch the throat and chest and feel the pulse. They rush to the mirror and scan their features. Then they discover that the eyes have lost their lustre, that a dark shadow skirts the lower lid, that the cheeks are hollow, and the face looks wan. One patient said, "My eyes are blood-shot; my tongue is coated. I look in the mirror, and the eyes look weary and beaten down." Many of the tribe continually touch and paw their skin and muscles and promptly discover what they are looking for: hardened glands, flabby tissues, swellings, dryness, moistness and what-not.

At times, the emotionalism is callously made use of for the purpose of keeping the members of the family in a state of commotion. One such example was furnished by a patient who stated, "I am disgusted with myself. I can't control my temper. The other day it was so bad that I cried out, 'I am sick and tired of living.' Of course, they were alarmed. I knew they would be."

CHAPTER FORTY

Sabotage Method No. 8
Failure to Spot Sentimentalism

If a patient is to spot his emotionalisms and sentimentalisms, he will have to acquire a working knowledge of what are emotions, sentiments and feelings. The first thing he will have to know is that these three varieties of inner experiences are particularly likely to *affect* the functions of the body. Any of them may cause the muscle of the heart to speed its action and to produce palpitations. They may throw the digestive organs into a state of excitement and give rise to vomiting, nausea, belching or gas formation. The muscles of the bronchi may be affected, and air-hunger and chest pressure may be the result. They may affect the muscles of the extremities and cause weariness and heaviness, that is, "nervous fatigue." Affecting the functions of the body, emotions, feelings and sentiments have been properly called affections or *affects*.

Everybody has feelings and sentiments every moment of his life. What he feels can be expressed in two terms: a sense of security or insecurity. If you feel secure, you are vigorous, cheerful, happy, enthusiastic, enterprising, self-confident. All of this can be summed up in the word "joy" or its finer shades of satisfaction, contentment, serenity. The reverse of joy is grief. The latter is the result of a feeling of insecurity. If you feel insecure, you lose your vigor, and lack your customary enthusiasm, happiness and initiative, and are deficient in courage and self-confidence. Grief may shade off into sorrow, gloom, concern, misgiving. All these feelings affect the *physical and psychological person.* If the affection spreads to the *social personality,* we speak of sentiments. Sentiments are exercised in a group, feelings can be experienced apart from the group. Animals and babies can feel happy or grieved. But the sentiments of sympathy, companionship and fellowship, of duty accomplished and responsibility discharged can be operative in adult or adolescent members of a group only. If a person is commonly affected by these sentiments, practicing them systematically, he lives up to the standards set down by the group and, by this token, acquires the title of a mature personality.

Feelings of security give the person a sense of efficiency and adequacy. They are exciting, stirring, stimulating. They make the person feel vital and dynamic. The converse is true of the feelings of insecurity. They produce a sense of weakness, helplessness and inadequacy. If they predominate, the person lacks the sense of vitality and dynamism. This is different with sentiments. If you are moved or affected by sympathy or by the spirit of fellowship, you will hardly experience the flush of vitality or the push of dynamism. You will merely acknowledge that you did a good turn or that you conformed to the group standards of duty and responsibility, that you did the right thing and lived up to your principles. This will give you a sense of right-thinking and right-acting. Your behavior was in accord with established values; it was valid but not necessarily vital. Feelings express *vitality* or the lack of it; sentiments stand for *validity* or the lack of it. A person driven on by his feelings is vital, perhaps also colorful and forceful; a personality guided by group-approved sentiments is valid, perhaps also colorless and dull.

The daily life of the average man is so arranged that his feelings and sentiments are held in a fair state of equilibrium. You feel distressed at a rebuff suffered in your place of employment, but returning home in the evening, you enjoy the comfort and peace of your home, the loyalty of your wife and the loveliness of your children. The grief experienced on the job is neatly balanced and perhaps cancelled out by the joy accorded you in the domestic sphere. Or, you are worried by the thought of having defaulted on some duty, but your sense of failure is soon counterbalanced by the evidence of an accomplishment that raises your morale. Today you have misgivings about your standing among neighbors and friends; tomorrow you will have proof positive that you are well thought of. Grief is balanced by joy, failure by accomplishment. In this manner, both your vitality and your validity are kept in a satisfactory state of adjustment.

This serene, happy and complacent life may be interrupted suddenly by a blow dealt you by fate. Your child is stricken with an incurable disease. He is or may be crippled for life. Now you are seized with a grief which is deeper and far more intense than that caused by the pinpricks, failures and rebuffs encountered in the daily round. The mild feelings of routine existence, coming and going, causing only transient disequilibrium, have now been replaced by a feeling of extraordinary depth and duration. This is still a feeling, deeper and more intense than the average variety, but a feeling, nevertheless.

The question is: Will you "process" or "work up" this deep *feeling* into a fierce, turbulent *emotion?* Will you, for instance, permit yourself to think and exclaim that life is now unbearable, that all is lost, that no joy can henceforth enter your existence? Will you rave against fate that has betrayed you? Against medical science that has failed you? Against Divinity that has forsaken you? Will you go into rages and explosions against yourself and others? If so, your deep feeling has changed into an emotion that is loud, boisterous and furious but lacks the depth of genuine inner experiences. You are now the victim of *emotionalism,* and your affect is one of *emotional hysteria.*

There is another possibility. Instead of venting your wrath on fate, humanity and Divinity, you may turn it against yourself, mainly or solely. You will then embark on a wild crusade against your own deficiencies. Why did you wait before you called the physician? If you had summoned him immediately, the calamity might have been averted. What kind of a father are you? How depraved, how devoid of the most primitive sense of duty and responsibility? If your child is doomed to lifelong suffering, it is you who wrought his doom. You charge yourself with carelessness, neglect and indifference to the welfare of your family and set yourself down as a man without morals, without character, without judgment. You doubt whether you are possessed of the ordinary sentiments expected of a father. You give yourself over to a paroxysm of self-accusations and self-torture. If that happens, your ordinarily deep or average sentiments have degenerated into a disordered, unbalanced, frenzied *sentimentalism*. Your affect is now one of *sentimental hysteria*.

In the instance of the child stricken with an incurable disease, the father had ample opportunity to display genuine feelings of grief and pertinent sentiments of devotion. A combination of this kind would have led to plans and actions meant to remedy or mitigate the affliction. The grief would have inspired a mood of resignation and might have prompted a reappraisal of previous valuations and ambitions. The father might have realized that in the past, he spent too much time and energy on vocational and social pursuits, that as a consequence, home life was neglected, that the domestic scene suffered from a deficiency of affection and intimacy. Considerations of this kind would have suggested settled plans to rearrange time schedules and work habits. As a result, the needs of the family would henceforth have taken their rightful place side by side with the demands of social and business obligations. The genuine feelings would have produced a reorientation of goals and aims.

In a similar fashion, the sentiments of sympathy and parental devotion would have led to decisions to do everything to shape and prepare the future of the handicapped child. There was the issue of how to substitute home training for school education, how to implement projects for medical supervision, recreation, group life, play, travel. The father might have given thought to a suitable though limited career for the boy, perhaps even to the possibility of married life in spite of the handicap. In all of this, the father would have thought of the boy and the family first and of himself last. Instead, he gave himself up to a burst of emotionalism and sentimentalism, and now he thought of himself first and the boy last. He lamented *his* own fate, the frightful loss which *he* suffered. His wails and moans centered on the sorrowful reflection how *he* would be able to bear up under the strain of anguish and despair. His feelings and sentiments were primarily focused on *his* own self, on *his* poor ego, secondarily only on son and family.

The difference is clear: genuine feelings and sentiments tend to produce plans and actions designed to manipulate or remedy a situation *outside* the person who experiences the affects. Emotionalism and sentimentalism have the opposite effect. They turn the attention of the affected person *inside,* to his own inner experiences, to his own woes, anxieties and anticipations. The difference is one between fellowship and individualism. Genuine affects make for fellowship and group-centered interests; emotionalism and sentimentalism produce stark individualism and self-centered egotism.

The tendency today, in daily life, literature, art, and popular scientific pursuits, is to emphasize emotions (fear and anger) to the neglect of genuine feelings and sentiments. Unfortunately, this trend has served to put the stamp of approval on the emotional and sentimental hysteria practiced by the nervous patient. Experiencing disturbing sensations or thoughts, the patient's first impulse is to concentrate his attention on his dear self and his poor ego. He expatiates in unending tirades on the nature, quality and intensity of his inner perceptions. He picks them apart, goes into details of analysis and explanation, insists that his feelings and sentiments are real, not imaginary, that his sensations are excruciating and unbearable, that instant relief is imperative. Otherwise, how is he going to "stand them?" He appeals for sympathy and attention, demands understanding and, above all, a "friendly hearing," an opportunity to pour forth a stream of complaints, an occasion for "processing" his feelings and sentiments into wild orgies of hysteria. This patient is interested first and foremost in coddling and pampering his inner experiences. He "works them up" or "processes" them into excitements, frenzies and panics. The preoccupation with his experiences *inside* him keeps him from taking adequate courses of action *outside* him for the purpose of remedying the situation. Moreover, if such a course of action is suggested by his physician, he counters with reactions of sabotage, sensing keenly that outside action is bound to divert his attention from the painful delights of inside analysis and self-observation.

This patient is a confirmed individualist, self-centered and thoroughly egotistical with reference to his symptoms, oblivious to his own realistic needs and indifferent to the demands of fellowship. His endless complaints disrupt group life and aggravate his own hysteria and suffering. If this deplorable situation is to be rectified, the nervous patient will have to learn that emotionalism and sentimentalism are the enemies of his own welfare and a blight on the group he lives in. In order to do that efficiently, he will have to train himself to spot his inner experiences and to prevent his originally mild and innocent feelings and sentiments from being processed into emotional and sentimental hysterias by means of the "working-oneself-up" procedures. The technique for spotting emotionalism was described in the preceding chapter. Instructions for spotting sentimentalism are offered in the following examples.

Examples: A woman, who had been suffering from numerous disturbing sensations, obsessions and compulsions, released a veritable torrent of moans, sobs and complaints whenever she found somebody willing to listen to her. She had been given instructions in classes and in private conferences to the effect that moaning, sobbing and complaining are done through the medium of speech muscles and that muscles can be controlled at will. The precise technique of practicing this type of muscle control had been discussed with her repeatedly. There was no doubt but she understood the procedure. She also understood that restraining muscles meant to produce increased tenseness in the restrained muscles, but that the tenseness disappears in a few minutes or seconds if the "command to the muscles" is maintained resolutely. She understood but failed to practice control. Instead, she bewailed her fate. "I know I am a drag on my family. I hate to torture them, but I cannot help it. Honestly, I don't understand how they stand up under the strain. I know I'll be their ruin." She loved to pamper her inner sentimentalisms and refused to control her muscles for purposes of inner control or for proper outer action.

Another patient, with a similar bent for incessant complaining, exclaimed, "I am afraid I ruin my family." The following conversation developed between patient and physician:

PHYSICIAN: The best way to stop ruining your family is to stop working yourself up. You can do that easily if you control your speech muscles.

PATIENT: I try, but I can't. Maybe I don't understand you.

PHYSICIAN: Don't work yourself up over your inability to understand. Stop making an issue of it.

PATIENT: How can I avoid making an issue of the health of my family? I certainly can't stop worrying about that.

PHYSICIAN: Don't make an issue of your worries.

PATIENT: And I can't stop this daydreaming.

PHYSICIAN: Daydream, but make no issue of it. Don't work yourself up over it.

PATIENT: And why can't I shake off these ugly thoughts?

PHYSICIAN: Have the thoughts, and wait till they disappear. But, above all, make no issue of your having thoughts.

PATIENT: But, Doctor, you don't listen to me.

PHYSICIAN: The most important thing is that you listen to what I tell you. You told me of your inner experiences and your sentimentalisms so many times that I know them by heart. You should stop talking about your worries and issues and start controlling them by using your muscles.

A male patient had difficulty controlling his temper. But instead of making an honest effort to "command his muscles," he relished indulging in sentimental self-accusations. "I strike my children," he exclaimed, "Is that human?" He was told, "Control the muscles of your arms, and command them not to strike. But, above all, don't become emotional and sentimental after you have struck your children. Avoid working yourself up." The patient replied, "Maybe I haven't got the mental capacity to do that."

PHYSICIAN: I asked you to use your muscles for control, not your brain.

PATIENT: But how can I carry out your orders if I don't think?

PHYSICIAN: You do an excellent piece of thinking right now arguing with me. The trouble is you think too much and too well when it is a matter of convincing yourself that you cannot do what I ask you to do.

Like so many other patients, this man made use of sentimental self-condemnations in order to prove to himself and the physician that he is desirous but incapable of improving.

One articulate patient expressed the relationship between sentimentalism and the will to sabotage in the following words: "I like to think of myself as a lost soul. I feel I am irretrievable. If I went with as much enthusiasm about the job of getting well as I go about moping and feeling sorry for myself, I'd be well in no time." Another patient expressed a similar thought when she said, "I am getting more tired in the morning thinking about what is to be done than doing it." These patients love to pamper their sentiments but hate to control their muscles.

CHAPTER FORTY-ONE

Sabotage Method No. 9
Failure to Practice
Muscle Control

Recovery stands for simplicity. Its systems of instruction and training are meant to enable the plain, humble and untutored patient to practice self-help. An objective of this kind cannot be achieved by means of involved explanations and complex techniques. Self-help in psychiatric after-care calls for simple methods of interpreting and manipulating symptoms. It is for this reason that Recovery offers to its members plain common sense instead of intricate philosophies, and artless techniques of training in place of elaborate procedures.

Whatever else a disturbing nervous symptom may mean, its main effect is that it interferes with the adjustment of the patient. And adjustment is effected through action, and action is carried on through muscles, including the muscles of speech. The patient says he suffers from fatigue. The fact is, however, that he thinks his muscles are exhausted and fears or neglects to use them for the purposes of walking or working. "Fatigue," then, thwarts proper muscular behavior. With the thought of exhaustion in his brain, the patient is doomed to inactivity and incapacity. The conclusion is plain: convince the patient that his muscles are neither weak nor damaged, and he will regain the courage and determination to use them for his daily activities. Adjustment will be restored and action reinstated.

Nothing is more convincing than muscular performance. A letter is waiting to be written. The message which you are to deliver is embarrassing or difficult to present in proper language. You doubt whether you can choose the right phrasing to express it without being too sharp or over-courteous, or too dull. Finally, you decide to proceed with the irksome task and find, to your surprise, that in the end, your communication is little short of a fine accomplishment in wording, style and composition. You are proud of your product and have gained considerably in self-confidence. The action of your muscles conquered and convinced the anxieties of your brain. Instances of this kind are too common to need amplification. The underlying principle is of universal application and finds its pertinent formulation in the proper prescription: try and you will find out. To a mind reared in the tradition of intellectual pomposity, such a naive method may appear to be too simple to deserve the name of a technique. But self-help is based and predicated on simplicity, and simple rules only will serve the mass of nervous and former mental patients who, in the mass, are composed of simple folk.

Nobody will doubt that a patient can convince his brain through the muscles, that he can walk on, in spite of his "exhaustion," without incurring the danger of collapse. All he has to do is to step out in forceful movement, and if he fails to "keel over" or to "cave in," he has given incontrovertible evidence that his muscles are anything but exhausted and that the menace of collapsing is a myth. Nor will anybody dispute the fact that a temperamental person can cut short his emotionalism by commanding his speech muscles to stop arguing or his skeletal muscles to stop fighting. Temper of this kind creates an impulse to strike or shout, and since the shouting or striking must be done by the muscles, they can be stopped by an order to the same muscles to refrain from striking or shouting.

The same transparent relationship obtains in the case of many disturbing sensations. An itch mobilizes the impulse to scratch, and it is well known how difficult it is for most persons to resist the temptation. Nevertheless, in company or on the street, intuitively or reflectively, the itch is successfully controlled, that is, the muscles have been commanded to refrain from scratching. Similar examples of effective blocking of symptomatic reactions through control of muscles could be quoted from experiences with other disturbances, for instance, the control of restlessness and agitation through determined motionless sitting, the conquest of "sleeplessness" through persistent lying in bed without turning and twisting.

But these illustrations refer to sensations that have, or seem to have, their seat in the skin or the muscles of trunk and extremities. How about sensations which are produced in inner organs? How about experiences other than sensations, for instance, fears, obsessions, preoccupations? Can muscle training stop a lump in the throat, pressure in the head and churning in the abdomen? Can muscles do away with the thought that the body is expanding or that people are looking at you?

An intelligent approach to these questions will have to consider the nature and character of both sensations and obsessions. Sensations are notorious for their transient and ephemeral existence. They come and go. All you have to do is to observe yourself for a few minutes' time, and you will have no difficulty spotting numerous mild sensations rising to consciousness and instantly falling back into unawareness. You can then notice, in quick succession, a warm feeling in the lobe of the ear, some tenseness in the neck, a tickle in the throat, a momentary heartburn in the region of the sternum, a pulling in the shoulder, an itch somewhere and a pressure somewhere else. Some sensations, if mild, are pleasing, like the warmth, the tickle and the itch; others are displeasing, like the heartburn, the pulling and the pressure. In this manner, stimulation and irritation alternate. The one set of sensations are relaxing; the others are tensing.

This continuous ebbing and flowing, appearing and disappearing has been likened to the systolic and diastolic phases of the action of the heart and has been called the "sensation pulse." How is it, one may ask, that the sensations felt by nervous patients come but do not go? What causes them to lose their transient character and to acquire the quality of sustained duration? To express it differently, why do the sensations experienced by nervous patients tend to lose their pulse?

The same consideration may be applied to the obsessions which plague nervous patients. An obsession is a thought, usually a suspicion. The suspicion may be directed at others, as in jealousy, or at one's self, as in the case of the obsessive thought that one's body is changing or that people stare at you. Of thoughts, it is just as axiomatic as of sensations (and feelings) that they are of transient duration, flitting through the brain, coming and going, unless they are concentrated on. Just give yourself over to a few moments of revery or daydreaming, and you will realize how your thoughts wander across the field of experience, now reaching out into the future, then roaming through the past with a motley assortment of ideas, opinions, plans and dreams crowding in on one another, the ones just entering your brain, the others leaving. This ceaseless hustle and bustle of an up and down flowing mentation has been called the "stream of thought."

The question is again permitted: How is it that with nervous patients, the ordinarily fading and floating thought elements harden and crystallize into perennial and unending suspicions and obsessions? Why does their stream of thought cease streaming? Obviously, some factor operating in nervous patients upsets the pulse of their sensations and interrupts the stream of their thoughts. That factor is an abiding sense of insecurity, producing, through concentrated preoccupation, sustained tenseness and preventing the nervous system from relaxing.

If the patient could gain the unquestioned assurance that his condition is "just nerves," distressing but not dangerous, he would have no difficulty relaxing his organs and reinstating the pulse of sensations and the stream of thought. Unfortunately, the assurance given the patient by his physician is verbal, mainly or exclusively, and words do not necessarily carry conviction. Usually, the patient is an "experienced complainer," has made the round of physicians and clinics, and numerous past attempts at reassuring him met with failure. He is now skeptical, listens but is not convinced. The physician's "sales talk" strikes against the patient's "sales resistance." Verbal explanations, no matter how skillful, usually fail to reach the "expert sufferer."

The thing that will convince him is his own performance. Make him walk ten blocks, and the action of his own muscles will demonstrate to him that he *did not* collapse in spite of his feeling of exhaustion. The myth of exhaustion is then reduced to absurdity by the patient's own muscular movements. Or, to give another illustration: the patient is tense, restless, in constant motion. He is unable to sit through a theatre performance. Hence, in a show, he chooses a seat near the aisle so he can make a hasty escape if the tenseness becomes "unendurable." Patients of this sort are gripped with fear that unless they rush instantly out of the door into the fresh air, they will faint or burst. Train them to force the muscles to sit through the ordeal of tenseness, which is "extremely distressing but utterly harmless," and the first trial, as a rule, will convince them that the "intolerable" tenseness can be tolerated and that the burst or faint do not materialize.

If the patients have been exposed to group psychotherapy classes and Recovery meetings, the example of other patients who "have done it" prepares the new practitioner for the first trial. In classes and meetings, he has obtained the conviction that others have conquered fears by the muscular route. Later, his own practice reinforces the assurance gained from the reports of the others. After a few more trials, the fears disappear, the tenseness recedes and relaxation reestablishes itself. And under conditions of relaxation, the suspended pulse of sensations regains its balance, and the disordered stream of thought restores the regularity of its flow.

The following illustrations will demonstrate the details of technique which patients are taught to employ in order to conquer disturbing sensations and obsessive thoughts by the simple means of "commanding the muscles to do what you fear to do." That most patients bungle the method in the beginning ought to be understood. Many patients not only bungle but also sabotage the method.

Example 1. A woman patient had been suffering from numerous anxieties, obsessions and compulsions for upward of three years before she was assigned to classes and Recovery membership. She feared going out unaccompanied, anticipating fainting spells although she had never experienced any. Her most distressing difficulty was the compulsion to "repeat." Whatever she did had to be done over numbers of times, sometimes for hours on end. Making beds was a never-ending procession. After the sheet was tucked in, it had to be pulled out and smoothed and stretched and tucked in again. Then the pulling out and smoothing and stretching had to be done again, undone, redone. In this manner, every task took hours to perform and seemed never finished. Washing the hands, cleaning the bathtub, locking the door required the same protracted ceremonial. No matter how well the original act was performed, it had to be done over in interminable repetitions.

Particularly agonizing was the compulsion to repeat sentences and questions. It was hazardous for the patient to engage in any kind of conversation because each statement made by her had to be reiterated until it finally "sounded just right." If a statement was made by another person, the patient had to ask question after question to make sure that she had actually understood what was meant. If the ritual of repeating was interrupted because a visitor appeared on the scene or the doorbell rang, the patient experienced an "unbearable" tenseness, tremors and tightening of the throat. The repetitions had to be resumed instantly after the visitor was disposed of or the telephone message was received.

The patient learned soon that what she feared was not rumpled bedsheets and dirty bathtubs, misphrased sentences and misunderstood questions but rather the "intolerable" tenseness, tremor and tightness which resulted from the fears. "I know that, Doctor," she replied, "but the knowledge doesn't help me." She was then trained to do with the muscles what her brain feared to do; to command her speech muscles not to repeat statements and questions; to order the muscles of the arms to interrupt the movements of washing, scrubbing and straightening after a reasonable amount of time had been spent on these activities. Above all, she was asked to be prepared to stand the tenseness resulting from a frustrated impulse and to know that it was "distressing but not dangerous."

With the example and encouragement of other patients, she practiced but with partial success only. One day she remarked, "I can now stop the repeating with regard to bedmaking, dusting, locking the door, and I no longer repeat statements and questions as much as I used to do. But with washing the hands and cleaning the tub, I have had no luck." It was not easy to persuade her that the tenseness was the same in both series of tasks, and that if she was able to brave it in one type of activity and not in the other, the reason for this senseless discrimination was her tendency to sabotage. Prior to joining classes and Recovery, she had been treated with methods of verbal assurance and found the technique of muscle training tedious, absurd and "not suited to my case." Many patients offer this negative reaction. They resent simple methods of this kind as an insult to their intelligence. The procedure is likely to appear insulting and, indeed, humiliating, because if excruciating tortures of years' duration can be disposed of with such simple means, why were the pains and pressures and dizziness made the object of years of wailing, temper tantrums, neglect of duty and financial sacrifice? The question is unanswerable but is rated as sabotage in Recovery and countered with the alternative question: Is the fact that you suffered needlessly in the past sufficient excuse to continue the suffering into the future just because the mode of treatment fails to impress you as intricate or dignified? In the present case, the sabotage against the "indignity" of being treated with a too-simple method was overcome after months of therapeutic effort, and the patient has done well for the past seven years. When her husband was called into service in 1944, the wife had no difficulty taking over his business and conducting it till months after Armistice Day.

Example 2. A young woman had been afflicted with a most distressing condition for upward of four years prior to being assigned to classes. On walking along the street, the sidewalks seemed to heave up against her, and the buildings appeared to bend toward her. This caused dizziness, tightening of the abdomen and, of course, panicky fear. After due explanations concerning the utter absence of any danger that she might be caught and crushed by the collapsing buildings or by the uprising pavement, she was trained to walk on in spite of the threat of the sensations. She soon learned to step out fearlessly into the street and acquired mastery in ignoring the "symptomatic idiom" of her sensations. But after a while, she complained that although she had conquered successfully the fear of being swallowed up by pavement and buildings, she still had the tightening of the abdomen, the dizziness and tenseness. "How can I get rid of this by practicing muscle control?" she asked.

She was told: "When the abdomen tightens up, command your muscles to continue the meal regardless of the pains and spasms in your stomach. Discipline your body by means of your muscles, always keeping in mind that no danger whatever is involved. If, sensing the tightness of the stomach, you refrain from eating, you incidentally tell yourself that the condition of your stomach is one of a crippling disease. This intensifies your tenseness, and the tenseness keeps your stomach from relaxing. The abdominal spasms and pains are thus perpetuated. They will disappear only if you relax, and you will relax only if you are fully convinced that no danger threatens. This conviction you can gain if you continue to eat, demonstrating to yourself that nothing happens if you do continue. After a few performances of this kind, your confidence will return, and your conviction will be established. Then your body will relax, and the stomach will follow suit. And the dizziness will subside because there will be little tenseness left to sustain it." After a short period of bungling trials and attendant sabotaging thoughts, she manipulated walking and eating with the aid of muscle control and has been comfortable for the past six years.

Example 3. A woman patient complained of an itch in the rectum. The itch had been with her off and on for over twenty years. It was experienced for weeks and months during the day, never at night. At times, it disappeared for a few days or weeks spontaneously. She had done well with regard to a number of other nervous symptoms but was unable to get rid of the itch. "It just drives me crazy," the patient said. "How can I control that?" She was asked, "Do you scratch when you are in the streetcar?" "Isn't that strange?" she replied. "Now that you ask me, I remember I never scratch when I am in the streetcar. I don't even have the itch there. I don't have it anywhere riding or driving." She was then told, "You sat in my waiting room for over an hour today. Did you scratch there?" "Why," she said, "I didn't have to scratch. I didn't itch. Isn't that funny?"

"That is not at all funny," the physician remarked. "When you are among people, you give the order to your muscles intuitively and instinctively not to scratch, and muscles always carry out orders that are "meant"–orders which are resolutely passed on to them. After you have given that order, you know by experience that it will be obeyed implicitly and don't give a thought to the itch any more. Removing your thought from the itch, you are without preoccupation, and there is neither itch nor scratch. But once you approach your home, you know that there scratching is permitted or at least possible. Now your mind is preoccupied with the itch which is trouble and pleasure at the same time. Again, intuitively and instinctively, you decide that now at last you will be able to indulge the pastime of scratching." The patient, a member of Recovery, soon learned to command the muscles discursively and reflectively and got rid of the itch in a short time.

Brief examples: A patient was obsessed with the fear of dying. As a consequence, he dreaded reading the word *death,* shied away from funeral parlors and gave up reading newspapers from fear of encountering reports of killings or sudden deaths. After proper explanations in classes and during office interviews, he was trained to command his muscles to stand in front of funeral parlors and to practice reading newspapers deliberately and assiduously. He had little difficulty shedding his fears.

Patients with fears of crossing streets, riding in elevators, looking down from high places are currently treated by the method of "commanding the muscles to do what you fear to do." Success is almost always prompt and lasting.

Of particular interest are patients who suffer from outright delusions subsequent to discharge from the hospital as improved but not fully recovered. One patient still complained that the neighbors were knocking at the walls; another that automobile lights were again flashing their headlights, signalling threatening messages. In these and other instances, it is sufficient to train the patients to first spot the experience as a "nervous symptom, distressing and annoying but not at all dangerous;" second, to exhort them to ignore the symptom and not to act on it. If the patient commands his muscles not to shout at the neighbors who "knock at the wall" and not to knock back at them, or to ignore the flashing of lights, not to draw the curtains or retire to another room, then he avoids the process of "working himself up." And with no hysteria engendered, the symptom disappears. It "comes and goes." The sensation and thought pulses re-establish themselves even with such pathological experiences.

An experience, reported by an observant relative of a patient, threw light on the mode of operation of some delusions. The patient complained of being stared at by people. Her cousin stated that when she was in a restaurant with her, nobody did any staring during the first few minutes. But then the patient, suspicious that she may be stared at, began looking at people, turning her gaze in all directions, staring at everybody and anybody, thus attracting the attention of the diners at various tables who actually began staring at her. In this manner, the suspicion of being stared at had produced the staring.

PART IV

GROUP PSYCHOTHERAPY INTERVIEWS

CHAPTER FORTY-TWO

The Myth of "Nervous Fatigue"

Evelyn had been irritable, restless and tense for the past ten years. Sleep was poor. Appetite had declined to the point of making a meal an ordeal. There was a constant tightness of the throat, pressure in the head, palpitations and gastric discomfort. Overshadowing all complaints in importance and intensity was "an awful fatigue, an exhaustion that starts right when I get up in the morning and continues without letup till late afternoon. Then it eases up, and in the evening, I feel almost well."

In spite of this sustained suffering, "without letup," Evelyn managed to keep her job for years, supplementing her husband's income. It was only in the past two years that the fatigue and exhaustion became "unbearable." She resigned her position and tended to her household and her young son. "But in taking care of my home, I have to drag myself all morning and the greater part of the afternoon. I am exhausted most of the day."

E –EXAMINER

P –PATIENT

E: You have attended classes for several months. Has your condition improved during these months?

P: It has. I sleep well, and my appetite is much better. The pressure in the head has hardly bothered me lately, and the pain in the abdomen is getting less and less. But I am still fatigued. In the morning, I have to drag myself and can hardly keep on my feet. Then I take lunch, and right after I have finished eating, I am all exhausted, my eyes droop, and I have to lie down for an hour or so.

E: You say that you are "all exhausted." May I ask you what precisely you mean when you use the word "exhaustion?"

P: Why, I am all in. I have no pep and must force myself to do the simplest thing.

E: Look here, Evelyn, an exhaustion that has lasted for years, day after day, even hour after hour, ought to have finally reduced you to a physical wreck. Your muscles should have shrunk, your face should by now look gaunt and haggard. Instead, you maintained your weight, your complexion is blooming, and your capacity for working is equal to the task of taking care of house, family and social activities. Several months ago, when sleep was poor and appetite scant, your claim to be exhausted might have been logical. But with a good appetite and sound sleep, it is difficult to think that you are suffering from a state of exhaustion.

P: I don't understand it myself, but it is a fact that I feel tired and weary all the time, except in late afternoon and evening.

E: You say you "feel tired and weary all the time." I do not deny that. You alone are competent to state how you feel. What interests me is whether your so-called fatigue is a mere subjective feeling or an actual and objective condition, whether you merely feel tired or actually are tired. You seem to be puzzled by the sharp distinction, and I shall try to be more specific. You understand that if somebody says he feels guilty, that does not necessarily mean he is guilty. And if somebody feels feverish, that does by no means establish the objective fact that he has fever. These examples will prove to you that a subjective feeling does not necessarily point to an objective condition. And if you say you "feel tired and weary all the time," I shall ask you whether you consider your tiredness a subjective feeling or an objective condition?

P: All I know is I am miserable all day. I wake up in the morning, and the fatigue is there the moment I open my eyes.

E: You told me, Evelyn, that for the past few months, your sleep has been good. Suppose you awoke this morning after a good night's rest. Would you nevertheless have felt fatigued immediately after awakening?

P: I feel fatigued immediately after I wake up in the morning regardless of whether sleep was good or poor.

E: If this is true, then it is established that you suffer from the subjective feeling of tiredness and weariness, and not from the objective condition of fatigue. I shall tell you why I can afford to be so positive about my statement. You see, Evelyn, soldiers after a long march, athletes after an exhausting race, laborers after a strenuous effort, may sometimes be too tired to fall asleep. But once they lapse into a sound sleep, they invariably and inevitably feel refreshed after awakening. These are examples of extreme fatigue. Even in these utmost exertions, sleep eliminates fatigue with unquestioned certainty. In minor exertions, mere rest without sleep will have the same effect. The only exception to this rule is physical ailment, like an anemia or tuberculosis. In these conditions, even a sound sleep may not do away with fatigue. But with physically healthy persons, sleep never fails to remove fatigue. If it is true that for several months past you have enjoyed good sleep, you have no reason for being tired in the morning. To sleep means to rest the muscles. How can your muscles be fatigued if they are rested?

P: I don't know what to say. The fact is that I am all in no matter how well I slept. If you call that a subjective feeling, you must think it is mental. But I didn't even have time to think about it. It is there the moment I wake up.

E: I do not know what precisely you mean when you use the word "mental." Presumably you refer to the possibility that you may have the thought of fatigue in your mind and instantly feel the fatigue in your muscles. This instantaneous response of the muscles to a thought seems to puzzle you. I do not see why it should. You have certainly gone through similar experiences hundreds of times. Remember the occasion, for instance, when you were at a meeting and were called upon to make a speech. Instantly, your heart began to palpitate, your face reddened, your abdomen trembled and the knees shook. To use your own words, you "didn't even have time to think" of the speech; you merely heard your name called, and the muscles of your heart, abdomen and legs were thrown into violent tremors "in no time." In the instance which I quoted, the thought in your mind which caused your muscles to shake was the fear of not being able to deliver a well-constructed address. It was a fear, or you may call it a fear idea, or the idea of danger. Do you understand now that if an idea strikes or occupies your mind, the muscles may respond with a violent reaction in a fraction of a second?

P: I understand that. But when I get up in the morning, there is no idea of danger in my head.

E: The question is what you mean by danger. If you wish to indicate that, in the morning, you are not trembling with the fear of being killed or trapped or burned, I shall fully agree with you that no such idea may occupy your brain immediately after awakening. But there are subtler forms of fears and dangers. These subtle anxieties and apprehensions go by the name of *preoccupations*. I happen to know from your own account how readily you fall victim to such preoccupations. Let me remind you, for instance, of the anguish you experience whenever you expect visitors for the afternoon or the evening. You fret and worry days in advance, anticipating some bungling or clumsiness while performing the part of the hostess. You know that when finally the much dreaded day arrives, you feel troubled and helpless "the very minute" you awaken. The day stares you in the face as a threat, as an event fraught with heavy responsibilities. You are without pep or zest. Your vitality is at a low ebb. A heaviness seems to descend on your limbs. Everything is done with effort. You have to drag yourself, feel "all in," exhausted, lifeless, fatigued. Do you understand that all of this is caused by your preoccupation, and that the preoccupation is based on the idea of danger?

P: It is true I am worrying my head off when I expect guests. People are critical, and it is not easy to please them and make them feel at home. But we don't have visitors every day, and there is not a day when I feel relaxed. I am always tired.

E: I mentioned your preoccupation with your guests as an example only. The example will demonstrate to you that a preoccupation of this kind is apt to produce, in a split second, a condition in which you feel "all in," dragging, exhausted and listless. Being a nervous patient, you are always preoccupied with your disability. This preoccupation is a kind of worry which hardly ever leaves you. You are always on guard against something untoward happening in some part of your body. Looking back on your unhappy experiences of the past ten years, you can recall numerous instances in which you planned a social engagement, a card game, a show, a trip and were stricken with a severe head pressure or palpitations or abdominal pain or numbness. The card game had to be interrupted, or you managed painfully to go through with it in wretched agony. You remember the frequent occasions when dinner parties had to be cancelled because your throat suddenly "locked," and you were afraid you might not be able to swallow or speak; or the dances that had to be called off because a heaviness settled on your legs so that you could hardly walk. It was observations of this character that in time suggested to you that it was no use planning. The unpredictable suddenness with which your symptoms could make their appearance gave you no guarantee that if you made a plan, you could go through with it. Gradually, the inability to plan spread to the trivial chores of everyday life. You set out to prepare a meal, and your eyes blurred. Or you decided to darn your husband's socks, and the hands trembled. The symptoms came without warning. They shot through your body without cause, without provocation. To use your own words, you "didn't even have time to think about them."

I may tell you that symptoms which shoot up so unexpectedly, in a mere fraction of a second, are called "trigger symptoms." They shoot forth with the rapidity of a bullet after the trigger has been pulled. Their trigger character makes them appear weird, mysterious, threatening. In essence, they suggest to you that you have utterly lost control of your primitive bodily functions. Having noticed time and again that your organs may go on a rampage without warning, you feel you cannot trust your body. You must always be on the alert for some sudden disturbance. You cannot plan with any assurance of carrying out your decisions. But if you are deprived of the power to plan, your day is carried out without accomplishment. Moreover, without planning, you miss that singular joy of looking ahead to accomplishments. The joyous trembling of watchful anticipation is taken from your daily routine. Life becomes a never-ending drabness and drudgery.

It is this type of life that you look forward to when you awaken in the morning. In a flash, before you had "time to think about it," the dismal dreariness of your existence stares at you. Again, one of those empty days with no plans, no decisions, no accomplishments. You become discouraged, disgusted with the dead monotony that is in store for you, and it is the self-disgust that robs your tissues of their vitality. There is no vigor, zest or incentive with which to start out on the daily routine. Your body is devoid of stimulation; it feels uninspired, flabby, limp. This feeling of limpness you call "fatigue."

You will now understand why, towards evening, your vitality returns and why, after supper, you "feel almost well." There is nothing left for planning after supper, no drabness to be anticipated, no drudgery to be performed in self-disgust. The dreadful day is gone or going. Nothing is expected of you any more. You breathe freely now, and your vitality returns. Do you realize now that what you call "fatigue" is nothing but a psychological reaction to the anticipated and dreaded boredom of daily existence? Do you understand that the tiredness of which you complain is not in your muscles but in your mind?

P: You are right, Doctor. I realize now that everything you say is exactly as I feel it. My mornings are dreadful. I have nothing to look forward to. I can't plan; I am afraid to plan. You are right, Doctor, but why was I never told what is wrong with me? I have seen all kinds of physicians, and the one told me I was suffering from nervous exhaustion; another said my energy was running down, and I should take it easy. One blamed it on my thyroid gland; another told me I had a poor constitution, and he couldn't do anything about it. I was warned not to overwork, was told to take long periods of rest, to go on trips and vacations. If you say that my trouble is nothing but boredom and disgust, why did nobody tell me that before? It would have spared me ten years' suffering, and I could have saved thousands of dollars spent on cures, sanitariums and trips.

E: It is painful for me to answer this question. I do not like to be critical of what other men think or believe. Unfortunately, there are superstitions that refuse to die. One of them, very preposterous and pernicious, is the myth of nervous fatigue or nervous exhaustion. All I can tell you is that, in 1880, a New York physician formulated the absurd theory that a group of patients, whom he called "neurasthenics," suffered from a state of nervous exhaustion.* How uncritical this man was is evident from the fact that he did not hesitate to make unwarranted and extravagant claims, for instance, that the "disease runs in families," that it is due to inheritance, that it has its origin in the spine, that it is typically American and, hence, proposed to call it "American Nervousness." Somehow this fanciful idea spread all over the globe and is still widely accepted today as a message of scientific truth. I cannot tell why a theory of this kind has been permitted to figure in textbooks and to be practiced on hapless sufferers. All I can state is that superstitions are born easily but die with difficulty.

I do not blame you for feeling resentful of the unnecessary hardship that was imposed on you during ten long years of anguish. But resentment will not help you. It will only serve to whip up your emotions and throw an addi-

---

*George M. Beard, *A Practical Treatise on Nervous Exhaustion (Neurasthenia)*, New York, 1880, William Wood.

tional load on your nervous system. What you need is re-education. You must learn to reject as untrue all the silly notions that were crammed into your head and to accept the explanation which I gave you. Up to now, with the thought of exhaustion in your brain, you were afraid to move, to work, to tax your "weak" muscles. I take it for granted that, henceforth, you will throw to the winds all this drivel about nerve exhaustion and will not hesitate to tax your muscles to your heart's delight.

P: You told me that before, and I made every effort to accept your view. On many mornings, I jumped out of bed without paying attention to my fears. I ignored the heaviness in my muscles and did my work, but it was certainly difficult. Your assurance that the fatigue is in the brain and not in the muscles helps me at times. But after I continue with my work for awhile, the thought strikes me that maybe the other doctors were right when they warned me not to strain my muscles. After ten years, it seems not easy to shake off the fears.

E: You said you made every effort to accept my views about fatigue. This is, of course, an exaggerated claim. I do not expect anybody to make "every" effort in any endeavor. What you mean is that you tried hard but did not succeed. But remember, Evelyn, I never asked you to "accept my views." I asked you to practice them. My view, with regard to "nervous fatigue," is that you can safely ignore it, that it is a bugaboo and not a real danger. This view cannot be "accepted" and, as it were, placed in your brain, there to preside over your actions. In order to make a view direct your action, it must be acquired, digested and absorbed through patient practice.

This is true of every sphere of life in which you wish to plant views into the thoughts and brains of a person. In bringing up your children, you did not merely present them with lovely notions and lofty principles, asking them to accept them. These views had to be practiced, again and again, till finally they were incorporated, and lived, and experienced and acted out spontaneously. When you intended to make your boy adopt the view of group responsibility, you did not tell him to accept your principle of group behavior. Instead, you told him not to make noise in the presence of people. You urged him to say "thank you" and "please." This you did for months and years until finally the new habits took root. After ceaseless practice, your boy finally incorporated the view in his system, made it part of his organism. The practice made the view "sink in" and take its firm place in the brain from where it then directed action. In this process of child training, you influenced your boy's muscles, and through them, established a firm structure of habits. It was these good habits that represented your view. You understand now that I asked you to practice my view, not merely to accept it. The continued practice would have brought acceptance in its train.

You will perhaps remember what precisely I asked you to do. I told you to jump out of bed and to go about your work, fatigue or no fatigue. But I also warned you to avoid all actions that embody the view of danger. I specifically instructed you not to look in the mirror to watch your so-called fatigue in your anxious features. I asked you to avoid the practice of touching the muscles of your arms and legs to investigate the degree of their flabbiness. I cautioned you not to sit down after a few steps or a few manipulations. Most important, I enjoined you not to complain about your fatigue, not to moan or sob, not to ask for help or sympathy. If you had complied with these instructions, you would have established a new set of habits of how to deal with this legendary thought of nervous fatigue. The old habits of fear would have been crowded out of your mind, and a new set of constructive trends would have settled down or sunk into your brain. My view would then have occupied and taken possession of your brain without any effort on your part to accept or adopt it.

If you say that "after ten years it is not easy to shake off the fears," I shall advise you that you had no business assuming that it might be easy. Mere acceptance of a view is easy, but practicing it means sustained application, with endless trials and endless failures till finally you score the ultimate success. You thought of merely accepting a view. That would have been easy but ineffectual. What I wanted you to do was to practice, i.e., to direct your muscles to carry out my view. I presume that after tonight's interview, you will no longer entertain the unrealistic notion that mere lip-service to a principle will reestablish a new set of habits. Practice alone will do that.

CHAPTER FORTY-THREE

Sabotaging Sleep

Bill complained of episodes occurring every few weeks in which he experienced intense fatigue and numbness in both legs from the knees down. On these days, he felt choked and had difficulty breathing. The condition lasted upward of eighteen years but improved greatly after he attended classes. The spells no longer interfered with his work. "In the past," he said, "I was out of circulation because of these spells. The choked feeling and numbness and weakness were with me for several days on a stretch. Then they became milder but would start again after another few days. I was in bad shape even on good days. On a Wednesday, I might want to buy tickets for the coming Saturday. But I was afraid I might go through a spell on Saturday and dropped the plan. Gradually, I stopped going out with people, except that I kept associating with one boyhood friend."

When questioned concerning the degree of improvement since attending classes, he stated that the spells were milder now and the intervals between them longer. "But I am still having trouble with sleeping. It takes me a long time to fall asleep, and the slightest noise gets me awake again. The other night, I couldn't get to sleep till after four A.M., and when I got up in the morning, I was worn out and felt I hadn't slept a wink."

E –EXAMINER
P –PATIENT
E: You say you could not fall asleep till after four A.M.

Suppose you retire at eleven P.M. What did you do while you lay in bed between eleven P.M. and four A.M.?

P (Bill): I retire late, usually after midnight. I hate to go to bed early and lie there fighting for sleep.

E: If you retire at one A.M. and fall asleep at four A.M., what do you do between one and four? Do you lie in bed? Or do you get up walking, smoking, reading?

P: I may lie in bed for awhile. Then I become tense and feel I have to get up. I take a book and read, or I go to the kitchen for a drink of water or get myself a bite from the icebox. After that, I may return to bed and lie down for awhile, but the trouble starts all over, and I get up again.

(Ethel is asked to join the interview.)

E: Ethel, several months ago, when I first saw you, you also complained you were unable to fall asleep. Is that still the case?

P (Ethel): I have no trouble now. I sleep like a rock.

E: How do you do that?

P: I used to go to bed fearing that another one of those dreadful sleepless nights was in store for me. Now I know it was this fear that kept me awake. Ever since I stopped fearing the sleepless nights, I don't have any.

E: To put it differently, the fear of not sleeping made you tense, and the tenseness kept you awake. After you eliminated the fear, you were no longer tense and had no difficulty sleeping. But tell me, Ethel, how did you manage to eliminate the fear of not sleeping?

P: I did what you told me to do.

E: What was it I told you?

P: You said there is no such thing as lack of sleep except in acute diseases. If a person is not suffering from an acute ailment, he may have trouble falling asleep, or his sleep may be broken and interrupted. But he will get a good deal of sleep if he keeps lying in bed. You also said a person may not get sufficient sleep in one particular night but will get enough of it the next following night to compensate for what he missed the night before. I remember you saying that difficulty of sleeping deprives one of comfort but does not interfere with health.* After I grasped that, I no longer worried about sleep.

(Bill rejoins the interview.)

E: Bill, having attended classes for many months, you certainly know the rules mentioned by Ethel. How is it you do not practice them?

P (Bill): I know the rules and practice them night after night. But I can't sleep. I know you will call that *sabotage*. If it is, I am not aware of sabotaging. I go to bed, keeping in mind that sleep is nothing to worry about; nevertheless, I feel tense the minute I stretch out. Is this sabotage?

E: It could hardly be anything else. You say you practice the rules for sleeping but cannot sleep. How is it that Ethel, practicing the same rules, applies them successfully? Obviously, Ethel's practicing is done with determination, yours without. She carries out my orders resolutely, you halfheartedly. The halfhearted practice is sabotage. If you were determined to carry out my instructions, you would not wait till after midnight before you retire. You say you are without worry or fear about sleep. Why, then, do you wait for hours, hesitating to retire? Hesitation is fear and the reverse of determination. Do you understand now why I call your effort undetermined and halfhearted?

P: I admit it must be fear that keeps me from going to bed on time. But I don't see why it is sabotage if I can't get rid of my fears. I certainly try my best.

E: That is all you do. You try your best which is the halfhearted practice I mentioned. Every sabotaging patient offers the excuse that he tries his best. What you try is a method, the method of initiating and maintaining sleep. You described your method. It may be your best. However, my instructions do not call for your method, poor, good or best. They demand that you employ that method which I have

---

*This does not, of course, apply to growing children whose health may suffer from insufficient sleep.

outlined here repeatedly. You sabotaged that method first when you delayed the process of retiring by hours, second when after retiring at a late hour, you failed to lie quietly but instead kept jumping out of bed, reading, walking or rummaging for a drink and food. Both sequences of sabotaging acts were carried out through the medium of your muscles. You may have difficulty controlling fears and worries. But muscles can be controlled "at will."

Everybody has it within his power to command his muscles to effect an act or to refrain from effecting it. That is all my instructions require you to do. They direct you to order your muscles to walk toward your bed at a given early hour, to lie down and to maintain the recumbent position until you fall asleep. If you permitted your muscles to do otherwise, you may have tried your best, but you failed to carry out my instructions. Of course, it is difficult to forbid the muscles to stir when you are tense and feel the imperative urge to move. The muscles become more tense and press with greater vehemence for relief through motion. But you heard me state repeatedly that no matter how agonizing muscular tenseness may be, it disappears after a few minutes if you refuse resolutely to move the muscles. A resoluteness of this sort requires that you are ready to pass for a few minutes through the torture of lying quietly when every fiber of yours is aching for motion.

P: In the beginning, I frequently did what you asked me to do. I went to bed early and stayed in bed without leaving it. At times, I kept that up for hours. Finally, I got so tense, I couldn't stand it. I don't think you can call that "sabotage" or "halfhearted practice."

E: I must challenge your statement that you couldn't sleep, although you stayed in bed for hours. That may happen occasionally and does happen with great regularity in the instance of persons suffering from acute distressing ailments. Otherwise, *to lie in bed for hours means to sleep part of the hours*. The sleep may be of poor quality and may proceed in fitful snatches. After each snatch, you awaken, having the feeling that you "did not sleep a wink." Nevertheless, you slept a considerable portion of the time which you spent in bed.

P: I know I don't sleep. I am aware all the time of everything that goes on. I hear every little noise and am wide awake all the time.

E: What you said right now is nothing but an act of sabotage. After I explained that everybody who lies in bed for hours sleeps part of these hours, you exclaim, "I know I don't sleep." With this, you contradict my statement. Apparently, you intend to engage me in an argument. After months of attending classes, you ought to know that I do not permit patients to question my statements. If you do that, you set your own immature knowledge against my seasoned experience. Indeed, you challenge my authority. You know that this is one form of sabotage, perhaps its worst form.

P: I don't understand why you speak of arguing. Am I not supposed to tell my side of the story?

E: The trouble is that you consider this a story of which you take one side, and I the other. Why should we take sides? If you think we should, you conceive of an interview as an argument or debate with "two sides to the story." While interviewing a patient, I do not engage in storytelling, not even in story listening. An interview deals with an account of symptoms, not with the telling of a story. Your sleeplessness is a symptom, not a topic of conversation. In a conversation, you are permitted, even desired, to state "your side of the story" which is based on your common knowledge.

But in a discussion of symptoms, you cannot rely on common knowledge. In order to understand the nature and action of symptoms, you are required to possess special and authoritative knowledge. Where and when did you acquire authoritative knowledge about sleep and sleep disturbances? All you were ever able to observe were your own difficulties of sleeping. What you observed was one single case, which is a slender basis for any kind of knowledge. I shall ignore the fact that your manner of observing was naive and amateurish. You are, of course, not trained in making valid and expert observations. This I will ignore. But tell me, Bill, would you apply to me for help if you knew that I had experience with only one case like yours? You would not consider me an expert with authoritative knowledge unless you were certain I observed and studied hundreds and perhaps thousands of cases. You see, Bill, when you said, "I know I don't sleep," you referred to your own haphazard and hazy knowledge, which you obtained by means of untrained observation and inexpert interpretation. In relying on your own irrelevant knowledge, you rejected my authoritative opinion. You told "your side of the story" and "took sides" against me. Do you realize that this is sabotage?

P: I cannot get it into my head that I should not be able to know whether I am awake or asleep. That doesn't seem to require expert knowledge.

E: I grant that you know when you are awake. But after you awaken from a brief snatch of sleep, you do not have to know at all that you have slept. I have heard it stated a hundred and perhaps a thousand times from patients and non-patients that last night they "didn't sleep a wink." Some people go to absurd extremes, claiming they "did not sleep a wink" for solid weeks or months. I told you that to lie in bed for hours means to sleep part of those hours. I added that the quality of this kind of sleep may be poor proceeding in snatches. The snatches may last ten minutes, or half an hour or an hour or longer. The sleep, being light and superficial, it is easily interrupted by every sound, by a mild muscular pain, by a moderate irritation of one's bladder or a slight spasm of the intestines. Awakening from this superficial slumber, the sleeper is not aware of having slept. Added together, the successive snatches may have amounted to a sizeable total, let me say, five or six hours in the aggregate. During these five or six hours, the muscles rested, and the conscious attention was relaxed. This is all that sleep is required to do for purposes of health.

For purposes of comfort, it is desirable to enjoy deep sleep from which one awakens refreshed with new vigor. But I do not cater to your comfort; I tend to your health. And health is adequately served by the brief snatches of light and superficial sleep. You will now realize that you have a fitful, broken and superficial sleep. It serves your health but does not give you the subjective feeling of having slept. Lacking this subjective feeling, you think you have been awake and express this conclusion in the wholly unwarranted exclamation, "I know I did not sleep." By making this statement or thinking this thought, you oppose your common sense observation to my expert knowledge, and this is sabotage.

(Lester joins the interview.)

P (Lester): Doctor, is a question in order?

E: If it is to the point.

P: I think it is. I frequently read health articles and listen to health broadcasts in which sleep is said to be essential to health. I know you are our only authority in matters of health, and I know it is sabotage to accept other opinions. And if you say that sleep has little to do with health, that settles it for me. But I hear plenty about the importance of sleep from friends and relatives, and I should like to know how to answer their arguments.

E: Your point is well-taken, and I shall be glad to oblige you. Since I am supposed to be your only authority on health, as every physician ought to be to his patients, you are entitled to know the sources of my authoritative knowledge. They are, first, my own experiences; second, the studies of leading men of science who are unquestioned authorities in this field.

I shall first tell you of my own experiences. They are manifold and concern observations on patients mainly, but also observations on my own sleep performance. I am of course not immune to "sleepless nights," which means that I pass occasionally through nights in which my sleep is fitful and superficial. When this happens, I also awake in the morning with the subjective feeling that I "did not sleep a wink." On one such night, years ago, I noticed that precisely at a moment when I felt distressed at my wakefulness, I still had in mind the tailend of a dream that had just occupied my brain. At that moment, there was no doubt that I had slept. Otherwise, how could I have dreamt? I then decided to look out for these dream fragments, and the method seldom fails me. Whenever I feel wretched because I seem to waste futile hours trying to fall asleep, I instantly recall the last dream fragment that I can bring to consciousness. Then I know I have been sleeping and dismiss anxiety and apprehensiveness. You will be well advised to hunt for these dream portions of the past few seconds or minutes whenever you are obsessed with the idea that you have "not slept a wink." Do you understand, Bill, that if you know you had a dream, you must have been sleeping?

(Bill rejoins the interview.)

P (Bill): I shall certainly look out for these dreams when I can't fall asleep. I hope I'll catch them.

E: If you say, "I hope I'll catch them," you indicate that you are by no means certain about succeeding. With this, you express doubt whether you will be able to convince yourself that lying in bed for hours means sleeping part of the hours. Perhaps I shall be able to furnish you with more conclusive evidence. Since you have not gone through a mental disease but suffer from a so-called psychoneurosis, I shall quote observations from psychoneurotic patients first. On numerous occasions, I witnessed patients of this description sleeping and snoring, but when awakened, they protested they "didn't sleep a wink." Other patients of this kind were observed by my nurses, interns and resident physicians who reported that the patients who complained of utter inability to fall asleep, either snored or failed to respond when their names were called, when they were sprinkled with water or pricked with a pin. Does that prove to you that to lie in bed means to sleep?

P: I am making every effort to take in what you say. Nevertheless, it seems to me I don't sleep. Couldn't there be an exception to the rule?

E: I am sure you are not the exception. But I agree there are exceptions. I told you that patients with acute physical distress may actually fail to sleep, although they lie in bed all night. This is true also of acutely suffering mental (psychotic) patients. It is well-known that so-called depressed patients may go without sleep or with a minimum of it for nights and even weeks in succession. Nevertheless, after they get well, not a trace of evidence can be found that the prolonged vigils have caused any damage to their health. If any proof is needed that sleep has little bearing on health, these patients provide it.

More convincing evidence yet is furnished by the so-called manic patients. In the days when we had no shock treatment, many of these wretches spent weeks and months on the wards, raving day and night with scarcely any interruption. They hardly slept or rested. Day after day and night after night, they were in almost continuous motion, talking incessantly, jumping, running, fighting. In this manner, their well-nigh complete sleeplessness was combined with a terrific expenditure of energy. If prolonged wakefulness is supposed to drain a person's strength and to undermine his health, these manic patients should have emerged from their spells as irreparable physical wrecks. Nothing of this kind, however, was observed. After they recovered their state of health, they gave no indication of having suffered as a result of the ordeal. Do you think, Bill, I have finally demonstrated to you that lack of sleep (1) is a myth as concerns persons not afflicted with acute physical or mental illness, (2) leaves no permanent damage if it actually does occur as, for instance, in the mental ailments which I mentioned?

P: You certainly proved your point. I am now convinced that to lie in bed means to sleep. But will I be convinced tonight when I lie down and my brain begins to rattle?

E: When your brain rattles, you must let it go on rattling, but you must remain calm. Your look of surprise indicates that you do not think it possible for anyone to be calm when his brain is in uproar. Many patients have told me about this rattling. They call it, variously, "brainstorm," "chasing of thought," "racing." What it actually means is that the brain has difficulty relaxing. The thoughts are in a welter of confusion. The "stream of thought," ordinarily calm and well-ordered, becomes stormy and feverish. Such disorder is frequently found in other organs. The heart may be thrown into sudden palpitations, the muscles into tenseness, rigidity and tremors. Every organ may begin to "rattle" at any time, to use your expression. This "rattling" is nothing but our old standby–tenseness.

After attending classes for months, you ought to know how to deal with tenseness. An organ that becomes tense is thrown into a storm of activity. A storm rises, but it also subsides after it has run its course. How is it that your storm of tenseness keeps up its fury for hours without subsiding? Tenseness is a sensation ordinarily produced by fear. I told you repeatedly that sensations and feelings rise and fall, provided you do not attach the idea of danger at the moment the curve reaches its peak. How is it that your fearful feelings and sensations rise but do not fall?

P: I know what you are driving at. I create a vicious cycle.

E: Correct. And I shall describe the precise manner in which your vicious cycle operates. When you merely think of going to bed, you are seized with an apprehensiveness, a not yet marked fear that you are again headed for one of those dreadful sleepless nights. Now you postpone the ordeal. You wait and hesitate and keep yourself busy with chores. Soon you notice that you have difficulty concentrating on the chores with which you busy yourself. The less you are able to concentrate, the stronger grows your tenseness; the greater the tenseness, the worse the concentration. You are already in the throes of a minor vicious cycle.

After hours of tinkering, you finally retire, apprehensive, anxious, disheartened. You said, "I feel tense the very minute I stretch out." I presume you meant to suggest that the very act of contacting the bed makes you tense. Fear, you mean to say, has nothing to do with it. Rather, it is some mysterious habit which makes the muscles tense when they merely touch the bedsheet. But from what I just told you, it ought to be clear to you that you are choked with fear long before you "stretch out." The vicious cycle was set going hours before you touched the bed. Feeling tense, you have difficulty lying still. You twist, turn, throw yourself from side to side, thereby increasing your tenseness many times its original intensity.

You say you "hate to lie there fighting for sleep." There is nobody and nothing to fight, and be certain you do nothing of the kind. What you do is to work yourself up to a paroxysm of rage and fury. Against whom do you rage? Presumably against yourself. Or, it is nothing but a blind anger, directed against nobody in particular. At any rate, to the original fear of not sleeping is now added this senseless anger that merely serves to accelerate the vicious cycle and to fan the tenseness to an intolerable pitch. Then the brain begins to "rattle." Do you understand that all of this is the result of fear? Fear can be remedied only by the certain knowledge that no danger threatens. You cannot gain this knowledge from your own experience which is amateurish and limited to the acquaintance with one single case. What must guide you is my authoritative knowledge which is based on solid study and expert observation. This alone can give you the conviction that no danger whatever attends a night spent in bed even if you feel you "haven't slept a wink."*

---

*The reader will notice that the author, who set out originally to buttress his argument both with his own experience and "the studies of leading men of science who are unquestioned authorities in this field," failed to quote scientific evidence. Omissions of this kind are unavoidable in interviews. They are due either to oversight or pressure of time. For the benefit of those interested in the subject, it may be pointed out that the experimental evidence that prolonged periods of sleeplessness cause little or no harm is fully dealt with in a study by Nathaniel Kleitman, entitled *Sleep and Sleeplessness*, University of Chicago Press, 1939.

CHAPTER FORTY-FOUR

Simplicity Versus Complexity in Combating Fears

Nancy had been apprehensive and self-conscious all her life. After she married and had children, the responsibilities of caring for the family weighed heavily on her tender conscience. One day, about twelve years ago, she became panicky, with palpitations, dizziness, dry throat and body tremor dominating the picture. She was so scared, that she feared she was losing her mind. She recovered from the first scare, but the fear of mental collapse persisted. Her sleep was poor. She watched herself, continuously magnifying minor observations. When she discovered that her memory or concentration failed her on some occasion, she considered this as incontrovertible evidence that her mind was slipping. In time, she developed other well-defined fears. The main fear was to be confined in a closed space. She suffered agonies of dizziness, sweats, churning of the stomach, sinking feelings, faints and palpitations whenever she ventured to take a ride in an automobile, streetcar, elevated or railroad train. Rides in an elevator were less disturbing if they were short stops, but if the point of destination was a high upper floor, the performance was a nightmare. Since the physician's suite was situated on the 17th floor of a downtown building, a visit to his office was looked forward to with great apprehension and required a companion to reassure her.

As the years passed, Nancy's fears expanded. She grew to fear her impulses. She dreaded the thought of being alone with her daughters or with her husband for fear she might do harm to those she loved. "My impulses," she said, "become confused. I feel the urge to be helpful, but once I have done a good turn, I instantly resent it and feel a hatred against the person to whom I was friendly a minute ago. Isn't that proof that I am going insane?" She attended classes and Recovery meetings and begged to be interviewed after merely four weeks of participation in the self-help program, before she had a reasonable opportunity to stage an initial improvement. Such early requests for class interviews are generally considered a good sign of cooperation.

E –Examiner

P –Patient

E: You have been in classes for only four weeks, and I do not expect you to have improved a great deal. Are you still afraid of closed rooms and high places?

P: Right now I feel awfully weak and exhausted after a thirty-minute ride on the I.C. (Illinois Central).

E: If that is so, I presume that your other fears have not improved either and that you are still obsessed with the thought that you will lose your mind and that you might do harm to the members of your family.

P: I have not noticed any change, except that I am now more hopeful.

E: Let me ask you, Nancy, what precisely do you fear when you enter an automobile or train coach or an elevator? Are you afraid of an accident?

P: I was in three major accidents and was not a bit scared. As a matter of fact, I was the calmest person in the crowd, perhaps because I don't care if I die. Another thing: I am afraid to be in an automobile even if it stands in the garage.

E: I understand, Nancy, that if you notice a weakness of memory and attention, you think of a possible mental ailment. I also understand that if you have frightening impulses, you fear you might some day carry them out. These fears are exaggerated, but they are not absurd or ridiculous. But if you state that you fear being in an automobile even when it is not moving, well, that is absurd. You cannot possibly think of danger under these circumstances, and your fear is without rhyme or reason. Can't you tell me what makes you quiver with fear in situations that neither you nor anybody else considers dangerous?

P: I get so worked up when I step into a car or an elevator, that I fear I am going to collapse the next minute.

E: People get "worked up" on many occasions but do not fear they will collapse. Why do you?

P: I get those awful palpitations and the sinking feeling in my stomach. And I go into a cold sweat, and I feel so faint that I think that's my last moment. Right now when I merely speak of these things, I have my palpitations.

E: Now I know what you are afraid of. You don't fear cars and elevators or closed spaces and high places. What you fear is your sensations that are called forth by these closed or high localities.

P: You may be right, but it does not matter to me whether it is the sensations or the places that frighten me. I simply feel that I am going to pass out.

E: The distinction which I made may matter little to you. But to me, it is a fundamental difference whether your fears are caused by sensations within you or by objects without. If your fears are the result of frightening sensations and overpowering impulses, I ought to be able to teach you how to control them, but I am unable to give you directions how to exercise control over automobiles and elevators. I do not mean to be facetious if I mention in the same breath such disparate things as automobiles and sensations, elevators and impulses.

But it is about time that patients should know that the only things they are afraid of are their own inner experiences, their thoughts, feelings, sensations and impulses. I do not deny, of course, that some fears stem from objects outside you. There are holdups and burglaries and drownings and killings. But these objective dangers, as a general rule, hold little terror for nervous patients. What they are mostly afraid of are terrifying sensations, threatening impulses, obsessing thoughts and depressing feelings, that is, their own inner experiences.

You gave an excellent example of your indifference to realistic, objective dangers when you stated that in three separate automobile accidents, you were "the calmest person in the crowd." This is a common rule with nervous patients. In situations of grave realistic and objective danger, they may be calm and fearless. But let them be confronted with disturbing inner experiences, and they become panicky and hysterical. Do you realize now that what you fear is not automobiles, streetcars and elevators but your own inner storms and excitements that are aroused when you approach or enter these objects?

P: I understand. But will that stop my palpitations and sinking feelings?

E: Why do you question that? Common sense ought to tell you that you cannot conquer a fear unless you first know what it is that you are afraid of. And if I succeeded in demonstrating to you the true object of your fears, you ought to have gained some relief already. You ought to feel more confident now because at last you know what it is that scares you. The fact that you do not feel relief proves that you did not accept my explanation. You still doubt and question it. If this is so, I shall have to give you other and perhaps more convincing examples.

You know, Nancy, that many people hesitate to admit trivial misdemeanors, for instance, children to their parents. They hesitate even if the parents have seldom inflicted bodily punishment on them. What they are afraid of is that after confessing, they will have the tortured feelings of shame, embarrassment and loss of face. They do not fear anything realistic like being spanked; what they fear is their own inner feelings.

You have also heard of mature men who fear asking their employer for an increase in salary. They fear to advance their request even if they know for certain that the boss is a kindly person and by no means bossy. In most instances, this fear of approaching another person with an otherwise well justified request is due to the fact that on previous occasions, the making of requests was followed by a sense of embarrassment and sensations of tenseness, stammering, flushing and perhaps palpitations and faintness. That man who trembles at the thought of approaching his superior may try to analyze the nature of his fear. In all likelihood, he will then advance inconsequential reasons. He will say that what he fears is that his "boldness" may cost him the job or that, after all, his services are not worth more than he earns. In all of this, he will ignore or evade the real explanation that what he fears is the possibility of arousing unpleasant inner experiences. Do you think you understand better now what I am driving at?

P: You mean to say that I am afraid of my sensations when I fear rides in automobiles and elevators. I think I know that now. But will the knowledge help me get rid of the fears?

E: Knowledge alone will not help. But once you know what you are afraid of, you can devise plans for eliminating fear. You will agree that if you fear something, you think of that something as a danger. You will also admit that in order to fear a danger, you must believe it is real and not imaginary. In other words, you must take the danger seriously and be convinced of its reality. All you have to do to dispose of a fear is to refuse to believe that there is danger. Then you will ignore it or laugh it out of existence. If you laugh at a thing and ridicule it, you cannot possibly fear it. That is the reason why a sense of humor is such a strong antidote against fear. You see, Nancy, if at the moment you are gripped with the fear of your sensations, if at that moment you could reach the conviction that the danger is unreal, imaginary or not serious, you could laugh at it and make it disappear in an instant.

Unfortunately, the many scares you have gone through in the past ten or twelve years have cowed you into such an abysmal fright that you have lost every trace of a sense of humor with reference to that fear. Your only salvation is to gain the unquestioned conviction that the danger you think of is not existent. I have tried to convince you of that; I pointed out to you the reasons why a fear of this kind cannot possibly be based on a realistic danger. But it seems you are not convinced yet. Why do you still listen to the language of your body instead of accepting what your physician tells you?

P: I have tried my best to accept what you told me. I have read many times what you said about the symptomatic idiom and the temperamental lingo. I have listened to what the patients told me, and I have studied the interview with Ruth on the "Vicious Cycle of Panic."* I am convinced that you are right. And if I do not happen to be cooped up in a streetcar or in an elevator, I can reason with myself and realize that your authoritative knowledge is superior to my personal experience. I know all of that. But when I enter an automobile, my knowledge is gone. What can I do about that?

E: What you can do is to gain conviction. You have acquired knowledge, but you do not possess conviction. You say that your conviction fades the moment you enter an automobile. What happens is that the moment you reach the car, your heart begins to palpitate, your stomach churns, your throat contracts. To put it otherwise, your inner organs are "scared." That scare communicates itself to the muscles of your arms and legs. They feel tense and heavy and refuse to move. In a sense, they feel paralyzed. Having read the interview with Ruth, you will know that this is the proper setting for a vicious cycle. The panic "marches," as it were, from the inner organs to the outer muscles and to the brain. The greater the commotion of the organs, the more intense is the "paralysis" of the muscles, and the more threatening the paralysis of the muscles, the more terrifying is the fear in the brain.

---

*The interview with Ruth on the "Vicious Cycle of Panic" was published in volume 2 of *The Technques of Self-Help in Psychiatric After-Care*, page 31. Editors' Note: Please see "Other Books by Abraham A. Low, M.D." on pages 417—418.

You ask what you can do. Well, you cannot dictate to the heart to stop the palpitations or to the stomach to cease churning. But you can command your muscles to move, paralysis or no paralysis. And once you make the muscles move in spite of their apparent paralysis, the brain will instantly be convinced that at least one of the dread dangers it feared is without foundation and nothing to be taken seriously. That may not do away with the commotion of the inner organs. The palpitations and other sensations may continue. But a breach has been made in the solid rampart of the panic, and the implicit belief in the reality of the danger is shaken.

When on the next occasion you enter the car, the organs may again be thrown into a violent turmoil, but you will no longer be scared by the "paralysis" of the muscles. Assurance and conviction will now be more assuring and more convincing, with the result that the brain will be more calm, and with a calm brain, there is no possibility of a sustained panic. With the panic petering out in consequence of reassurance, the organs will soon quiet down, and this time, conviction will be strengthened. On the occasion of a third or fourth or a dozen other trials, you are certain to cut short the panic in its very beginning. Then conviction will score the final triumph, and you will be cured of your fear and incapacity. Do you realize that the way to shed your fears is to give the proper directions to your muscles?

P: Frankly, that sounds a bit too easy. It doesn't just seem possible that I should cure my fears by moving my muscles. It should take more than that.

E: It will be difficult for you to convince me that it is "a bit too easy" for persons to command their muscles to move if they feel paralyzed by the fear of making another step. You did not mean to say that my suggestion sounds too easy; you thought it sounds too simple. I shall not enter into a detailed discussion of this very important distinction. I shall merely tell you that I do not want my patients to believe that cures and remedies must necessarily be complex, involved and time-consuming. It is easy to sit in a chair and to be given lengthy and interesting explanations about how fears arise and develop. That is complex but easy. But if a boy is afraid of swimming or diving, it is not at all easy to make him move his muscles for the purpose of a resolute jump. That jump is simple but difficult.

Do you realize that you expect to be cured of your fears by means of complex but easy and sometimes glib explanations instead of by means of simple but exacting directions? You want to be studied and analyzed and discussed, but you do not want to be told what to do and how to act. What will the most lucid explanations profit you if you are seized with a deep anxiety or a paralyzing panic? In a condition of this kind, you are utterly unable to make use of the ingenious and fascinating explanations you may have been given. If in a panic you try to remember what you learned and to reason out what is the sensible thing to do, your mind will fail you disastrously. The panic weakens your memory and blots out your reasoning power. All you will be able to do in a commotion of this sort is to apply simple rules. Their very simplicity renders them capable of being employed in a situation in which complex thought is impossible.

P: I do not mean to be contrary, Doctor. But it seems to me that when I get into a panic, I will not be able to carry out even simple rules.

E: That may be correct for the first and second trial. But if you continue to practice, you become ever more proficient in the application of these simple rules. Moreover, you have ample opportunity to practice in situations that are less disturbing or threatening. You mentioned that you are obsessed by the fear of doing harm to your husband and your daughters. This fear does not throw you into a panic. It is with you all the time, and being strung out over endless hours and days, it is milder, less vehement, less acute. This fear can be handled with a method that is not only simple but also easy.

You know that in consequence of the fear, you avoid touching knives or any sharp objects. Well, should you practice the simple method of deliberately touching sharp objects in the presence of those that you fear to harm, you would have no difficulty convincing yourself that your impulse to do harm is not dangerous. You would soon refuse to take that impulse seriously and would learn, thereby, that at least some of your fears are ridiculous and can be laughed at. Once you have succeeded in discarding one of your fears by the simple method of commanding your muscles to act against them, you will have learned the general principle that fears can be checked by a command to the muscles to counteract the suggestions of danger. The lesson that you have learned with minor fears will then carry over to the region of the major fears. As with most patients, your fears are many in numbers. Some of them are strong, some are mild. You may say that the fears form a chain with strong and weak links. If you wish to break a chain, you must attempt to pry it open at its weakest spot, not where the links are strongest. This is the Method of Attack on the Weakest Point, which I have mentioned in interviews repeatedly.

P: I have tried so often to touch knives. I wish I could, but I can't.

E: What happened when you stretched out your arm toward the knife?

P: Well, I felt I couldn't do it.

E: Don't tell me that you couldn't do it. Tell me what happened. Tell me whether you had a panic when you advanced your arm in the direction of the knife. Did you feel like fainting? Did you have violent palpitations, sweats, and weakness and churning?

P: No, I simply couldn't move my arm.

E: Do you see the difference between entering the car and picking up a knife? In both instances, you are afraid; that means you have the idea of danger in your brain. But in the case of the automobile, the idea of danger is attended by threatening sensations, while in the case of the knife, it is nothing but a thought. You will now understand why I call this fear of touching a knife a weak link in the chain of your fears. All you have to do to get rid of your fear of the knife is to convince yourself that your thought of danger is absurd. And the best means of reducing an idea of danger to its absurdity is to act against it. The moment you touch the knife and notice that nothing happens, not even a palpitation, certainly no fainting or any other sign of a panic, once you notice that, the thought of danger is immediately proved absurd.

Although you are a newcomer to this group, nevertheless, I am certain you heard the members of Recovery mention in their panel discussions how they learned to conquer their fears through their muscles. Many of my patients were afraid to be on their feet because they thought their muscles were exhausted by nervous fatigue. When they decided to walk on in defiance of their fears, they became convinced in an instant that their idea of danger was absurd. With some, success came on the first or second trial, with others, after a period of extended trials. But whether success comes quickly or slowly, the underlying principle is the same: attack the chain of your fears at their weakest point, and convince your brain through your muscles that its ideas of danger are absurd.

Chapter Forty-five

Vicious Cycle and Vitalizing Cycle

Virginia's health broke when she was 20. Her previous history was that of an average girl with a good record of school, job and social adjustment. But after she passed her twentieth year, she suffered an attack of depression. She lost weight, ate and slept poorly. Her interests weakened. She neglected her job and her appearance. She felt tired all the time and had to make an extreme effort to perform the trifling tasks of her daily routine. Dressing, speaking, walking required an excessive amount of energy. Her mood was down. She experienced the desire "to make an end of it" but lacked the courage to do so. Due to her dejected spirit, she blamed herself for past mistakes and petty misdemeanors. Finally, she had to be taken to the hospital.

She returned after six months and felt well for four years. Then she drifted again into a mood of depression. This time she received a course of electroshock treatment and regained her health after only five weeks of hospitalization. She resumed her activities, secured a position with a real estate firm but continued to be tired, restless and irritable. It was at this point that her mother heard of Recovery. Virginia joined the organization, practicing the system of self-help and conquering fatigue, irritability and restlessness. But in spite of her patient application, she was unable to shake off a sense of shyness which made her feel miserable and helpless when she was to meet people singly or in social groups. She volunteered for a class interview in the spring of 1947, stating that a previous interview two years ago had given her much relief.

E –EXAMINER

P –PATIENT

E: How are you, Virginia?

P: I feel all right. But I am so self-conscious. I shut up like a clam when I am among people. When I want to say something, I can't find a thought. It seems my brain freezes, and I can't think. It is all a fog and blank. If somebody asks a question, my throat tightens, and I can't speak a word.

E: Have you been working all the time?

P: I have worked continuously since shortly after I left the hospital.

E: That makes it close to four years of continuous work. Did you change jobs during this time?

P: No, I am still holding the same job that I got four years ago.

E: Do you think your employer is satisfied with your work?

P: I got three raises, and my boss leaves the running of the office practically to me.

E: I consider this a neat accomplishment and a very creditable comeback after what you went through. You ought to be proud of yourself. Instead, you shrink and almost swoon when you are asked to do nothing more than open your mouth and formulate a simple sentence. You say your brain freezes, and you cannot think, your throat tightens, and you cannot speak.

How is it you do a good piece of speaking and thinking right now? How is it your brain thaws up and your throat unlocks during this interview? You are certainly among people here. More than that, this is an audience and you the star performer tonight. You are in the limelight, watched by everybody in this hall. Many people, with strong nerves and no record of a past breakdown, wilt when they are asked to make a speech before a public gathering of this size. And, remember, what you say here is a tale of weakness, a recital of your shortcomings, a confession of personal inadequacy, while in a social group the conversation turns around more or less impersonal and indifferent topics. You show courage here in a highly embarrassing situation in which your failures and inefficiencies are laid bare, and exhibit fear in a social setting where courtesy and etiquette banish all possibility of being exposed. Can you explain this strange behavior?

P: I am relaxed here. But when I meet people on the outside, I am tense.

E: I am frequently tense myself. But that does not cause my brain to freeze and my throat to tighten. No matter how tense I sometimes am, I get my brain to think and my speech muscles to produce words and sentences. How is it you cannot think and speak when you are tense?

P: I don't know how to explain it. I simply don't get thoughts, and the words don't come.

E: I shall try to give the explanation. You will grant, Virginia, that to speak means to produce movements of the muscles of speech. To put it differently: speaking is a muscular act. I take it you know that muscles will act only if they are stimulated and will refuse action if they are frustrated. From this, you may conclude that your muscles of speech are stimulated here tonight but would be frustrated if you were to repeat this performance elsewhere. What stimulates muscles is courage and self-confidence, that means, the sense of security. What frustrates them is fear and self-distrust, that is, the sense of insecurity. Do you understand now, Virginia, that when you have the thought of insecurity in your brain, it will frustrate and tighten your muscles and keep them from acting and speaking?

P: It seems to me I have no views or thoughts in my brain when my speech stops. My head feels like a blank, and no thoughts come, not even the thought of insecurity.

E: If you say you have no thoughts in your brain, you seem to believe you know how your brain works. In this, you presume a trifle too much. Right now you sit on this chair. Moreover, you keep sitting. You do not jump up or run away. How could you maintain your seat unless you were certain that the chair is solid and you are in no danger of falling? Yet, you may insist the thought of security was not in your brain while you kept up your sitting activity. Do you realize that you could never sit down or continue sitting unless your brain told you that the act of sitting is safe and secure? The same consideration holds good for every variety of acting, for eating, standing, walking, speaking. You would never dare voice a sentence unless your brain told you that the statement you are about to release will not endanger your social, moral or ethical security; that the remark you intend to make is neither offensive nor compromising. This rule applies to every act, no matter how simple or how insignificant. You could never make a step unless you were sure you would not fall and fracture your leg. You could never ask even the most innocent question unless you were reasonably certain it would not be resented.

These examples, which could be multiplied indefinitely, will tell you that, ordinarily, no act of yours will be released unless the brain first takes the view that no danger is involved. After the brain has, in the flash of a momentary decision, reached the conclusion that the situation is one of security, it stimulates the muscles to release the appropriate act. The conclusion that the planned act is safe is formed without your conscious knowledge. We say it is arrived at intuitively and not discursively. When you came here tonight, you had already formed the conclusion in your brain that the situation of this interview is one of security. Hence, your thoughts did not freeze, and your throat did not lock. Why is there freezing and locking when you attend a social gathering?

P: I guess because there my brain forms the conclusion of insecurity.

E: Correct. But how is it that this conclusion of insecurity keeps occupying your brain all the time you attend the gathering? Why is there no letup, no change of conclusions?

P: I think I know what you have in mind. I produce a vicious cycle.

E: That is correct, if you specify what kind of vicious

cycle you have in mind. The most common varieties of vicious cycles are those of fear and anger. But fear and anger are part of life, indeed, a most significant part of life; and if they run in vicious cycles, their action represents a very stormy, an almost tempestuous sort of life. However, when your thoughts freeze and go blank, they can hardly be said to be stirring with life. In a sense, they are dead. Their life pulse has gone out of them. If you speak of freezing, of fogs and blanks, of shutting up like a clam, that means that you pass into something like a state of lifelessness. Your vicious cycle affects the pulse of your responses and reactions. You know what a pulse means. It means something that rises and falls, something that begins, matures and finally fades away. This is true of muscular movement, of glandular activity, of nerve impulses, of thoughts, sensations and feelings. All of them have their life history of being born, of maturing into full action and of passing out of activity. For the sake of simplicity I shall limit the discussion and consider the pulse cycle of thought only.

You know that if you now happen to think of the weather, that thought will not occupy your brain for a great length of time. Your attention will soon wander from the topic of the weather to that of your office, or home or mother. It will then turn to the book you are just reading, then to the friend who phoned you yesterday, then to the subject of the atomic bomb which was discussed in the morning paper. In order to make the mind hop and skip in this rather careless manner, you must be reasonably carefree. That means, you must have a reasonable sense of security. If you feel insecure, your thoughts will be focused on the object that threatens, and your attention will be riveted on the topic of danger. The one thought of danger will *preoccupy* your brain and will prevent it from *occupying* itself with other thoughts. The thinking pulse will then be interrupted by your preoccupation. The preoccupation will make one single thought dominate the brain, with the result that the remaining thoughts will no longer rise and fall. The thought pulse will be suspended and life will seem abolished. The brain will then feel as if in a fog, dense, blank, lifeless, pulseless. How is it, I shall ask, that your thought pulse shows life and vigor during this interview and loses its vitality in other groups?

P: I still think it is the vicious cycle that does that.

E: I told you I am ready to accept the explanation. But it will have to be qualified. There are many types and degrees of vicious cycles. One of them is that of fear, another of anger. These are the most common varieties. If yours were that of fear, the vicious cycle would fan it into a panic. If it were that of anger, it would be raised to the pitch of rage. I have observed you in the company of other people, and you gave no evidence of being rocked by either panic or rage. Your face was smooth, perhaps even blank, and its muscles gave little evidence of lively expression. You sat motionless, staring into space. You give this a different wording when you say that your brain does not think and your speech muscles do not move. They are not lifeless, by any means, but you feel that life has gone out of them. The brain feels unable to think, and the muscles unable to act. The more helpless the brain, the more limp are the muscles; the more limp the muscles, the more helpless is the brain. This is the vicious cycle of helplessness. How is it, I shall ask again, that you are able to shake off this sense of helplessness when you are interviewed here in front of a large crowd?

P: I don't know exactly, but the nearest I can think of as an explanation is that I don't feel cramped here as I feel in groups on the outside.

E: That does not explain a great deal. It seems to me I shall have to do the explaining. We spoke of a vicious cycle. That means that some sort of circular movement is set up between the brain cells and the muscles. In this cycle, the brain acts on the muscles, and the muscles act on the brain. The two influence one another. The cycle begins its destructive work before you arrive at the particular gathering. For hours and perhaps for days, you have anticipated that your brain will be paralyzed and helpless. On the way to the social function which you are to attend, the "freezing" process begins, and when you reach your destination, it has deepened into what you call "a blank." The brain feels life-less and dispatches impulses to the muscles not to stir, not to move. In this manner, the helplessness of the brain communicates itself to the muscles, and the vicious cycle is set afoot.

I told you that brain and muscles influence one another in this cycle or circular movement. Since they interact or act on one another, it ought to be clear to you that if you cause the one to move, the other will follow suit. To state it differently: make the one move, and the other will perforce join the movement. You may not be able to get the brain moving. But you certainly can do that with muscles. Command your speech muscles to act, and the brain will instantly realize that its theory of helplessness is a myth, a fiction, an untruth. The more vigorously your muscles will move, the less will the brain be able to believe that it is help-less. That this can be done, you demonstrated here with your perfect speech performance during the present interview.

You remember the first occasion when you were interviewed about two years ago. You stammered, hemmed and hawed and had extreme difficulty squeezing a few words out of your throat. The first sentences leaped out of your mouth explosively. I had to proceed slowly and cautiously, giving you ample time to warm up to the task until finally you took heart and gained courage and gave an excellent account of yourself. At that time, you experienced a vicious cycle of helplessness at the beginning of the interview. During this cycle, your brain was devitalized and deprived your speech muscles of their vitality. But once you commanded your speech muscles to move, the very action of the muscles had a vitalizing effect on the brain. The movement of the muscles convinced the brain that speaking is possible. And when the brain witnessed the living, vital performance of the muscles, it acquired a new vitality itself and lost its lifelessness. The more forceful was the action of the muscles, the more vitalized became the brain; the more vital the brain, the more forceful the muscles. By commanding your muscles to move, you had thus transformed the *vicious cycle of helplessness* into the *vitalizing cycle of self-confidence*.

As the interview drew to its close, it was explained to Virginia that her energetic performance during the interview could be duplicated and multiplied on numerous other occasions inside Recovery and outside. What she had to do was to practice commanding her speech muscles to initiate the vitalizing cycle of self-confidence whenever she had an opportunity to do so. It developed that Virginia had neglected this practice by refraining from joining the panel discussions at family gatherings. She realized that this was her golden opportunity and felt that having gained revealing information about the nature and operation of the vitalizing cycle, she was now in a position to practice with understanding. Reports reaching the writer indicate that Virginia is making a good effort at participating in panel discussions and is ready to transfer to social engagements outside Recovery the experience she is gaining in the family gatherings of the ex-patients.

CHAPTER FORTY-SIX

Symptoms Must Be Attacked Where They Are Weakest

Roy was 35 years of age when he was first seen in the physician's office. He was married, had two children, loved his home and was well liked by friends and neighbors. His employment record was good. He had held his present position for fifteen consecutive years, advancing to the rank of a foreman. All in all, he had done well until three years ago, when suddenly, "out of a blue sky," his right arm and right leg went numb. The numbness had come on at the moment when he entered the plant to start on the afternoon shift. It disappeared as fast as it had come, lasting a few minutes only. But Roy was frightened into a senseless fear that he was headed for a stroke. Ordinarily stolid and unemotional, he was now pale, trembling, restless. His fellow workers noticed the change and drove him home.

The family physician ordered Roy to stay home for a week and to rest. The following week, an electrocardiogram was taken, and the doctor was heard to say that something in the graph was "flat instead of round." After that, Roy developed violent palpitations, headaches, dizziness, fatigue, air-hunger, difficulty of sleeping, fears of physical collapse and mental breakdown. He saw specks floating in front of his eyes and once "nearly went blind" for a couple of minutes. Some of his sensations were bizarre and intensified his fear of a mental breakdown. Looking at his hands, he saw them in a yellow tinge. He felt pains which settled in narrowly confined places, in the left wrist or in the space above the right knee. His teeth began to hurt. There was a pain around the heart. He lifted his little son and instantly felt a pain around his right ear. He lay on the left side, and something clicked in the right flank. The fingers of the right hand might hurt, and suddenly the pain shifted to the back of the head. He felt pressure of the throat, had night sweats which roused the fear of tuberculosis, pain in the chest, difficulty of sleeping, trouble in concentration and "confusion all the time."

A combined course of office and group treatment produced a good improvement. He returned to work and was able to attend to his job in spite of the fact that some of his sensations persisted as weak "reminders." He had learned in Recovery to ignore the threat of symptoms and turned his new knowledge to good account. There were minor setbacks, but he handled them well until, after about six months of successful self-management, a major setback occurred which he was unable to shake off. When he was interviewed in class, he stated that the present setback had lasted upward of four weeks already.

E –Examiner

P –Patient

E: What is it that has troubled you most in these past four weeks?

P: My eyes feel blurry, my memory is poor, and I have an awful fatigue, and the legs feel heavy and numb. And I have these headaches again and the pain around the heart.

E: You have been ill for three years before I saw you. Is that correct?

P: It was not quite three years but almost that long.

E: And during these three years, your trouble got worse and worse?

P: Well, I had some good days.

E: Your symptoms changed. They kept coming and going.

P: I can't say that. Some stayed on.

E: Some of your pains shifted from one part of the body to the other?

P: No, I didn't have that.

E: So far you have denied or corrected or rejected about every statement which I made. When I mentioned that I saw you for three years, you set me right by stating that "it was not quite three years but almost that long." You will understand that the difference between "three years" and "almost three years" is so insignificant that you could safely ignore it. Instead, you stress and emphasize this trifling distinction, underscore it pointedly and make an issue of things that have no importance. You pick flaws in my argument and turn this interview into an occasion for verbal fencing, sparring and skirmishing. This proves that you came here tonight in a fighting mood, which is merely another way of saying that you are in the grip of tenseness. You say that the tenseness has been in evidence for fully four weeks without letup. Does that mean that it was with you all day and every day during these four weeks?

P: It was easier the first few days and the first week. I could relax at a card game or at a show. I guess my mind was taken off my troubles when I had some diversion. But in the past three weeks, it got worse and worse. Even a show or a card game didn't help me. I got so tense that everything irritated me, even my little girl and my wife at home. Maybe you are right, I am in a fighting mood. It makes me mad because I like to get along with people. I simply cannot understand it.

E: Perhaps I can make you understand it. Look here, Roy, tenseness is a sensation. Having attended classes for close to a year, you heard me state repeatedly that sensations rise and fall. How is it that your tenseness has risen but did not fall?

P: I think I know what you mean. I attached the idea of danger to the sensation.

E: Correct. But what does it mean to attach an idea to a sensation? Can ideas be made to change places, to wander from one spot to another? In other words, can ideas be shifted and shoved and pushed around just as you may please?

P: Yes, you said that a person can choose to think of whatever he wishes. And I think that is right.

E: How about sensations? Can they be manipulated at will? If you have the idea of this table in your mind, can you now "attach tenseness" to the thought of the table?

P: I don't think so.

E: If you deny that, then, you obviously believe that thoughts or ideas can be handled, directed and manipulated at will but sensations cannot. You are right. You cannot say, "I am going to be tense from now on" and actually produce the tenseness by sheer wanting it. But you can say, "I am going to think of this table now," and the thought of the table will be in your mind and stay there as long as you choose to entertain it. If that is so, we may state it as a general rule that thoughts and ideas are subject to the action of will but sensations are not.

But why speak of sensations only? There are feelings and impulses. You know that when your eyes blur, when your head aches and the legs are numb, you do not merely experience these sensations; you also feel alarm about them. They depress your mood, they strike you with despair, with discouragement and the sense of helplessness. Think of the anguish and anxiety that go with the listlessness and fatigue that descend upon you in the morning. Think of the anger and resentment that you feel rising within you when you notice your pains and aches and work yourself up to a pitch of excitement. All of these are feelings added to the sensations. Do you think you can cut them short, or bid them to disappear and make place for other more comfortable feelings? Of course, you cannot do that. Feelings cannot be redirected or rearranged at the bidding of your will.

Neither can impulses. When you are in agony over your disturbing sensations, instantly there is the impulse to call off an engagement, or to summon the physician or to turn with fury upon your wife or child because of some innocent remark they may make. These impulses are just as spontaneous and passive as your sensations and feelings. They appear, and you know of their presence only after they have emerged. You cannot manage them as you can your thoughts. You cannot command them to come or to go. They come upon the scene spontaneously and passively. If they are to depart, the process is again passive and spontaneous. Do you understand now that thoughts are active and deliberate while sensations, feelings and impulses are passive and spontaneous? Do you also understand then that while you cannot drop your sensations, feelings and impulses by a command of will, you can do that with your thoughts?

P: I understand that, and I know you are right. But somehow I haven't been able to get rid of the thought of danger. I've tried many times to think of what you tell us about sabotage, and that we are not permitted to make our own diagnosis. I know that when you say there is no danger, there isn't any. But the idea sticks to me, and I cannot get rid of it.

E: Several months ago, it was just as difficult for you to shake off the idea of danger. But you did it and got well. There is no earthly reason why you should not be able to repeat that performance. But in order to succeed, you will have to practice as hard as you did months ago. That practice calls for a method. Do you remember which method you were asked to use at that time?

P: I came to classes and meetings, and I accepted your authoritative knowledge.

E: Of course, you have to accept my authority and must attend classes and meetings. But that is not what I meant by method. What you mention is the person who taught you the method and the occasions and places where you were supposed to learn it. You may have some opportunity to practice that method in classes and in my office. But the bulk of practicing will have to be done at home, in the shop, on the street and in all kinds of places and situations where there is no physician and no Recovery to help you along. What you did was to learn theoretically how the method works. But you failed to apply it systematically. You do not even seem to know which method I refer to.

What I want you to learn is to throw out of your brain one thought and to replace it with another. The thought that

I want discarded is the idea of danger, and the thought which I want to take its place is the idea of security. You know that the thought of danger is forced upon you by your sensations. You may, for instance, experience a numbness in the legs. The likelihood is then that the sensation will suggest that you are in danger of a physical collapse or a permanent handicap. I want you instead to think of the numbness as a harmless though distressing bodily feeling. Should you effect this change in thought, the sensation would fall soon after it has risen. Similarly, I want you to view your chest pressure and blurred vision as implying no danger to life or to mental and physical health. This requires the proper application of the method I taught you.

Now, if somebody wishes to master a method, he will have to begin his practice where the application is easiest. Suppose you wish to become an airplane pilot. You will first work on prints and models, then on parts, then on machines of simple design, and only in the last stages of your apprenticeship, will you venture to manipulate the more powerful engines. This gradual progression, from relatively simple to increasingly more complex tasks, is the system by means of which every method is learned. Do you think you have applied this procedure? You have not. Most likely you do not even know the name of the method I have in mind.

P: I don't think I know it.

E: I mentioned it frequently in past interviews. It is the Method of Attack on the Weakest Point. I shall refresh your memory by quoting examples. If a patient suffers from an explosive temper, it will be easier for him to control it where the temperamental deadlock is mild than where it is in full blaze. At home, with his wife and children whom he loves, the deadlock is milder than with the boss whom he may hate. Should he check his explosions more or less regularly whenever his little daughter irritates him, he would attack the chain of his temperamental flares at their weakest point. He might then transfer this practice to his wife, then to his friends and lastly to his boss who represents the strongest link in the chain. You may be inclined to doubt whether a method which works well with temper will also be effective with symptoms. Well, if you have read my books, you will know that temper, exactly like symptoms, is initiated by an irritation or annoyance, that is, by sensations. To these sensations, the temperamental person adds the ideas of either, "he is wrong" (angry temper) or the thought of "I am wrong" (fearful temper). You see here that in temper, as in symptoms, a thought is always linked to a sensation. Clearly, the same method can be applied to both situations.

I shall give another example. You know that many of my patients suffer agonies because of their self-consciousness. They hesitate to address people, to offer opinions or to take part in conversations because they fear they might say the wrong thing or they may display a clumsy and awkward manner in speech, movement or carriage. Most of them are haunted by suspicions of being misunderstood or of being considered below par. Obviously, there is here again a linkage between disturbing sensations and thoughts of insecurity. The sensations are those of discomfort on meeting people, and the thought is that of the danger of compromising oneself. In order to check the idea of insecurity, the first step to be taken by the self-conscious person will have to be to practice in an environment in which the chances of being misunderstood or underrated are at their lowest. This is one of the reasons, as you know, why I insist that my patients associate with their fellow-sufferers in Recovery. There they have an opportunity to attack their fears and suspicions where they are weakest. I hope you realize now that if you wish to get rid of your troubles, you will have to adopt this well-tried method, which means that you will have to attack those of your symptoms first which form the weakest links in the chain of your ill-balanced sensations, feelings and impulses.

P: It seems to me my symptoms are all pretty strong. It would be quite a job to find weak sensations among them.

E: I cannot agree with you on this point. You said your main difficulties are now (1) blurring of vision, (2) poor memory, (3) headaches, (4) pain around the heart, (5) fatigue with heaviness and numbness in the legs. It might be difficult for you to persuade yourself that the first four symptoms are without danger. The moment you experience the pain in the region of the heart, the thought of a stroke or sudden collapse shoots into your brain, and it will not be easy to shut it out by means of a simple procedure or formula. You may also find it difficult to believe that your blurred vision, your poor memory and your headaches are harmless and devoid of danger.

But this is altogether different with your fatigue. You think that your muscles are in danger of exhaustion should you continue to tax their fading strength. This thought of danger can be thrown out of your brain instantly if, accepting my authoritative knowledge, you conclude that yours is a psychological feeling of tiredness and not a physiological condition of exhaustion. If you do that, you can decide to step out vigorously and to walk on for dozens of blocks. The sheer act of brisk and steadfast walking will give you the conviction that your muscles can easily perform a good-sized piece of labor without withering or caving in. If you continue the walking practice day after day, the conviction will gain strength and become unshakable. The thought of muscular weakness and physical infirmity will give way to the idea of health, vigor and resistance; or the thought of security will replace the idea of insecurity. After you will have broken the link of fatigue in the chain of your symptoms, you will know that when your body spoke of danger in connection with the fatigue, it lied to you. Why should you believe the other symptoms if they voice threats and sound alarms? It seems to me that if the one symptom has been exposed as a liar, the other symptoms can no longer escape the same kind of exposure.

I shall make one more point: what you call *nervous fatigue* is a condition that has its highest intensity in the morning, dwindling in strength in the afternoon and disappearing in the evening. You know that this is the case with your own so-called fatigue. Now, if your muscles were weak to the point of exhaustion, why should they regain their strength after a day's exertion? This alone ought to convince you that your fatigue is a feeling and nothing else. Moreover, this feature of the afternoon decline gives you an added opportunity to practice replacing the thought of insecurity with the idea of security. If after a day's work you set out on an energetic evening walk of about one or two miles, you can easily persuade yourself that fatigued muscles, which are capable of doing strenuous exercise after a day's hard labor, cannot possibly have been exhausted in the morning and early afternoon. If you carry on your practice in the evening, your performance will not only be convincing, but it will have the additional advantage of being easy of execution.

CHAPTER FORTY-SEVEN

Temper and Symptom— Passive Response and Active Reaction

Peter told the story of his seven years of suffering. It began when one night he awoke and could not catch his breath. He rushed to the window, tried to draw in the fresh winter air, but the "air-hunger" persisted for what appeared to him hours of never-ending torture. He fell asleep again but in the morning belched incessantly. Although the breath-holding spell did not recur, he still shuddered when he remembered the ghastly experience of the preceding night. He was certain he had a heart ailment. His physician reassured him with the result that except for recurring belching reactions, he managed to maintain a precarious adjustment for five years. Then the belching increased in intensity and became associated with a pain about the heart region. This time, the physician's assurance that his condition was harmless failed to convince Peter. One day, while working in his shop, he jumped up and "couldn't breath." Now he was sure he was in danger of a physical collapse. He became panicky and intractable and was taken to the hospital. He was given electroshock treatment which added the suggestion of mental ailment to the fear of physical collapse. After discharge from the hospital, he returned to work.

He was now obsessed with all kinds of fears and tormented with suddenly rising violent impulses. The fears centered about lungs and heart, and the impulses were in the nature of indiscriminate aggressions, for instance, "to punch somebody in the face." The impulses were controlled, but the fears spread. He became afraid of swallowing because eating might lead to belching. If he occasionally exploded in a temper outburst, he felt wretched. If he controlled temper, he "felt like a rat." Trigger symptoms made their appearance. He thought of getting a spell of air-hunger, "and presto, I got it." His concentration suffered. At times he stammered. All of this made him feel confused, self-conscious, miserable. It was at this stage that he was seen in the office and assigned to classes. He made a fair improvement, got the belching, air-hunger and fear of swallowing under tolerable control, but what disturbed him most was his lack of self-confidence and the inability to check his temper.

E −EXAMINER
P −PATIENT

E: What seems to trouble you most is the fact that your self-confidence is reduced to a level in which you are no longer as cocky, argumentative, conceited and intellectually snobbish as you used to be. If my sharp wording displeases you, I shall remind you of the pertness with which you used to voice your political opinions, the intolerance you used to display in your tiffs with friends, wife and co-workers, of the delight you took in out-arguing anybody who might engage in an exchange of views with you. As I see it, you do not suffer from any lack of self-confidence. You merely resent the fact that your former vanity and inflated sense of importance are now gone. You consider that a loss, thinking you have become a dish rag; I regard it as a gain, thinking you are on the way to develop a measure of humility. What interests me is your failure to curb your temper sufficiently. As long as you continue to indulge your temperamental habits, your symptoms will persist. Eliminate your temper, and you will do away with your symptoms.

P: I have tried the hardest to get rid of my temper, and it seems to me I accomplished a good deal. At home, I have few arguments, and in the shop, I keep quiet most of the time. But, of course, I fly off the handle once in a while. And, good Lord, once I let myself go, there are the palpitations and the confusion and some air-hunger and belching. Can't I ever be natural and human like others?

E: I am not at all concerned with your being natural and human. My sole objective is to rid you of your symptoms. You seem to think it is your natural and human privilege to exercise your temper. It is just as natural and human to eat steak. But if a man is suffering from a gastric upset, he'd better relinquish his "natural and human right" to steak dinners. Are you willing to give up your temper for the sake of your health?

P: I guess I am willing. But this thing got me licked. I try to be calm, and I do pretty well most of the time. But if the boss is unreasonable and rides me the worst way, I cannot hold back, and tell him where to get off.

E: Give me an example of the manner in which the boss is unreasonable. Tell me what he does to "ride you the worst way."

P: The other day when I came to the shop, a tool was missing. I asked the boss whether he had seen it, and he said, "You lost it, and you will have to find it." That just burned me up. I came back with a saucy remark, and he laughed out loud. That dirty laugh made me boil. I let loose and gave him a mouthful. It didn't take a minute, and I had my belching, and it took me hours to get rid of it.

E: From what I know about you, it seems to me that this example is representative. It represents your customary habit of reacting to minor frustrations. You asked a question, and the boss returned a gruff answer. Instantly, you became irritated to the point of "burning up." The next link in the chain of events was that you came back with a "saucy" remark. The boss, refusing to become temperamental, laughed and made your blood "boil." The final result was that you belched for hours. You will realize that what "burned" and "boiled" was your temper. You know, however, that temper will neither burn nor boil unless you form the idea that you have been wronged. From this we conclude that prior to releasing your temper, you thought or decided that the boss was wrong and you were right. It was this temperamental thought in your brain that touched off the temperamental commotion in your body. This again led to the "saucy" remark and ultimately to the sustained fit of belching. Let me repeat: there was (1) the temperamental thought, (2) the temperamental commotion, (3) the "saucy" remark, (4) the belching. You will understand that the thought, "He is wrong and I am right," can be rejected, suppressed or dropped. You will also understand that your "saucy" remark could have been checked. In other words, in this fourfold series of incidents, two lent themselves readily for control. You could have rejected the thought of being wronged by the boss and could have prevented your muscles of speech from voicing the "saucy" remark. Do we agree on this point?

P: Of course. I heard you say that many times, and I know that ideas can be rejected and that muscles can be commanded not to move. I know that, but it doesn't seem to help me. That thing gets me, and I explode.

E: What you say means that control of thought and muscles is theoretically possible as a general principle but practically impossible in your particular case. Which means that you are an exception. But I do not recognize exceptions, and what one patient can do, another can likewise. We shall take it for granted then that you could have controlled the temperamental thought in your brain and the temperamental utterance of your speech muscles. How about the temperamental commotion ("boiling") and the belching? Do you think you could have stopped that?

P: I can only say what you told us in previous interviews. Temper runs its course, and symptoms do the same.

E: Correct. Both temper and symptom run their course, and you cannot stop them by an effort of the will as you can do with thoughts and muscular action. And if you say that temper and symptoms run on of their own momentum, that means that once they are set going, they continue on, rising and falling passively, without any possibility of arresting their progress until they exhaust themselves. For this reason, they have been termed the *passive responses* of the body to a disturbing event. They are called passive because they cannot be actively influenced by the intervention of will.

This is different with thought and muscular action. Your will can play on them as it chooses. If you now think that your boss emitted a "dirty laugh," you can in a second change your view and admit that the laugh was perhaps not so dirty after all. If the thought strikes you that his remark about the tools was provocative and offensive, there is nothing to prevent you from surmising that a more sympathetic explanation may be just as acceptable. And as concerns your muscles, well, that muscles can be restrained from moving is a commonplace fact that need not be stressed. And when you had the impulse to "let loose" and "tell the boss a mouthful," you could have decided to hold your tongue and to prevent your speech muscles from moving. Muscles and thoughts can be manipulated actively and, for this reason, are called the *active reactions* in contradistinction to the passive responses of temper and symptoms.

If you really wanted to get rid of the belching, all you had to do was to stop your speech muscles from voicing the "saucy" remark and to reject the absurd idea that you are the judge as to who is right and who is wrong. Had you done that, your temper would have been reduced to a flicker of an inner stir, and the belching would have been aborted. Do you understand now that your belching cannot be cured unless you control your temper and that the latter can only be checked if the brakes are applied to thought and muscles?

P: I understand that when I listen to you. But at the moment my temper gets me, I forget what you told me.

E: Which means that in your opinion, your temper is an overwhelming power that has you in its grip and leaves you helpless when it seizes you. But the grip is so tight only because you do not make the proper effort to loosen it. The time to make this effort is not when you are face to face with the boss. There, a deadlock has developed between you and him, and the mere sight of the boss makes your temper flare. In order to get a hold on your temper, you must practice control under circumstances which do not produce the situation of the deadlock. You must practice at home with your mother and wife and child. There is no deadlock at home, or if there is one, it is mild and can be handled with ease. With the members of your family, your temper rises slowly and perhaps never reaches excessive heights. There ought to be no difficulty rejecting the thought of "I am right and she is wrong" when your little girl irritates you with her childish pestering or when mother and wife ask annoying questions. These trifling impositions give you an opportunity for practicing temper control dozens of times each day.

From your own account and from reports that come to me from other sources, I know that you "let yourself go" in the morning before you leave for work and in the evening after you return from the shop. You permit yourself the expensive luxury of releasing wild thought and speech reactions. Once these active reactions are set off, the passive responses of temper and symptom follow promptly in their wake. When you arrive at the shop in the morning, you are already primed for the responses of temper and symptom because you failed to practice control of thought and speech reactions the evening before. On entering the shop, you are disposed to explode and belch because you pre-disposed yourself to flare-ups in the paltry domestic squabbles of the previous day. Your temperamental disposition at the shop in the morning is the result of the temperamental predisposition cultivated in the evening at home. If you wish to get rid of your belching, you will have to realize that the place to practice temper control is at home and not in the shop, and that the elements which have to be controlled are the active reactions of thought and muscles, not the passive responses of explosion and symptom.

CHAPTER FORTY-EIGHT

Intuitive Versus Discursive Thought in Temper

Lester had an accident five years ago in which he suffered a skull fracture. He recovered but was left with a persistent headache, spells of dizziness and difficulty of remembering. In the course of the interview, he made the following statement:

E –EXAMINER

P –PATIENT

P (Lester): After I returned to the office, I expected the people I worked with to be understanding and considerate. Instead, they did everything to irritate me and to make me feel sore.

E: What precisely did your co-workers do that showed they had no consideration?

P: Why, they slammed the doors and knocked against my chair and laughed and yelled when I was busy concentrating on my work. One fellow particularly made it a practice to brush against me whenever he passed me. When I told him to stop, he made a sassy remark and then kept moving his chair and dropping objects and scratching the table with his pencil. Anybody could see that this chap just wanted to provoke me. That sort of thing went on all day. Do you wonder why I lose my temper?

E: Indeed, I wonder. Since you have persistent headaches, the best thing for you to do is to control your temper. The surest means of producing or aggravating your headache is to lose your temper. Why don't you make every effort to control it?

P: If anybody does something to irritate me, it gets my goat, and I explode. I wish I could hold my temper, but I can't.

E: Have you been working in the same office all these five years?

P: I was transferred to another room but had quite a few battles there, too.

E: How are you at home?

P: I lose my temper at home, too. My mother pesters me, and my brother and sister wouldn't do a thing for me when I am suffering.

E: I know also that you have hardly any friends because they did not give you the sympathy you expected, and you threw tantrums whenever you did not have your way.

P: I think I am entitled to consideration. Can I help it if the headache drives me frantic, and I explode?

(Rhoda joins the interview.)

E: Rhoda, do you think Lester is unable to control his temper?

P (Rhoda): You told us there is no uncontrollable temper; his temper is uncontrolled, but not uncontrollable.

E: What you tell me, Rhoda, is what you heard in previous interviews in which we reached the conclusion that tempers are frequently uncontrolled but never uncontrollable. But tell me, Rhoda, why does Lester leave his temper without control?

P: That's difficult for me to say.

E: Now, Rhoda, you remember the examples which Lester quoted. He becomes enraged when the man near him scratches the table with the pencil or when somebody closes the door with more noise than Lester thinks proper or when somebody else brushes inadvertently against his chair. You know that people do not, as a rule, "fly off the handle" because of such trivial irritations. Ordinarily, a person will go into a rage only if he is injured or insulted. I might be provoked and react with a violent emotion if I were addressed in rude language or pushed off my chair with brute force. In an instance of this kind, I would feel outraged because my right to peaceful living was infringed upon willfully and intentionally. Let me tell you, Rhoda, that nobody loses his temper unless he is, or feels he is, wronged or insulted intentionally. Your temper does not flare up if you hurt your foot against a stone. The pain and irritation which you experience may be just as intense as if somebody throws the stone on your foot deliberately. But in the one case, the hurt was inflicted by accident, and you do not feel insulted; in the other case, the hurt was caused by intention, and that makes you feel insulted and arouses your anger or your temper. If you understand that, you will realize that when the man near Lester scratched the table with the pencil, he did so by accident and not by intention; and if somebody slammed the door or brushed against Lester, the "irritating" act of behavior was again the result of an accidental happening and not of a deliberate intention to cause offense. Why, then, did Lester go into a huff because of such accidental trivialities?

P: I guess he thinks they are intentional and not accidental.

E: That's it. Lester thinks of intentions where there are only accidents. And since accidents may happen every time and in every place, he is provoked everywhere and on every occasion. Did you listen, Lester, and do you agree with what I said about your temper?

(Lester rejoins the interview.)

P (Lester): I listened and tried to understand what you said, but I am sure I don't think of intentions when I am irritated. I simply go off and don't think at all. The explosion comes before I have time to think.

E: In a sense, you are right, Lester. But in one sense only. The word "thinking" has two meanings, and I wish to explain to you the difference between the two kinds of thinking. Suppose I tell a story and in the process say, "A man approached me; he walked slow." Be certain I shall instantly catch my error and correct swiftly, saying, "I meant to say he walked slowly." Do you think I did a great deal of thinking when I offered the correction? Did I stop and reflect and deliberate whether the adverb *slowly* is better grammar than the adjective *slow*? Presumably I did not do any reflecting but noticed the error intuitively and felt likewise intuitively that my statement needed correction. But while doing this intuitive job of noticing and correcting the error, I drew two discrete conclusions: I concluded (1) that "slow" was the wrong use, (2) that I had to correct to "slowly." In all of this, I did not debate within myself and did not reflect on the words *correct* and *incorrect* or on the words *adjective* and *adverb*. Had I done so, I would have discoursed (within myself) about the issue of the grammatical error, and my type of thinking would have been discursive. Instead, I drew the conclusions by way of intuition. Hence, my type of thinking was intuitive.

I want you to understand this distinction between discursive and intuitive thinking. You see, children correct themselves frequently. At a certain stage of their development, they may say, "I will go to kindergarten yesterday," and correct instantly to "tomorrow." We grownups could discourse in such an instance that the word "yesterday" connotes the past and clashes with the phrase "I will go" which connotes the future. If we do that, our conclusions are drawn discursively. The child has not yet learned how to engage in discursive thinking of this sort. He must draw the same conclusions by a process of intuitive thought. I would perhaps tell you how we come to acquire discursive thought. It is done through school instruction, mainly. How intuitive thought is achieved, I am unable to tell. It is one of the mysteries of life which I, at any rate, am unable to explain.

I hope you will now understand, Lester, that in order to draw conclusions about the meaning of a situation, one does not have to reflect or to do an act of discursive thinking. One may reach the same conclusion by means of imaginative or intuitive thinking. That's what you do when your co-worker scratches the table with his pencil. Intuitively, you draw the conclusion (without having time to think by reflection) that he intends to irritate you. Once you reach this conclusion, you interpret the situation as one in which an enemy attacks or provokes you, and instantly your anger (or temper) is aroused. You will now realize that the common variety of temper is a condition in which one person draws the intuitive conclusion that another person intends to offend him. The explosion and anger are merely the result of this preceding intuitive conclusion. Far less common is that variety of temper in which discursive conclusions are acted upon.

It was explained to Lester and the class that in order to gain control over his temper, a person must learn, through continuous practice, to avoid the intuitive conclusion of a deliberate insult which precedes the temperamental outburst. Several more examples were given to illustrate the difference between discursive and intuitive thought. Finally, the examiner asked:

E: Now, Lester, suppose your co-worker will scratch the table with his pencil tomorrow; what will you do then?

P (Lester): I will try not to draw the conclusion that he does that intentionally.

E: That would be fine. But I have reason to doubt whether you will be able to do that. You see, Lester, your temper has been with you for many, many years, indeed, since your childhood. True, it has become intensified and almost crystallized since your accident. But as such, it has been with you practically all your life. Do you think you can change such a life habit just by making up your mind to drop it?

P: Of course, I'll have to practice.

E: That's it. You'll have to practice, and to practice hard. Can you tell me how you will carry out your practicing?

P: I will think of what you told me and will stop arguing.

E: I doubt whether that will be successful. You see, Lester, a temperamental outburst runs in stages. First, you explode and go into a rage. In a given instance, you may rave on for two or five minutes. During this time, you are "out of your senses" and will not be likely to exercise a great deal of thought. You will certainly not stop to consult your memory, recalling what I told you about control of temper. So I take it that during this initial stage of your explosion, you will not think of the instruction I gave you. You will simply rave on until your anger will subside. I shall call this initial stage of your temper the "immediate effect of the temper outburst." I hope you realize that when I want you to practice avoiding intuitive conclusions, I do not ask you to do that during this stage of the immediate effect. But after the immediate effect is over, you enter a "cooling off" process which may last some ten or fifteen minutes. This is the temperamental aftereffect. Once the aftereffect sets in, you begin to think, perhaps not very clearly, but sufficiently so to be able to remember what I told you. Whatever thinking you do during the immediate effect is intuitive, vague and dim. But in the aftereffect, your thought becomes discursive again. You can then reflect and meditate.

The question is whether your type of reflection will be rational or emotional. If it is emotional, you will continue to fume, will brood over the outrage of which you were the "innocent victim." Burning with righteous indignation, you will justify the explosion which you released during the immediate effect and will give it your endorsement. Once you endorse your outburst as justified, you are primed for another explosion; you fairly itch to "pay that fellow back" and thus keep your temper boiling in anticipation of another bout. This is the last stage of the uncontrolled temperamental cycle which we shall call the *stage of anticipation*. It is called the stage of anticipation because in this third phase of the temper outburst, you anticipate a renewed squabble in which you expect to come out on top. You anticipate a victory which will wipe out the "disgrace" of the present defeat. You will understand now that the so-called temperamental cycle, if left to itself without an attempt to control it, consists of three discrete stages: (1) the immediate effect, (2) the aftereffect, (3) the anticipation of a renewed outburst. Can you tell me now which stage of this cycle you must make use of for the purpose of remembering what I told you in matters of control?

P: You said it can't be done in the immediate effect. So I think it will have to be done after that.

E: That's correct. You will have to make use of the aftereffect. Of course, I do not expect you to succeed the first time, nor do I expect full success the fourth, fifth and sixth time. Instead, I presume you will become emotional in the first few beginnings of your practice, and your aftereffects will be spent in spells of fussing and fretting, with the result that the temperamental cycle will be run unchecked through its immediate effect, aftereffect and the anticipation of the next temperamental "comeback." I hope, however, that after repeated practice, you will finally manage to stop short at the end of the immediate effect, and that henceforth the aftereffect will be given over to a sane, rational appraisal of the situation in which you will refrain from endorsing your explosion, thus avoiding the anticipation of and preparation for the next outburst. This will come to pass if, after a few initial failures, you will not permit yourself to be discouraged and will continue practicing with solid determination. You will do that if you have the genuine will to remedy and check your temperamental habits. Do you think you will make the effort?

P: I sure will. After all, my temper didn't do me a lot of good.

E: What harm did it do you?

P: Why, I have lost all my friends, and I know I am a pest at home.

E: That is correct. Your temper made you lose your friends and has destroyed what peace and happiness was left in your home. But let me tell you, Lester, I am not so much interested in friendship and home life. My main interest is to get my patients to lose their symptoms. It is important, of course, to have friends, and to have peace in the home is a desirable aim, indeed. But the patient's first obligation is to get rid of his symptoms. I do not think you will make a strenuous effort to curb your temper if you merely have your eye on the damage it does to friendships and home life. This ought to be a strong incentive. But experience teaches it is not. The only thing that will make you bend all your energies toward conquering your temper is the realization that you cannot get well unless your temper is prevented from creating emotional upheavals in your body and producing an incessant train of symptoms. Mark this, Lester: I am not primarily interested in temper as a disturbance of social relations. I am interested in it mainly because it maintains and intensifies nervous symptoms. This is the reason why I insist that my patients cannot get well unless they learn to control their temperamental cycles.

CHAPTER FORTY-NINE

The Patient Wants the Ends of Health, Not Its Means

Herbert had been in good health until four years ago, when waiting for a street car, he suddenly felt a "light-headedness" and was seized with the fear of "keeling over." The sensations passed quickly, and Herbert paid scant attention to the incident. But when three weeks later the sensations recurred in exactly the same fashion, again while waiting for a streetcar, the otherwise stolid man became alarmed. He feared he was suffering from a fatal illness. Henceforth, he was afraid of boarding streetcars and experienced sweats and palpitations when in the morning he prepared to leave the house. The "light-headedness" and "keeling-over" sensations became more frequent. He noticed they occurred in open places only. At home, he was free from them. He also observed that he was never subject to spells on the street if he was in the company of another person. When first seen at the office, he stated that for the past three years, he has not left his home unaccompanied. He was compelled to give up his position, and his wife had to secure employment to provide for the family needs.

Two months after joining classes and acquiring membership in Recovery, Herbert was able to take long walks without a companion. His "light-headedness" did not disappear altogether, but he learned to dismiss the idea of danger and to ignore the symptom. Numerous disturbing sensations which had established themselves in the course of his ailment–palpitations, sweats, crawling and numbness in the arms, fatigue and blurred vision–were on the point of fading away. At the end of the third month, he returned to work, resuming his position as the breadwinner of the family.

He continued classes and stated in an interview, "I have been swell for the past six weeks. I worked and didn't have any of these symptoms, except that I felt some of the sensations for a short time, occasionally. And they were very mild. I think you'd call them 'reminders.' But a couple of days ago, I had a severe spell of light-headedness again. That sure scared me. And some of the other sensations came back, too. I tried to ignore them, but it's not easy."

E –EXAMINER

P –PATIENT

E: When did you start on your new job, Herbert?

P: Six weeks ago.

E: Two months ago, you told me that you were taking walks of three and four miles all by yourself. Have you done that lately?

P: No. I work hard and feel tired when I quit the job in the afternoon. I still walk the five or six blocks to the streetcar. But then, I am all in.

E: How many hours per day do you work?

P: On some days it is four hours, on some, seven.

E: I told you to take long walks every day. You did that until recently. Why did you not continue the practice? With an average of five to six hours of daily work, you had ample time to take your walks. If you failed to do that, you sabotaged my instructions.

P: I am on my feet all the time when I am at work, and it's always a rush. When I leave the shop, I can hardly drag myself.

E: What you said is an excuse. You justify your failure to take long walks on the grounds of hard work, rush and fatigue. On this score, you do not only practice sabotage; worse yet, you claim you were justified in practicing it. If this is so, you will go on excusing and justifying, and the final result will be that the walks will cease, and you will slip back into your condition of fear and helplessness. Is that what you want? Don't you want to get well?

P: Of course, I want to get well. I keep going to the shop and coming to classes. Would I do that if I didn't want to get well?

E: In a sense, you may be correct in stating that you want to get well. But I am just as correct if I say you do not want to get well. You see, Herbert, if a man who is out of work says he wants a job, you will hardly deny that he really wants it. But then you observe that after he obtains the position, he complains about the hard work and the poor pay. He loafs and stalls and makes excuses and finally absents himself frequently. Will you say that this man wants the job in the sense that he wants to do a good day's work?

P: But I do a good day's work and don't gripe.

E: I did not mean you when I spoke of the man who loafs on the job. And if you assumed that my remarks were aimed at you, it merely shows that your conscience bothers you. That is a good sign and indicates that you are by no means happy about your backsliding. But to return to the man with the job: he wanted it, no doubt. He looked for it, took it when it was offered and kept it, although he didn't like it. What better proof do you need to conclude that he wanted it? But what precisely did the man want? He wanted the job, but he resented the things that had to be done on the job. In other words, he wanted the end but did not want the means that lead toward the end. Do you realize that the word "wanting" has at least two meanings? In the one sense, it means that you wish to obtain an end; in the other sense, it means you are ready to take every step to reach that end. In the first sense, you were correct when you said you want to get well. In the second sense, I was right when I objected that you did not want to get well. What I tried to make clear to you was that you wanted health as a shadowy, nebulous end but refused to employ the concrete means of hard application to accomplish that end.

P: I don't think I refused to work, and I certainly applied myself. If you ask my boss, he will tell you that I was on the job all the time.

E: I told you that "wanting" can be used in two different senses. That applies with equal force to what you said about your being on the job. What you have in mind is the work on the premises only. In order to get to the premises where you work, you must be able to take long walks; you must be able also to perform your task without being handicapped by "light-headedness" or fatigue or palpitations, sweats and numbness. Obviously, if you do not manage to get rid of your sensations, you will have to quit the job. If you want the job, you must, at the same time, want to be in good health to carry on with your job. You will understand now that your health is a means toward the end of securing and maintaining the job. You want the job but not the means necessary to accomplish it.

P: Can I help it if the "light-headedness" comes back, and I get those frightful palpitations and the sweats and the numbness?

E: I told you frequently that sensations come of their own account, not at your bidding. You are not responsible for their coming, but you are responsible for their persistence if you fail to handle them in accordance with my instructions. Every nervous sensation disappears after a short while if you refuse to get alarmed about it. If you permit yourself to become alarmed about the sensation, you establish a vicious cycle. The more you fear the palpitations, the worse they grow. The worse they grow, the greater is your alarm. This vicious cycle can be cut through instantly if you refuse to think of the sensation as dangerous.

P: I know that, and I have tried to be calm. I told myself that sensations are distressing but not dangerous, but it didn't help me. The palpitations went on, and the numbness got worse instead of better.

E: You repeated my formula but did not practice it. When your sensations started their rumble, you should not merely have thought they were harmless; you should have demonstrated that to yourself. You should have demonstrated your indifference to the danger. This you could have done by walking on, unhesitatingly, in spite of the palpitations. You know numbers of patients who have conquered their sensations by the simple expedient of acting on them with indifference. The indifferent act demonstrates that there is no danger. Here is Jane, sitting two seats from you. You know that while walking on the street, she had the frightful sensation that the pavement moved up toward her and the buildings were toppling over her. I take it you remember that several weeks ago, when Jane was interviewed, she told her method of dealing with these sensations. Do you recall what she did?

P: She walked on and disregarded the sensations.

E: Jane practiced the rules of fearlessness and got results. After three years of avoiding walks, she now has no trouble and moves about as if she had never been sick. Had you practiced the rules instead of merely remembering or repeating them, you would be well by now. You say you tried but did not succeed. Do you understand that what you tried was to achieve the goal without practicing the means? Jane had not only the goal in view but also the means that lead to it. If you really want to get well, you will have to consider the practical means and not only the theoretical goal. Will you do that?

P: I shall certainly try.

E: That's not enough. You must want and not merely try.

The interview was then devoted to a discussion of the terms *trying* and *wanting*. Herbert tried to walk long distances but relinquished his effort after an initial failure. The first failure discouraged him, and he gave up. Jane, on the other hand, experienced the same initial failure but kept practicing until she succeeded. She showed will and determination, which means to want the end but also the arduous means that lead to its achievement.

CHAPTER FIFTY

Mental Health Is Supreme Purpose, Not Subordinate Goal

E –EXAMINER

P –PATIENT

E: How are you, Helen?

P: I have been well for more than six weeks, but last week, I had a setback. It was during a card game. I didn't get my paralysis, but it was bad enough. I had a panic and couldn't shake it off for two days. Today, I am much better, but I am still shaky.

E: You speak of paralysis. Can you tell the class what you mean by that? You are a young woman, and why should you have a paralysis at your age? Tell your story briefly and try to explain what you mean by "paralysis."

P: I have always been restless. After I got married, I couldn't stand being alone at home in the evening, not even with my husband. We had to be in the company of people all the time. We either had people visit at our home, or we went out visiting. Usually, we played cards. One day, three years ago, while playing a game of bridge, my hands suddenly went limp. I tried to move them and couldn't. Of course, that scared the wits out of me. I pretended to have a headache and excused myself. The moment I left the table, my arms moved again. That was the first time I had that paralysis.

E: Did the condition return?

P: It did not for about three weeks. In between, I played cards repeatedly and had no trouble moving the arms. I actually forgot the whole thing. But one evening, I played again, and the arms gave out. This time, I was so scared, I didn't have the presence of mind to fish for an excuse but just ran out of the room. My husband called a doctor who said he couldn't find anything wrong with me. But I felt like in a daze, although I knew I could move the arms again. After that, I could not get myself to play cards when I was out of the house. I was in terror when I thought that the arms would stop moving again.

E: Were you able to play cards at home?

P: Yes. I played without trouble at home, even when visitors were present. I was also able to visit people, but I did not touch a card when I visited. I gave excuses, said I had a headache, or felt dizzy and couldn't concentrate. That helped for a while, but one evening, the hostess was insistent and wouldn't take an excuse. I gave in, and, sure enough, there was the paralysis. After that, I refused to accept invitations. I still had visitors at my home, but they gradually petered out because I did not reciprocate.

E: Did the "paralysis" ever appear when you played cards at home with only relatives present?

P: This didn't happen for a long time until, one evening, it finally happened. After that, there was no more card playing with anybody except my husband and my parents. With them, I never had the paralysis.

E: Did you have any other trouble aside from this "paralysis?"

P: For many months the paralysis was the only trouble. But then all kinds of other trouble came. The greatest trouble was meeting people. I hated their questioning me about my condition. I had to explain why I kept away from them, and it wasn't easy to find excuses. Finally, I kept out of everybody's way, that means, I avoided going out as far as I could.

E: Did you continue seeing your relatives?

P: I did. But they became bothersome, too. When they came to the house, the first thing they told me was, "Why, you are not sick; you just look the picture of health. You must be feeling fine." When I told them I still had my fears, they said, "Oh, it's all in your mind." Or they told me to snap out of it, to use my will power. I knew they were right, and the doctors had told me the same thing. But I hated their way of talking, perhaps because they were right.

E: That was an excellent description. I need not tell you, Helen, that what you just described was a very severe nervous condition. Had you continued avoiding people and shutting yourself up in your home, your life would have been that of a helpless cripple, doomed to lead a useless and miserable existence. If this is so, why don't you make an effort to get well?

P: If I had a setback, does that mean I don't make an effort to get well? You told us so many times that setbacks are unavoidable.

E: That is correct. But I also told you that you must learn how to handle the setback. Do you think you handled it in accordance with my instructions?

P: I got over it in two days. Is that so bad?

E: It is bad enough. You said you were panicky and couldn't shake off the panic for two days. Then you added that you are still shaky today. Had you done what I asked you to do, the setback would not have developed into a panic and would have lasted minutes or hours, and not days. What did you do when you noticed the setback?

P: I remembered what you told me. I knew that sensations are distressing but not dangerous. Wasn't that what I was supposed to do?

E: You did very little. You merely "remembered" and "knew" something that I said. That's not what I call "doing." I shall ask you: Did you attend the Recovery meetings? Did you go to family gatherings?

P: No, I didn't. I was so fine the past six weeks, that I was sure I was well and didn't need the meetings.

E: You spent three years in utter agony. Then you got well but were warned that the condition was likely to return unless you took part in classes and Recovery activities for at least six months. You attended my classes but neglected going to Recovery meetings. That means you made a half-effort. Why did you not make a total effort?

P: I did what I could. I had to come to your office twice a week. That took up two afternoons. The class took up an evening. Then I had to take care of the house and the children, and my husband is entitled to some of my time, I think. And you told me I should go and visit people, which I did. All of this took plenty of my time.

E: You mentioned the home and the children and social activities. They are all very important. I do not deny that. You may call them the domestic, social and marital purposes. You took care of them and deserve all the credit that is due for the accomplishing of purposes, especially if they are as worthy as the ones you mentioned. You might have added that you had to attend a church meeting or meetings of a civic club. These would be the purposes of citizenship, community and church interest. All worthy and commendable purposes.

But when you are ill, your main and all-absorbing purpose must be the will to get well. All other purposes, no matter how inspiring and exalted, must be subordinated to the one leading and supreme purpose of getting well and keeping well. Unless you regain and maintain your mental health, all other purposes will be frustrated. Only if you keep well, will you be able to discharge your duties as mother, wife, friend, church and club member. I do not mean to say that health is more important than motherhood or religion. I merely say that motherhood, religion, citizenship and fellowship cannot function unless health is made to function first. To a patient, his health must have unquestioned priority over all other purposes. Health must be the supreme aim to him; all other aims must be subordinated to the demands of health. You spent your effort on subordinated purposes and neglected that aim that ought to be supreme now. Instead of concentrating all your strength on the main issue, you frittered away your energies on a number of side issues. Why are you so careless of your welfare? Don't you want to keep well?

P: Of course, I want to keep well. I just shudder if I think of my suffering in the past.

E: You say you want to keep well. In a sense you are

right. You would like nothing better than to have done with the "paralysis" and the awful difficulties into which it got you. That merely means that you wish to have your health. It does not mean that you have the will to health. I shall not enter into a comprehensive discussion of what is the difference between a loose wish and a determined will. This much I will say: A wish does not commit you to exercise all your energies toward attaining it. You wish to make a trip to a distant country. You may say you want the trip. But you don't want it hard enough to sacrifice other aims in its favor. You will not sacrifice your life savings or the welfare of your family for the sake of that wish. That wish is not directed toward a supreme aim. You do not give it priority over the family purpose. Should you, for some foolish reason, make that trip a supreme aim, you might perhaps sacrifice all other purposes to it. Then you would pursue your aim with the force of a total effort. The trip would no longer be backed by a loose wish but would be insisted on with the vigor of a determined will. I hope that you understand now the difference between a supreme and subordinate purpose. Health was to you a subordinate aim, a loose wish, something that you thought you might be able to attain at the cost of a half-effort. You know better now. You know that health must take precedence over all other purposes and must be attended to with the energy of a total effort. If you keep that in mind, you will not have to worry about your setbacks. You will be prepared for them and will shake them off in minutes instead of hours or days.

The examiner then pointed out that the real reason for Helen's failure to attend Recovery meetings was her sense of shame. Helen, he commented, is still harassed by the idea that her nervous ailment is a disgrace to her and her family. She still suffers from the pressure of stigmatization. To feel stigmatized means to be tense. The tenseness creates pressure on the nervous system and may produce or revive symptoms. As long as Helen continues to feel stigmatized, she will be in danger of becoming "paralyzed" again. If she wants to prevent a return of the symptoms, she will have to learn how to shake off embarrassment and stigmatization. One of the purposes of Recovery gatherings is to rid the patient of his feeling of being stigmatized. If Helen continues to shy away from the meetings, she will have demonstrated that her will to avoid embarrassment is stronger than her will to get well. That will is a mere wish, not a solid determination.

CHAPTER FIFTY-ONE

Spontaneity and Self-Consciousness

Irene, a woman of 30 and mother of two children, developed a depression of mood which persisted for five years, with only brief intervals of fair health. When she was first seen by the examiner, she complained of a "complete absence of interest," difficulty of sleeping, lack of appetite, fatigue. She claimed she had no zest, pep or initiative. She could not plan, make up her mind, decide to get things started. In the morning, it took her literally hours to get dressed, to choose the proper attire, to get started with cooking, dusting and cleaning. When she finally began to do her work, she had to drag herself. Everything was done with extreme effort. Even such simple acts as turning on the faucet or lighting the gas range required her to use all of her strength. She could only do things if she forced herself to do them. A simple conversation was "hard labor." Walking was an ordeal. On the other hand, sitting or lying down was intolerable because it made her restless. Because speaking and walking called for extreme effort, she avoided going out and meeting people. After several weeks of combined office and group treatment, she recovered her health and staged a comeback that surprised both her and the members of the family. When interviewed in class, she reported that all her symptoms were gone and that she was as well "as anyone might wish to be."

E –EXAMINER
P –PATIENT

E: I have observed you closely for the past two months, and there can be no doubt that you have regained your health. But tell me, Irene, what do you plan to do for the purpose of maintaining your health?

P: I shall attend classes and Recovery meetings, and I will study your books and the *Recovery Journal.** Isn't that what you want me to do?

E: Of course, I want you to do that. But the maintenance of health is a lifelong task, and I do not expect you to attend classes all your life. And whether you will continue membership in Recovery forever is questionable. So, what is your program for keeping well, aside from your present activities in classes and meetings?

P: I certainly intend to take part in Recovery for good. I know that many members feel the way I do. They think they are in Recovery for keeps.

E: I like your spirit. But you cannot depend on Recovery exclusively. Suppose your husband will be transferred to an out-of-town branch of his concern? Then you will be separated from Recovery and will be thrown on your own resources. Are you prepared for a development of this kind? Are you ready to practice self-help?

P: I never thought of that. But it seems I'll be able to manage.

E: Look here, Irene, you have suffered for almost five years and have only been well some two months. In these two months, you have heard me state repeatedly that every patient must be prepared for setbacks. You have listened to several interviews in which patients reported that they drifted into setbacks after months and years of good health. Last week, you had an opportunity to listen to the interview

---

*The *Recovery Journal,* edited by Abraham A. Low, M.D., was published from June 1946 to June 1947.

with Emily who had enjoyed good health for three years in succession and then developed a severe spell that landed her in the hospital. You remember that when I criticized Emily for neglecting her participation in our aftercare project, she gave the excuse that three years ago she felt sure she was able to manage herself without the aid of classes or meetings. Emily paid dearly for her false sense of security. Now you also say you think you'll be "able to manage." Are you going to repeat Emily's mistake?

P: I don't know what more I can do than come to classes and work in Recovery.

E: Be certain, I appreciate your loyalty to Recovery. But I must repeat what I mentioned before. Suppose some day you will be deprived of Recovery support. Are you prepared to practice self-help? Do you know how to go about it? Do you know which method to employ? You wish to keep well. That means you want to prevent a recurrence of your ailment. But prevention must be practiced correctly, methodically and systematically. Do you think you know the method which will help you maintain your health?

P: I don't know what to say.

E: You see, Irene, you told me that when you were ill, you had no interest, zest or initiative. You could not plan or decide. Making up your mind and getting things started was difficult or impossible. Simple tasks, which are ordinarily done without hesitation, required extreme effort. All of this can be summed up in the statement that you lost your spontaneity. Do you understand now that if you are to keep well, you will have to know (1) what is the nature of spontaneity, (2) what you can do to strengthen and preserve it?

I shall try to tell you something about that. While I am speaking here before the class, I have in mind a plan or intention. My intention is to express certain ideas and to make this class accept them. This intention must be carried out by my muscles. The muscles of my lips, tongue and cheeks must pronounce my sentences, the muscles of the throat must provide the proper intonation. The face muscles will have to mold and fashion my features in such a manner that they give adequate expression to everything voiced by my lips. Add the gestures of my arms, the carriage of my frame, all of them must fall in line with the central intention conveyed by my spoken word. In the space of one hour, I shall have to set in motion hundreds of muscles in thousands of combinations, and all the movements they will perform will be required to give expression to one intention, one plan, one idea. Let me tell you that what I described here is the pattern for every act of every description, no matter what may be its meaning. You may say that *every act expresses one single intention through a multiplicity of muscular movements.*

Suppose now that when I arrived tonight, I felt tired, discouraged and dispirited, the reason perhaps being that I experienced a grave disappointment in the afternoon. If this is so, then, my intention may still be to plant certain ideas in your brains. But that intention will now be coupled with another intention: to go home and rest, to get this class out of the way, to be finished with it in record time. My mind will no longer be "made up" or determined by one single intention. Instead, it will be torn between two intentions. The intention to continue this address will grapple with the opposite intention to go home and relax. The result will be that two sets of antagonistic impulses will reach my muscles of speech, intonation, facial expression and gestures, and the muscles will sometimes express the one group of impulses (to make a good and effective speech) and sometimes the other group (to be done with that speech that keeps me from taking a rest). The dual intention will distract my attention and will involve me in contradictions. Before long, I will notice that I stray from the theme and that I do not hold the interest of the audience. The observation will scare me. I will lose my assurance and will be self-conscious. And once I become self-conscious, I am not spontaneous.

You will understand now that spontaneity is interfered with or destroyed by self-consciousness. You will also realize that self-consciousness is produced by the fact that two contradictory intentions endeavor to make the muscles express two different ideas at the same time. The muscles are thrown into disorder, expressing portions of the one idea and fragments of the other, with the result that the speech loses clarity and gives the impression of confusion. Do you understand, Irene, that when you lacked spontaneity, your mind was the seat of two contradictory basic intentions and was not "made up" in favor of one single plan?

P: I know I was always self-conscious when I was ill. But when you speak of contradictory intentions, I don't know whether that was so. I know I wanted to do something and felt I couldn't. I had to drag myself, and when I forced myself to cook or clean, I did it with great effort.

E: You say you wanted to cook but had to force yourself to do it. That means your intention or plan to cook met with resistance. You know that at present, if you intend to cook, you simply send an impulse down to your muscles, and they perform the act. They do that with ease, without effort. You no longer drag yourself, which means that strain is eliminated. You hardly think of, and certainly do not reflect strenuously on, what your muscles are doing, which means that you are no longer self-conscious about your actions. Since your cooking proceeds without effort and without self-consciousness, you can say that you are now spontaneous. Your spontaneity has reestablished itself because your impulse to cook is no longer resisted and thwarted by the contrary impulse not to cook.

You will understand this situation better if you consider another example in which resistance hampers prompt and effortless action. I shall quote the act of buying necessities or conveniences. Should you want to buy a loaf of bread, all you would have to do would be to have the proper intention and to impart the corresponding impulse to your muscles to walk out of the home, to cross the street, to enter the bakery shop, to pick up the bread and to pay for it. All these actions would be executed promptly, and without effort and without self-conscious hesitation. You would act spontaneously.

In the afternoon of the same day, you might want to purchase a coat. The question will be: cloth or fur? Now you will no longer just dispatch an impulse to your muscles, fetch a seal coat, pay for it and stroll home. Now there will be stalling, hesitation, plenty of thought and an abundance of reflection. You may want that sealskin very insistently, but the intention to buy it will be crossed by the contrary intention to save the money. Your spontaneity will be gone because two antagonistic impulses will impinge on your muscles.

I shall try to tell you what is at stake in situations of this sort. You see, when it was a matter of securing a loaf of bread, you were sure you needed it, you were certain that your intention was proper, reasonable, harmless. You know with absolute assurance that after the purchase of the bread, there will be no self-blame, no compunction, no threat to your moral ego. In other words, you felt secure with regard to carrying out the impulse once you conceived it. This sense of security was absent in the instance of your intention to buy a coat. You had the intention to acquire the cloth coat, but it was not sufficiently dressy. Then the seal caught your eye, and now you were uncertain whether you could afford it. The impulse to buy engaged in a running fight with the impulse not to buy, and the result was a sense of insecurity, strain, and tenseness (effort), and stalling and hesitation (self-consciousness). In the end, you were left without spontaneity. You will now be in a better position to understand the factors which tend to do away with your spontaneity: (1) there is a conflict of intentions and impulses, (2) a sense of insecurity, (3) effort and self-consciousness, (4) inability to decide, plan and act. The inability to decide, plan and act is the outward expression of your defect in spontaneity; the conflict of impulses, the sense of insecurity and the self-consciousness are its inner causes.

In the subsequent portions of the interview, it was explained that if Irene meant to preserve and strengthen her spontaneity, she had to cultivate ideas of security and to reduce as far as possible her thoughts of insecurity. The examiner then demonstrated, with suitable examples, that patients can weaken their sense of insecurity if they learn to adopt the philosophy of averageness in preference to thinking in terms of exceptionality. Irene had been brought up as a perfectionist. Her ambition was to keep her home "perfectly clean," to do a perfect job in the education of her children, to attain excellence as hostess, wife, friend, neighbor. Trivial errors, trifling mistakes and insignificant failures caused her to sweat and fret, to wear herself out with vexation and self-reproach. She worried, felt provoked at her fancied inefficiency, was perpetually flustered and confused. The confusion multiplied her record of bungled trivialities and botched irrelevancies. A vicious cycle developed: The more she was confused, the more she bungled; the more persistently she bungled, the more disturbing became her confusion. In the end, she lost confidence in her ability to do things "correctly," developed an exaggerated self-consciousness and lost her spontaneity.

After joining Recovery, she learned to be human and average, to permit herself to be "like others," to bungle as much or as little as people bungle "on an average." She rejected the grotesque idea of the "perfect job" and the "flawless performance" and imbibed the now familiar Recovery doctrine to "have the courage to make mistakes in the trivialities of everyday life." If Irene continued to practice these Recovery doctrines in her everyday activities, if she practiced methodically to laugh at the paltry consequences of her trivial mistakes, she was certain to develop self-assurance and to rout her self-consciousness. Then her muscles will not be wedged in between two sets of antagonistic impulses, her spontaneity will be established on the firm ground of self-confidence, and her solid habits of thinking in terms of averageness will prevent her from becoming discouraged, despondent and depressed.

OTHER BOOKS BY ABRAHAM A. LOW, M.D.

The following books are published by Willett Publishing Company, Glencoe, Illinois 60022

Manage Your Fears, Manage Your Anger: A Psychiatrist Speaks

The ongoing presence of crippling fear and uncontrolled anger calls for effective methods of managing these disruptive forces. This book reveals Low's complete identification with the suffering that fear and anger create, his sense of humor and his deep concern for those who sought his help. It is also available on audio cassettes.

Peace Versus Power in the Family: Domestic Discord and Emotional Distress

Many people who want domestic harmony lack the means to achieve it. The reader will find here a comprehensive system for understanding and controlling the forces at work in the domestic environment.

Mental Illness, Stigma and Self-Help: The Founding of Recovery, Inc.

In 1937, the establishment of a self-help association of former mental patients was unthinkable. Abraham Low braved criticism and rejection as he formulated the principles and techniques of self-help aftercare. Low's unique vision attacks the pervasive stigma of mental illness, not only in the general public, the media and the legislatures, but also in the patients themselves and their families.

The following book is published by Recovery, Inc., 802 North Dearborn Street, Chicago, Illinois 60610.

Selections From Dr. Low's Works (1950-1953)

The reader will find articles and comments written by Low between 1950 and 1953 for the bimonthly *Recovery News*. The brevity and clarity of this book further demonstrate Low's ability to render complex subjects understandable to the layman.

The Techniques of Self-Help in Psychiatric After-Care (1943)

This series, written by Low and published by Recovery, Inc., in 1943, is now out-of-print. It contained the following three volumes, two of which have been republished, as indicated below, by Willett Publishing Company, Glencoe, Illinois 60022.

> *Vol. 1: The Historical Development of Recovery's Self-Help Project.*
> Republished in 1991 as *Mental Illness, Stigma and Self-Help: The Founding of Recovery, Inc.* See previous page.

> *Vol. 2: Group Psychotherapy: A Record of Class Interviews with Patients Suffering from Mental and Nervous Ailments.*
> This volume is out-of-print.

> *Vol. 3: Lectures to Relatives of Former Patients.*
> Republished in 1984 as *Peace Versus Power in the Family: Domestic Discord and Emotional Distress.* See previous page.

APPENDIX A

(TAKEN FROM THE SECOND EDITION, 1952)

PREFACE

The present volume is meant to give an account of the psychotherapy methods evolved in the past fifteen years by Recovery, Inc., a nonprofit group whose purpose it is to train post-psychotic and psychoneurotic persons in the practice of psychiatric self-help. An extensive report on the association's history, scope of activity and mode of operation was offered in 1943.* A concise but fairly comprehensive description was published in 1949.†

The contents of the book are, in the main, reproductions of panel discussions conducted by the ex-patients and group psychotherapy interviews held by the author with his private patients in the years 1944 to 1949. Several essays on "sabotage" have been added, describing the manner in

---

*Low, Abraham A., *The Techniques of Self-Help in Psychiatric After-Care*, Chicago, 1943, Recovery, Inc., 3 volumes.

†Low, Abraham A., Recovery, Inc., "A Project for Rehabilitating Post-Psychotic and Long-Term Psychoneurotic Patients," published in *Rehabilitation of the Handicapped*, page 213, New York, 1949, the Ronald Press Company. The latter article has been incorporated, with the publisher's permission, as a revised reprint in the present volume, page 15 (page 424 in this edition).

which patients offer resistance to the physician's instructions. The bulk of the material was previously published in the *Recovery Journal* and "Recovery News," issued by Recovery, Inc., and edited by the author. It deals with a system of group psychotherapy evolved by the writer since 1933.

Psychotherapy, individual or group, is invariably based (1) on a philosophy, (2) on techniques. In years past, the field was dominated by three main philosophies and techniques: Freud's psychoanalysis, Adler's individual psychology, and Jung's approach which, because of its vagueness and mysticism, defies precise classification. More recently, the psychoanalytic doctrine has taken the lead and all but crowded out its erstwhile rivals. It established its hegemony in universities and philanthropic foundations and gained unquestioned prominence in the province of psychotherapy. The doctrine appears to be in firm control in the official psychiatric organizations, in the mental hygiene activities of the national government, in the Veterans Administration, presumably also in the hospitals of the armed forces. Official psychotherapy in the United States today is essentially psychoanalysis.

The author rejects the psychoanalytic doctrine both as philosophy and therapeutic technique. In point of philosophy, he cannot share the view that human conduct is the result of unconscious drives, sexual or otherwise. To his way of thinking, adult life is not *driven* by instincts but *guided* by Will. In emphasizing the priority of Will over Drives, he is merely echoing the principles and teachings of the late Professor Emil Kraepelin, founder of modern psychiatry, and those of the late Professor Wilhelm Wundt, father of modern psychology. Quite proudly he claims also to echo the voice of common experience and common sense. Whatever may be meant by drives, be they instinctual cravings (the favorite psychoanalytic term), or emotional trends, desires, wishes, yearnings and leanings, they all eventuate in impulses, acting or ready for action. To the author, it is inconceivable that adult human life can be ordered without a Will holding down impulses. What precisely is meant by the term *Will* is amply demonstrated in the text.

In point of psychotherapeutic techniques, psychoanalysis must be accounted a failure on the evidence of its own testimony. The most startling defect is the insignificant number of patients which can be reached by the method. The Chicago Institute for Psychoanalysis, for instance, has been able to report no more than 319 patients treated six months or longer during a ten-year period.* The Menninger Clinic of Topeka, Kansas, tops this record of poor productivity with a report[†] of 100 patients similarly treated for six months or longer in the course of ten years (1932-1941). In order to fully appreciate the story told by these astonishing figures, one must remember that the two institutions are generously staffed and richly financed.

Knight, tabulating the results of treatment as published by the psychoanalytic institutes of Berlin, London, Topeka (ten-year surveys) and Chicago (five years), was unable to quote more than 660 cases treated for upward of six months in the four clinics during a ten-year period (five years in Chicago). Of this total, 363 patients were treated in Berlin, 114 in Chicago, 100 in Topeka, 74 in London. Stating it otherwise, the productivity of the psychoanalytic techniques, as reported from four leading clinics, ranged, in point of the number of patients carried per year, from 7.4 (London) to 36.3 (Berlin). Figures of this kind admit of one conclusion only: The psychoanalytic techniques are available for a small fraction only of the multitude of post-psychotic and psychoneurotic patents.

The reason for its restricted availability is the egregious amount of time needed for the administration of the treatment, an overall average of hundreds of hours being required for each individual patient. For patients cared for in private practice there is the added handicap that the time-

---

*Institute for Psychoanalysis, Ten Year Report, 1932 — 1942, Chicago.

†Knight, Robert P., "Evaluation of the Results of Psychoanalytic Treatment," *American Journal of Psychiatry,* volume 98, page 434, November 1941.

consuming process involves a necessarily exorbitant expense. Whether the emphasis be on the time factor or the cost element, in either case, the method is all but unavailable for the masses of patients.

Aside from its limited availability for numerically significant groups of patients, psychoanalysis is also, again on the evidence of its own testimony, therapeutically ineffective. Knight, assaying the therapeutic results obtained in 660 analyses conducted for six months or longer in the institutes of Berlin, London, Chicago and Topeka, tells us that 183 patients (27.7 percent) were considered "apparently cured"; 186 (28.2 percent) were "much improved"; 291 (44.1 percent) were either somewhat improved or worse, or showed no change. Needless to say, a 27.7 percent yield of "apparently cured" patients, even adding the 28.2 percent of the "much improved" contingent, constitutes a serious indictment for any psychotherapeutic method.

Oberndorf* is authority for the statement that 40 percent of the "psychotic cases treated by psychoanalysis plus institutional regime at the Menninger Clinic" were discharged as cured. He comments that this is also the percentage of those "discharged as cured from mental hospitals in the United States." It is well-known, however, that the 40 percent figure for cures of state hospital patients represents the spontaneous recovery rate. Is it permissible, then, to draw the inference that, for psychotic patients at any rate, the results of psychoanalytic treatment are identical with their spontaneous chances for "outgrowing" their psychosis? Taking either the hint offered by Oberndorf or the disappointing figures supplied by the above mentioned statistics, the conclusion seems inescapable that psychoanalysis has failed as a therapeutic technique.

It is not intended here to criticize psychoanalysis with a view to extolling the work of Recovery, Inc. But, inasmuch as the psychoanalytic method has well nigh monopolized

---

*Oberndorf, C. P., "Consideration of Results with Psychoanalytic Therapy," *American Journal of Psychiatry*, volume 99, page 374, November 1942.

the field of psychotherapy, it is incumbent on a diverging approach to measure its record of accomplishment against that of the recognized procedure. A few simple figures culled from the files of the author will demonstrate that the combination of office treatment with the group methods practiced in Recovery, Inc., achieves a range of availability which dwarfs that of psychoanalysis.

Between January 1, 1946, and December 31, 1947, in a representative two-year period, the author was able to examine in his office a total of 425 new patients. Deducting from this figure those patients who did not return after the initial examination (140) and those who suffered from somatic or neurological conditions (24), there remained 261 subjects who were available for psychotherapy. Of this final group, 156 were given treatment for six months or longer. In other words, employing the method described in this book, one man was enabled to give active psychiatric care to a considerable multiple of the patients serviced in a comparable period by large staffs of psychoanalytic institutions. Clearly, the Recovery method is vastly superior to psychoanalysis in the matter of availability to the masses of patients seeking psychiatric care.

As concerns the therapeutic effectiveness of the Recovery techniques, as distinguished from mere availability, it is sufficient to point to the basic character of the organization: the members know one another; they meet frequently and regularly in classes and at parties; they get together in family gatherings and consort socially; they form sewing clubs, bowling parties and dancing teams; many of them spend evenings or Sundays together, dining or visiting theatres and amusement places. One can readily surmise what would happen if no more than a negligible 28 percent of the lot would finally reach the status of "apparently cured." The organization would explode in no time. Instead, the association–staffed by one physician, financed without outside assistance, shunning though not completely escaping publicity–has prospered close to fifteen years. This record speaks for itself. It needs no statistics to support its claims.

APPENDIX B

(TAKEN FROM THE SECOND EDITION, 1952)

A CONCISE OUTLINE OF RECOVERY'S SELF-HELP TECHNIQUES*

Recovery, Inc., was founded, November 7, 1937, by thirty ex-patients who regained their health after receiving shock treatments and/or other therapies at the Psychiatric Institute of the University of Illinois medical school, the predecessor of the present psychiatry department of the Illinois Neuropsychiatric Institute. The author was at the time the assistant director of the Institute. Between 1937 and 1940 the organization limited its services to the patients admitted to the wards of the Psychiatric Institute. In the fall of 1940, it expanded its work to include the psychoneurotic patients of the outpatient department.

In September 1941 the group severed its connection with the University of Illinois Medical School and established headquarters of its own in the Chicago Loop district where it is now located at 116 South Michigan Avenue. In the years since 1942, the bulk of its membership was recruited

---

*Revised reprint, with the publisher's permission, of a paper contributed by the author to "Rehabilitation of the Handicapped," a volume issued, 1949, by the Ronald Press Company, New York. The paper bore the title, "Recovery, Inc., A Project for Rehabilitating Post-Psychotic and Long-Term Psychoneurotic Patients."

from the author's private practice. As is evident from this brief description, Recovery, Inc., has had the opportunity to try out its techniques (1) with an intramural patient population, (2) with an outpatient group and (3) with private patients.

The object of the organization, apart from its tendency to save time for the physician and money for the patient, is to help prevent recurrences in mental diseases and to forestall chronicity in psychoneurotic conditions. Its techniques place the emphasis on self-help.

The "Residual Symptom" of the Recovered Mental Patient

After leaving the hospital, the mental patient is supposed to be restored to health. This is true in most instances if by "mental health" is meant the absence of delusions and hallucinations, of violent impulsiveness and indifference to group standards. But returning home, the patient still suffers from restlessness, tenseness and preoccupation. His inability to relax is aggravated by the sense of being stigmatized. Many returned patients are so suspicious of being watched or mistrusted that even simple inquiries like, "How do you feel?" or "How are you today?" are likely to cause irritation. These innocent questions may suggest to the patient that the reality of his recovery is doubted.

Feeling stigmatized, the patient becomes self-conscious and introspective. On a given night, he might have difficulty falling asleep. This is apt to alarm him. The alarm increases the difficulty of sleeping. Then more alarm, more sleeplessness and more alarm yet. A vicious cycle is thus set going which may keep the patient from properly resting night after night. Other vicious cycles may soon establish themselves. The patient notices a sense of fatigue which in itself may be as insignificant as any sensation of fatigue experienced by the average person. But feeling stigmatized, he correlates his tiredness with the possibility of a relapse. And the more he dreads the relapse, the more intense becomes his fatigue; the heavier the fatigue, the more haunting the fear of the relapse.

One patient had a nocturnal itch after returning home, another complained of a twitch in one arm, a third felt a hair on the tongue. Experiences of this kind are distressing enough to conjure up the vision of an impending relapse. The experiences become far more terrifying when the patient observes, for instance, that the arm suddenly begins to shake in automatic motion or when "awful flashes" shoot across the eye. Patients reported an "electric buzz running through the muscles," that "the tongue lay stiff in the mouth," that "my own voice sounded strange," that "the ear felt pushed in," that "I can't seem to hear myself when I speak." Palpitations, numbness, head or chest pressures, dizziness, difficulty of concentration, dimness of vision, air-hunger, headaches, nausea and scores of other disturbances were reported by numerous patients.

Observations of this sort may give rise to the vicious cycle which has the familiar character of the symptom increasing the fear and the fear intensifying and perpetuating the symptom. While there are no statistics to substantiate the claim, it is fair to assume that many recurrences of mental ailment are the direct result of these "residual symptoms" which, fanned by the fury of the vicious cycle, produce anxieties and panics which finally necessitate the much dreaded recommitment.

Recovery, Inc., insists that the patient, prior to leaving the hospital, attend group psychotherapy classes in which he is given adequate instruction how to face the threat of the residual symptom and the pressure of stigmatization. At the time, the members of the family are urged to attend discussion courses in which similar instruction is offered. In this manner, the pre-discharge care prepares for the aftercare effort.

The Defeatism of the Chronic Psychoneurotic Patient

Most residual symptoms from which the returned mental patient is likely to suffer are similar to, or identical with, the common complaints voiced by psychoneurotic patients. Hence, the possibility of treating both groups by the same method. The psychoneurotic patients admitted to Recovery, Inc., belong in the category of chronic, protracted cases mainly. Patients with symptoms of a few months' duration are rarities in the ranks of the group. Most members have a record of from two to twenty years of suffering. These "experienced sufferers" have made the rounds of physicians and clinics and were assured on numerous occasions, explicitly or by implication, that some therapeutic measure would cure them. The assurance never materialized, with the result that they no longer believe a cure possible. They know, however, that some or most of the past therapies had a transient, palliative effect. The palpitations were milder after a reassuring talk; the dizziness yielded to a sedative. Hence, they treasure the "pep-talk" or the prescription.

In order to secure these elusive aids, they must complain; they must convince the physician that they "really" suffer, that their pains are not imaginary, that they can "positively not stand" their fatigue. To get a hearing from the doctor is all the more important because at home their complaints are likely to be met with impatience or ridicule. Complaining, then, becomes a vital part of their daily routine. In the course of years, they develop the consummate art of the "expert complainer." What these long-term patients crave is a sympathetic ear which, after years of griping, they can no longer secure from their relatives and friends. They delight in a lengthy discussion of their fears and frustrations. Their ideal is to be explored, analyzed, sounded and probed. Essentially, they have decided that their case is beyond repair. What they expect is a hearing, perhaps some temporary relief, but not a final cure. The "chronicity" of this group has little to do with the nature of the symptoms, with diagnosis or etiology; it is self-appointed defeatism.

Since Recovery places the emphasis on the self-help action of the patients, it must ignore investigations and explorations which are not within the province of inexperienced lay persons. Complexes, childhood memories, dream experiences and subconscious thought play little part in the class interviews conducted by the physician and are entirely eliminated from the self-help effort carried on by the patients. The psychoneurotic individual is considered a person who, for some reason, developed disturbing symptoms leading to ill-controlled behavior. The symptoms are in the nature of threatening sensations, "intolerable" feelings, "uncontrollable" impulses and obsessive "unbearable" thoughts. The very vocabulary, with its frenzied emphasis on the "killing" headache, the dizziness that "drives me frantic," the fatigue that "is beyond human endurance" is ominously expressive of defeatism.

The first step in the psychotherapeutic management of these "chronic" patients must be to convince them that the sensation can be endured, the impulse controlled, the obsession checked. Unfortunately, the physician is far from convincing. His attempt to "sell" the idea of mental health arouses the "sales resistance" of the patient. "The physician doesn't dare tell me the truth," muses the patient. "It would be against his ethics to declare me incurable." The resistance is easily overcome in the group interview. The fellow sufferer, who explains how he "licked" his frightful palpitations after years of invalidism, cannot possibly be suspected of trying to sell something. That "colleague" is convincing. He convinces the novice that "chronic" conditions are not hopeless.

THE PATIENTS MEET ON THREE DAYS EVERY WEEK

On three separate days each week the patients take part in group discussions, either as panel members or listeners. On Wednesday, family gatherings are held in private homes in the various neighborhoods of Chicago. The patients are subdivided into seven neighborhood groups, each comprising from ten to twenty families. Three such family groups function on the North Side, two on the South Side, one on the West Side of the city; one serves the West suburbs. On the occasion of the family meetings, panels of three or four experienced members discuss a chapter of the author's three volumes on self-directed aftercare or an article from the now discontinued *Recovery Journal* or from its successor, the "Recovery News." The theme is centered on the topic of symptoms and the proper means of conquering them. The physician is not present at the family gatherings although he reserves the right to attend occasionally to check on the effectiveness of the procedure. Reports are currently conveyed to him by the panel leaders.

Tuesday evening is devoted to a group psychotherapy class, conducted by the physician. Saturday afternoon, a public meeting takes place at Recovery headquarters, 116 South Michigan Avenue. It is attended by the patients, their relatives and friends. The first half hour is given over to a panel discussion similar to that held at the Wednesday home gatherings. In the second half, the physician delivers an address in which he sums up the conclusions reached by the panel, approving or correcting their statements. The panel members are led by a panel leader.

TREATING THE "SETBACK"

Patients are required to attend classes and meetings for at least six months. The average patient experiences a considerable improvement in the first or second week of participation in the program. But the improvement is, as a rule, as short-lived as was the relief which the patient used to gain from the visits to clinics and doctors' offices. No meetings are held on four days of the week. During these days, the novice is apt to suffer a "setback." He is again tortured by "that awful fatigue" or has been unable "to sleep a wink for three nights in succession," or the fear of doing harm to the baby reappears after it was gone for a short while.

Every patient is warned to be on guard against the unavoidable setback. He is cautioned to contact a veteran Recovery member immediately after the symptom has reappeared. The assurance offered by the veteran is in accord with the language used by the physician, and the interpretations given to the novice coincide with those used in the physician's classes and in his writings. New members are assigned to veterans whom they may call in distress. The veteran functions in the capacity of the physician's "aide." The contact is generally made by telephone but may be done by a personal visit to the aide's home. If the result is not satisfactory, the novice is permitted to call on the leader of his local panel. If this is ineffective, he may contact the chairman of the organization who serves as deputy to the physician. Finally, he may call the physician. The effectiveness of the scheme is evidenced by the fact that few instances are recorded in which the physician was called by novices.

The Symptomatic Idiom

If the patients are to help and teach one another, they must be instructed to use a language which is not confusing. This is particularly important because language, if used glibly, tends to be alarmist and defeatist. By dint of its defeatist insinuations, language frequently engenders tenseness which reinforces and perpetuates symptoms. To avoid the fatalistic implications of the language used by the patient, the physician must supply a terminology of his own in matters of health. There are many languages. Features and gestures speak. So do symptoms. Their language is a one word idiom: DANGER. This is called the "symptomatic idiom." Accepting the suggestions of the symptomatic idiom, the patient considers the violent palpitations as presaging sudden death. The pressure in the head is viewed as due to a brain tumor. The tenseness is experienced as so "terrific" that the patient fears he is going to "burst." His fatigue does not let up "one single minute," and "how long can the body stand it?"

In these instances, the implications of the symptomatic idiom are those of an impending *physical collapse*. If phobias, compulsions and obsessions dominate the symptomatic scene, the resulting fear is that of the *mental collapse*. After months and years of sustained suffering, the twin fears of physical and mental collapse may recede, giving way to apprehensions about the impossibility of a final cure. This is the fear of the *permanent handicap*. The three basic fears–of the physical collapse, mental collapse and permanent handicap–are variations of the danger theme suggested by the symptomatic idiom.

The Temperamental Lingo

Another source of defeatism is temper. The patients are taught that temper has two divisions. The one comes into play when I persuade myself that a person has done me wrong. As a result I become angry. This is called the *angry or aggressive temper*, which appears in various shades and nuances: resentment, impatience, indignation, disgust, hatred, etc. The other variety of temper is brought into action whenever I feel that I am wrong. This gives rise to moral, ethical and esthetic fears or to the fear of being a failure in pragmatic pursuits. I am afraid that I sinned, failed, blundered, in short, that I defaulted on a moral, ethical or esthetic standard or on the standard of average efficiency. This is called the *fearful or retreating temper* which may express itself in many different qualities and intensities: discouragement, preoccupation, embarrassment, worry, sense of shame, feeling of inadequacy, hopelessness, despair, etc. The fearful temper is likely to lead either to a feeling of personal inferiority or to the sentiment of group stigmatization. Whether it be of the angry or fearful description, temper reinforces and intensifies the symptom which, in its turn, increases the temperamental reaction. In this manner, a vicious cycle is established between temper and symptom.

The temperamental reaction is kept alive mainly by the unsympathetic and unthinking attitude of the relatives. By means of coarse statements or subtle innuendo, they provoke loud explosions or silent agonies on the part of the patient. They tell him to use his will power, implying that he makes no effort to get well. With this, they indict him as a weakling, worse yet, as purposely shamming disease. They urge him to "snap out of it," indicating that the symptoms are so easy to deal with that a mere snap would shake them out of existence. Other insinuations frequently levelled against the psychoneurotic or former mental patient are equally disconcerting. Complaining of fatigue, he is told not to be lazy; mentioning his "awful palpitations," he is admonished to be a man. The net result of this concerted environmental assault is that the patient is continually angry at his detractors and, gradually accepting their insinuations, becomes ashamed and fearful of himself.

In telling the patient that wrong was done to him or that he is wrong, his temper speaks to him. The language which it uses is called the *temperamental lingo*. Its vocabulary is limited to the terms "right" and "wrong." Unless the patient learns to ignore the threats, warnings and incitements of the temperamental lingo, he will be the victim of angry outbursts and fearful anticipations. His tenseness will be maintained and intensified; new symptoms will be precipitated and old ones fortified. Temper is most dangerous when it plays on the symptom itself. By labelling sensations as "intolerable," feelings as "terrible," impulses as "uncontrollable," the lingo discourages the patient from facing, tolerating and controlling the reaction. The very sound of the labels ("intolerable," etc.) is apt to rouse fear and defeatism. All a patient has to do is to call a crying reaction by the name of "crying spell," and no effort will be made to check the burst of tears. The word *spell* suggests uncontrollability. Make the patient substitute "crying habit" for "crying spell," and the impossibility of stemming the flood at least will not be taken for granted. Similarly, if the patient raves about the "splitting" headache, the dizziness that "drives me mad," the pressure that "I can't stand any longer," the fatalism of diction is bound to breed a despondency of mood. In order to prevent the temperamental response, the patient must be trained to ignore the whisperings of his temperamental lingo.

THE "RECOVERY LANGUAGE"

The combined effects of symptomatic idiom and temperamental lingo are checkmated if the patient is made to use the physician's language only. The members of the Association call it proudly the "Recovery language." The most important parts of its vocabulary are the words "sabotage" and "authority." The authority of the physician is sabotaged if the patient presumes to make a diagnostic, therapeutic or prognostic statement. The verbiage of the temperamental lingo ("unbearable," "intolerable," "uncontrollable") constitutes sabotage because of the assumption that the condition is of a serious nature, which is a diagnosis; or, that it is difficult to repair, which is a prognosis. It is a crass example of sabotage if the claim is advanced that, "My headache is there the very minute I wake up. I didn't have time to think about it. It came before I even had a chance to become emotional. How can that be nervous?" A statement of this kind throws a serious doubt on the validity of the physician's diagnosis and sabotages his authority. Likewise, it is a case of self-diagnosing and consequently sabotage to view palpitations as a sign of a heart ailment, of head pressure as meaning brain tumor, of sustained fatigue as leading to physical exhaustion.

Once the physician has made the diagnosis of a psychoneurotic or post-psychotic condition, the patient is no longer permitted to indulge in the pastime of self-diagnosing. If he does, he is practicing sabotage. Patients are expected to lose their major symptoms after two months of Recovery membership and class attendance. If, after the two-month period, the handicap persists in its original intensity, the indication is that sabotage is still in action. The patient still listens to the suggestions of the symptomatic idiom, fearing impending collapse and permanent handicap. Or, he gives ear to the verbal vagaries of the temperamental lingo, feeling helpless in the face of suffering. Clinging to his own mode of thinking, he sabotages the physician's effort.

Contrary to expectation, it is comforting to the patient to be called a saboteur. Considering himself as such, he knows that he has "not yet" learned to avoid resisting the physician. The "not yet" is reassuring. It suggests that in time he will learn. The patients encourage one another to wait until they get well. They warn one another against impatience. The most effective slogan handed down from veteran to novice is, "Wait till you will learn to give up sabotaging."

THE "SPOTTING TECHNIQUE"

If the patient is to check his sabotaging propensities, he must be trained to "spot" the inconsistencies and fallacies of his own language, whether it is merely conceived in silent thought or given formulation in vocal speech. To this end, a system of "spotting techniques" was evolved by means of which the members learn to reject the suggestions of the symptomatic idiom and the temperamental lingo whenever a symptom or a temperamental reaction occur. An extensive, though necessarily incomplete, description of the spotting techniques is furnished in part 3 of this book.

SOCIAL ACTIVITIES

The social calendar of the organization is remarkably crowded. The activities are largely spontaneous, little supervised. Practically all events, be they group psychotherapy classes, public meetings or family gatherings, are somehow linked to sociability. After a group psychotherapy class, the patients form small groups heading for the nearest drugstore or restaurant where they rehash the theme discussed in class or chat about private affairs.

The most stimulating social event is the "kaffeeklatsch" following immediately upon the Saturday afternoon public meeting. After the panel and the physician have finished their discussions, the assembly hall is speedily converted into a sort of lounge. The patients, relatives and friends seat themselves around small tables and are treated to coffee and cake. Mothers and fathers then exchange views about the progress of their still suffering or already recovering offspring. The patients join the chat, and the atmosphere is one of mutual encouragement, gratitude and hopefulness. The "kaffeeklatsch" may last an hour or longer. The physician moves from group to group, engaging in brief conversations or listening to the stories and views presented by members and guests. This informal mingling with patients and relatives provides the physician with information which he could hardly obtain otherwise. The men and women speaking to him are spontaneous, divorced from the official and cramping situation of the interview carried on in the ordinary examining room. Mrs. Jones reports an incident which she observed in Mrs. Smith's home on the occasion of the last family gathering. The account is unreflective, reportorial, descriptive. These casual chats with the members are an invaluable means of acquainting the physician with the personal details of the patients' home life.

The family gatherings are similarly patterned. A panel discussion of about thirty minutes is followed by a modest repast furnished by the family in whose home the meeting is held. The physician does not attend the family panels but is currently kept informed by the panel leaders about what transpires about adjustment or maladjustment of the patients and about the quality of home life prevailing in the particular family. The panel leaders meet with the physician once a month to receive special training in the matter of conducting the panels. This is again an occasion when a vast mass of information is conveyed to the physician about the home life of the patients. It need hardly be stressed that the type and quality of information which the physician is thus enabled to collect is vastly superior to that obtained in his examining room while interviewing the questioning parents and relatives.

The members seem to have an almost unquenchable thirst for social contacts. They visit one another in their homes; they go together to shows and concerts, meet for lunches, for short trips, for joint visits to museums or parks or for plain walks. Some groups have regular schedules for bowling, barn dancing, hiking and swimming. The families of one North Side and one South Side group formed sewing circles. Consciously or unconsciously, the trend is to break through the dismal isolation and loneliness which have always been the blight of neurotic or post-psychotic existence. The patients state it explicitly that formerly they merely existed, now they live again. Formerly they were lonely individuals, now they are thoroughly integrated with the rich, pulsating life of a closely knit group.

A happy outlet for this burning desire for sociability is afforded by the informal afternoon gatherings which take place at Recovery headquarters, 116 South Michigan Avenue. A number of veterans, housewives mainly, volunteer each to spend one afternoon a week in the Recovery office, supervising the activities of that afternoon. Patients or relatives working in the Loop district drop in, partake of simple refreshments and spend time chatting or asking advice or seeking reassurance for disturbing symptoms. The physician's office is two blocks distant. New patients are asked to visit the Recovery office immediately after the termination of the initial examination. There they are met by the other patients and given information about the work of the organization. Panics, anxieties and apprehensions are easily soothed by the calming influence of meeting other patients who, having suffered similar disturbances, are now presenting the picture of good health.

MEMBERSHIP, FINANCES, ADMINISTRATION

Membership, at three dollars per year, is open to any psychoneurotic or former mental patient. At this writing (January 1950) the membership stands at 376. About 75 percent of the total is secured from the author's private clientele. The organization is financed by membership fees, donations, proceeds from the sale of Recovery literature and collections at meetings. The organization is almost, but not quite, self-sustaining. The yearly deficit is met by the author.

In April 1948, the organization moved to its present larger quarters. With a considerably increased rental and the necessity for new furniture and office equipment, it was deemed wise to create a guarantee fund. The members responded promptly and generously to an appeal for contributions. The goal was 5,000 dollars, and close to 4,400 were collected.

The affairs of the organization are conducted by a board of three directors, all ex-patients. Mrs. Annette Brocken, ex-patient and assistant principal of a Chicago public school, is president of the organization and chairman of the board of directors. Serving with her are a vice-president, a secretary, a treasurer and six councilors. The author does not hold office but functions as the medical director. An ex-patient is the editor of the "Recovery News." Another ex-patient holds the position of the executive secretary, doing all the routine work, including dictation and typing. This is the only salaried employee. The monthly compensation is almost nominal.

RECOVERY LITERATURE

Between 1938 and 1941, the organization published a bimonthly magazine, *Lost and Found*. The author was the editor, contributing the bulk of articles. The pages of the magazine were devoted mainly to a thorough discussion of the influence of domestic temper on the fortunes of the patients. In 1943, this material was issued in book form in three volumes entitled, *The Techniques of Self-Help in Psychiatric After-Care*. The issue is now exhausted after a total sale of close to 1,000 copies.

From June 1946 to June 1947, the *Recovery Journal* was published. In consequence of rising cost of printing, it was discontinued after the eleventh issue. It was succeeded by a phototyped news sheet, the "Recovery News," which appeared eight times a year. Each issue contains a contribution from the author. Subscription is included in the membership fee, and $2.00 per year for non-members. A second edition of the *Self-Help Techniques* is in preparation.

RECOVERY BRANCHES OUTSIDE CHICAGO

Eight branches of Recovery, Inc., are now functioning outside the Chicago area. Following are their locations and dates of formation: Muscatine, Iowa (1946), Brighton,

Michigan (1947), Evansville, Indiana (1950), Louisville, Kentucky (1951), St. Louis, Missouri (1951), Burlington, Iowa (1951), Denver, Colorado (1951), Dixon, Illinois (1951). Other branches are in the process of formation. The Denver branch is superintended by a local psychiatrist; the others are led by ex-patients. The members meet regularly in their homes, read the Recovery literature, cite examples from their own experience and conduct panel discussions which are modelled after the pattern established in Chicago. The branches are visited by officers of the Chicago organization in intervals of about six months, and the leaders of the branches, in turn, come to Chicago to attend meetings and to perfect themselves in the techniques of panel leadership.

RESULTS

It was stated that the objectives of the organization are (1) to help reduce the incidence of relapses in mental ailments and to prevent chronicity in psychoneurotic conditions, (2) to save time for the physician and expense for the patient. It would be easy to furnish imposing tables detailing percentages of improvements and failures. Tabulations of this kind, posing as objective statements, are usually nothing but subjective opinions no matter how heavily they are buttressed by charts and graphs. They are particularly objectionable if compiled without the benefit of a well organized, long-range, follow-up investigation. Since the latter was not available, no computation was attempted.

Nevertheless, reasonably valid conclusions as to the therapeutic effectiveness of the system can be drawn from the very nature and structure of the organization. The patients and relatives know one another, and if relapses or continued chronicity were frequent occurrences, the membership would inevitably become discouraged and lose confidence.

An unfortunate event, which took place in October 1947, illustrates the point with striking force. A well-known member of the group relapsed into a depression and one morning ran into the path of a speeding train. It was not clear whether the fatal incident was suicide or accident. Nevertheless, something in the nature of a demoralization swept the organization. Several of the ex-patients developed severe reactions. One of them had to be hospitalized. The fact that this has been the only instance of suicide, if such it was, in a period of close to fifteen years during which many hundreds of manic-depressive patients had joined as active members, ought to be considered an eloquent testimony to the therapeutic efficiency of the system. This system would rapidly disintegrate if it failed to accomplish its therapeutic objectives. Statistical evidence does not seem required to demonstrate its success.

Statistical figures, however, are available in support of the organization's second objective, i.e., its endeavor to effect substantial economies in the physician's time and the patient's expense. Due to the fact that the patients are disciplined, there is little quibbling and arguing in the physician's office, which means that the so-called "resistance" to his explanations and directions is reduced to a minimum. This alone allows an impressive saving in time. Another time-saving factor is the massive instruction given the patients in classes and meetings and the insistence on continual study of the physician's writings. With resistance restricted and the patient coming to the office reasonably well instructed, the private interview can be terminated in a surprisingly small space of time. As a general rule, the author manages to see from four to five patients during one hour of his office time. Accordingly, the charges for the brief visit can be held to a moderate figure. In addition, the intensive class training and the equally intensive patient-to-patient contact make it possible to achieve improvements after a relatively short period of treatment. The total charges are thus lowered considerably. All patients are required to visit the physician's office for six consecutive months after the initial examination. They are seen once a week during the first month, once in two weeks in the second month. During the third through the sixth month, the office visits are reduced to once every four weeks if symptoms and difficulties are significantly ameliorated. But the two-week ratio continues if improvement lags. The average number of visits in 1947 was 11.9 per patient in a representative six-month period. The maximum was 23 visits, the minimum was 5, the median was 12.

Index

Editors' note: This index includes only major references to terms listed.